INTRODUCTORY SIGNALS
AND CIRCUITS

Introductory Signals and Circuits

University of Illinois

JOSE B. CRUZ, JR.

Princeton University

M. E. VAN VALKENBURG

GINN AND COMPANY

A Xerox Company

Waltham, Massachusetts • Toronto

Consulting Editor / *Charles D. Hendricks, Jr.*

Preface

The rapid rate of progress and the increasing number of new applications in circuit theory should call for frequent examination of the content and approach used in teaching the subject at the introductory level. In considering this examination, we must note that progress in integrated circuit fabrication requires that additional models be incorporated into the study. The widespread availability of digital computers for the solution of equations makes a more general formulation meaningful and necessary. The increased emphasis on the electric network as a signal processor requires that more attention be given to properties of signals. Further, there is a need to utilize a concrete vehicle for introducing topics in systems engineering; experience indicates that the electric circuit is the most successful such vehicle.

In this book, we present our attempt to adapt the body of knowledge known as electric circuit theory to the developments cited above. The book is intended to provide foundation concepts which are believed to have lasting significance and broad implications. We assume that the student who studies from this book will pursue the subject further in one or more advanced courses.

In keeping with this plan, the topics we have selected have been treated in sufficient detail to arouse student interest, but not in such depth that he will lose sight of the end objectives. We believe this kind of treatment will give the student an accurate picture of the objectives and methods of circuit theory. With this background, he will be more effective both in subsequent studies of circuit theory *per se* and also in many applications of circuit theory to the topics within the discipline of electrical engineering.

A number of the authors' convictions concerning teaching methods will be evident throughout the book:

(1) We believe that the fundamental principles should be expressed in their most general forms, to encompass applications to nonlinear, time-varying, or distributed systems, or for computer solution, but that at this point we can best illustrate principles for the linear, lumped, time-invariant case. Appreciation for the limitation and consequences of the linearity assumption is heightened by introducing occasional examples of nonlinear circuits and systems.

(2) We believe that the student should study simple ways for solving simple problems first. Most beginning engineering students are unable to comprehend the beauty of a completely general solution!

(3) Students must have extensive drill at this point in their careers, and this drill must make it possible to first understand the principle, and also to extend it to the solution of complex problems. Thus there is a need for both easy and more difficult problems.

In implementing these goals, we have provided numerous examples, drill exercises with answers for the student to test his understanding, and problems, some quite difficult, for the student to apply his knowledge and thus establish a learning situation. We have also postponed the general method of analysis of networks to the later parts of the book.

Given the philosophy we have just outlined, there remains the problem of selecting material to be covered. Which subjects should we treat, and which can be delayed for later study? To explain our choice of topics, we state that our experience over years of teaching is that for complete understanding to be achieved *frequency-domain ideas are more difficult for beginning students than time-domain ideas.* And of the frequency-domain ideas, one of the most difficult is that of the frequency spectrum. While the Fourier series and transform are excellent artifices for unifying the understanding of the subject, and indispensable in understanding signals in communication systems, these subjects best come later in the student's program of study. Having made this decision for the Fourier transform, we have decided to exclude the other transform methods also.

In stressing concept over specific facts, we have chosen to delay the study of methods for the efficient solution of simultaneous algebraic equations until Chapter 15. There will be no serious difficulty, of course, if this material is covered earlier, even before Chapter 1. Each instructor should decide the point at which this information has maximum usefulness. His decision will be influenced by the degree to which the computer will be used as an adjunct to the course.

We believe that the student should not be taught three-phase circuits as a *special topic*, for he may then tend to regard them as different from other circuits, which is certainly not the case. While three-phase problems are treated in the book, they are distributed throughout rather than being lumped in a single chapter.

The material in this book can be covered in about seventy class hours at the sophomore level. At the junior level, progress may be somewhat faster. There is enough material for a first course and perhaps part of a second course. It is assumed that the later courses will include transform methods.

We are indebted to many people who have assisted in the writing of the book, and most important of these are the students in our classes who provided the motivation for writing and who tested the product. We are deeply indebted to the community of scholars engaged in the study of circuits and systems at the University of Illinois who over the past years have provided a stimulating and congenial milieu in which this book could be developed. These include William R. Perkins, Donald A. Calahan, Leon O. Chua, Franklin F. Kuo, S. Louis Hakimi, Wataru Mayeda, James A. Resh, Ronald A. Rohrer, the late Sundaram Seshu, Manoel Sobral, Jr., Timothy N. Trick, Nelson Wax, and James R. Young. We have benefited from discussions with fellow authors Charles A. Desoer, Ernest S. Kuh, Benjamin J. Leon, and Leon O. Chua concerning conventions and symbols that should be used. We express special appreciation to Franklin F. Kuo and Jack Bourquin who read the complete manuscript and made numerous suggestions for improving the presentation. Finally, we are indebted to Mrs. Divona Keel, who typed the various drafts of the book with efficiency and spirit.

J. B. Cruz, Jr.
M. E. Van Valkenburg

January 1967

Contents

Signal Sources and Signal Processing   **1**

1.1 Reference conventions for signal entities

We use the word *signal* to mean a time history of voltage or current in an electric network. The voltage or current variation with time may represent a message, music, a television picture, etc. In our elementary study of signals, we will include the sinusoidal waveform used to transmit energy. We exclude signals which must be described by statistical properties, leaving this important subject for later study. All signals we study may be described by real numbers which may be either positive or negative (and zero). It is important that we first understand the meaning of the positive or negative sign identified with the signal.

Consider a battery, an electric-energy source, which has its own exclusive symbol, that of Figure 1.1(a). The terminal of the battery with an excess of positive charge is called the *anode*, that with an excess of negative charge the *cathode*. It is conventional that the anode be distinguished by a plus sign and the cathode by a minus sign, as shown in the figure.

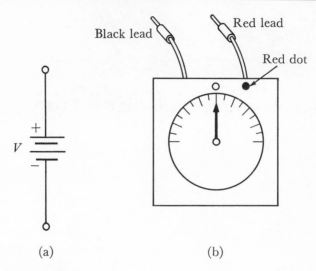

Figure 1.1   (a) Symbol for a battery. (b) Representation of an ideal voltmeter.

The battery voltage may be measured by a voltmeter. An idealized voltmeter or galvanometer suited to measurements of our interest measures instantaneous voltage, has a zero center scale, and is capable of deflecting to both the left and the right as in Figure 1.1(b). Reversal of voltmeter leads reverses the direction of deflection. It is usual to call one direction of deflection positive and the other negative. This is the *second* use to which we have put the words positive and negative, but this need not be a source of confusion if we make clear which use we intend.

Consider the experiment in which the two leads of the voltmeter are connected to the battery and the deflection is positive. The lead connected to the plus terminal or anode is designated as the positive reference lead (red); the other is the negative reference lead (black).† With these identifications defining the voltmeter deflections, we consider a general electric source. This source may reverse polarity with the passage of time. How can we describe this polarity variation?

We first postulate that the output terminals of the source have reference marks painted on them, one a plus and one a minus, these assignments having been made *arbitrarily* at the time the source left the factory. To this source we connect our calibrated voltmeter with the red lead of the voltmeter connected to the plus terminal of the source, and the black lead to the minus terminal. With this connection, a positive deflection of the voltmeter (or its counterpart in the form of an oscillograph) implies that the plus terminal of the source has an excess of positive charge and the

† In the laboratory, our red lead will often be called the "live" or "hot" lead, and the black one the "ground" lead.

source polarity is like that of the battery. Similarly, a negative deflection implies a source polarity opposite to that of the battery. Thus we see that the plus mark on the general source has a different meaning than the plus mark on the battery. In the case of a battery, the plus mark implies positive polarity; for the source, the plus mark is a *reference* in terms of which the polarity variation with time may be described. For this reason, the plus mark on the general source could just as well be a sign of the Zodiac. We can make the identifications "like the battery" and "opposite to the battery" only in terms of the reference marks on the source. Plots like those in Figure 1.2(b) have meaning only in terms of the reference marks.

For example, if the equation of a recorded voltage is $v(t) = V \sin t$, where V is a positive number, then the plus terminal of the source has a positive polarity from $t=0$ to $t=\pi$, a negative polarity from $t=\pi$ to $t=2\pi$, etc. A number of schemes are used instead of the plus and minus we have used; three of the most common alternate designations are shown in Figure 1.2(a).

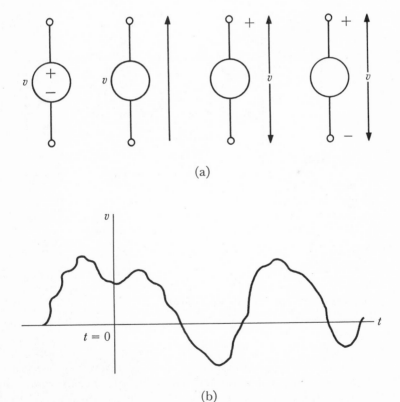

(a)

(b)

Figure 1.2 (a) Several alternate representations of voltages and their associated reference marks. (b) Plots of *v* versus time.

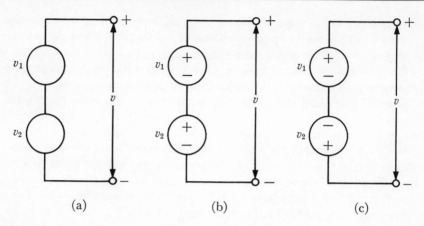

Figure 1.3   Two voltages in series, illustrating the need for reference marks in describing the voltage of the combination.

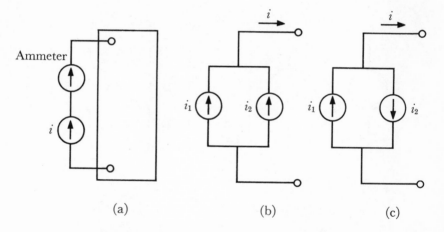

Figure 1.4   Conventional reference for currents.

The need for reference marks is further illustrated by the connection of two sources shown in Figure 1.3(a). Without reference marks on the sources, we do not know the relationship of v_1, v_2, and v. With the reference marks of Figure 1.3(b), we see that $v = v_1 + v_2$; with those of Figure 1.3(c), we have $v = v_1 - v_2$.

Statements similar to those given for the voltage reference apply to the current reference. The symbol used to indicate reference direction† is shown in Figure 1.4(a). The ammeter deflects in a positive direction when current is in the reference direction, negative when in the opposite of the

---

† Ammeters found in the laboratory are marked with plus and minus signs. The plus goes with the tail of the arrow, the minus with the head.

reference direction. The marks of Figure 1.4(b) imply that $i = i_1 + i_2$, while those of Figure 1.4(c) imply that $i = i_1 - i_2$.

In our discussion of source notation, we have used a single-subscript symbol like v_1 together with reference marks (plus and minus) to describe sources. Another notation commonly used in circuit theory is known as the *double-subscript notation.* If we use this notation, the voltage v_{jk} is *defined* to be the voltage between j and k with the plus mark implied at j. Thus we read v_{12} as the potential at 1 with respect to 2, meaning the voltmeter reading with the red lead connected to 1 and the black lead to 2.

In describing current sources by double subscripts, we see that i_{jk} is the current in the path from j to k with the reference arrow from j to k. Thus i_{12} is a current with the reference direction such that the tail of the arrow is at 1, the head at 2.

The equivalences for the two forms of notation for voltage and current are illustrated in Figure 1.5. Observe that for both cases, the reversal of subscripts implies a change of sign; thus we have

$$v_{12} = -v_{21}, \qquad i_{ab} = -i_{ba}, \qquad \text{etc.}$$

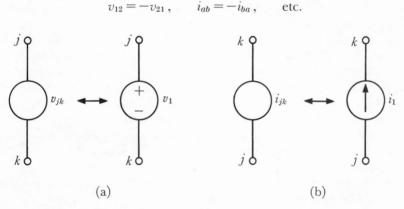

(a)   (b)

Figure 1.5 Equivalent representations, using double-subscript and single-subscript notation.

● **EXERCISES**

1.1-1 The voltage signal from a source is described by the equation $v_1(t) = 5 \sin (2t + \pi/6)$ volts. When $t = \pi/2$ sec, determine the terminal voltage and its polarity with respect to the reference marks of the source.

1.1-2 The current in a circuit is $i_{12} = 5 \sin (2t + \pi/6)$ amps. At $t = \pi/2$ sec, what is the current direction? The direction of electron flow? Repeat for $t = 0$.

1.1-3 Two identical ideal voltmeters are connected across a time-varying source. The red lead of one meter and the black lead of the other are connected to the same terminal of the source. The remaining leads are connected to the other terminal. What is the algebraic sum of the readings of the meters at all instants of time? How do the readings of the two meters compare?

1.2   Models of signal sources and notation

The devices associated with electric networks are commonplace: coils, capacitors, resistors, transistors, vacuum tubes. In studying circuit theory or network theory, we are not concerned with these devices per se but with abstractions or idealizations of them known as *models*. Good models are required to be simple and yet must accurately represent the device (or system) under specified conditions. In general, the choice of a model represents a compromise between simplicity and accuracy requirements.

Devices which are important sources of electric energy include the battery, electromechanical generators, and electronic generators. These and other electric energy sources may be represented by two models: the voltage source and the current source.†

Let a source of electric energy be connected to an arbitrary network as in Figure 1.6(a) and let the resulting current be denoted by $i_1(t)$ and the voltage across the terminal pair by $v_1(t)$. Suppose that instead of using Network No. 1, we had used some other arbitrary network as in Figure 1.6(b). In general, the resulting $i_2(t)$ would be different from $i_1(t)$ and $v_2(t)$ would be different from $v_1(t)$. However, if $v_1(t) = v_2(t)$ *no matter what arbitrary network we use*, then we define the source as an *ideal voltage source* or simply a *voltage source*. The voltage-source model is a source of electric energy with a prescribed voltage across its terminals. The resulting current depends not only on $v(t)$ but also the nature of the connected network.

If in Figure 1.6, $i_1(t) = i_2(t)$ *no matter what arbitrary network we use*, then we define the source as an *ideal current source* or simply a *current source*. This time, the source has a prescribed current through its terminals. Both

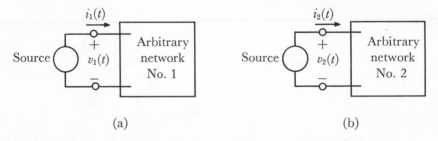

(a)   (b)

Figure 1.6 Arbitrary networks connected to identical sources of electrical energy. If the sources are voltage sources, $v_1(t) = v_2(t)$. If the sources are current sources, $i_1(t) = i_2(t)$.

† More elaborate source models will be introduced later.

the network and the current source $i(t)$ determine the resulting voltage $v(t)$. To distinguish between voltage and current sources, we will adopt the symbols in Figure 1.7.

When the voltage of a voltage source or the current of a current source is controlled by or depends on another voltage or current, the resulting model is distinguished by the name *controlled source* or *dependent source*. The symbols that we will use for the controlled voltage source and the controlled current source are shown in Figures 1.8(a) and 1.8(b), respectively. An example of a controlled voltage source is one which depends on a voltage $v_1(t)$

$$v_2(t) = \mu v_1(t), \tag{1.1}$$

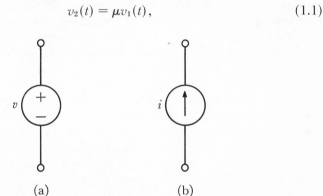

(a)   (b)

Figure 1.7   (a) Symbol for voltage source. (b) Symbol for current source.

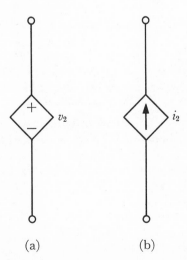

(a)   (b)

Figure 1.8   (a) Symbol for a controlled voltage source. (b) Symbol for a controlled current source.

where μ is a real constant. The voltage $v_1(t)$ does not have to be a voltage source. It may be a voltage resulting from electric sources somewhere in the system. Such a controlled voltage source is called a voltage-controlled voltage source. An example of a controlled current source is one which depends on a current $i_1(t)$ such that

$$i_2(t) = \alpha i_1(t), \qquad (1.2)$$

where $i_1(t)$ is a current in some part of a network and α is a real constant. The current $i_1(t)$ does not have to be a current source.

A number of conventions have been introduced in the foregoing discussion, as well as in the preceding section. Throughout the book we will continue to use lower-case letters for time-varying quantities. This will be explicit when we write $v_1(t)$ or implied when we write simply v_1. Upper-case letters will be reserved for time-invariant quantities: real constants and later complex numbers.

In writing $v_1(t)$, we have assumed that the student is familiar with the usual function notation by which it is read as *the value of v_1 at t*. Here v_1 will be a voltage or, as determined by the context of the discussion, a general signal; t is time, usually in seconds. We usually think of $v_1(t)$ as given by an equation (in closed form) although it need not be. A function will sometimes be expressed by two sets of numbers occurring in ordered pairs as in Table 1.1.

Table 1.1

t	v_1
0	1
1	3
2	3.4
. . .	. . .

A graph of a function is made by plotting the two numbers of an ordered pair such that v_1 is the *ordinate* and t is the *abscissa*. Such a graph of a signal as a function of time is called a *waveform*.

The time t is reckoned with respect to an arbitrary reference. A common reference is the closing of a switch; another is the firing of a gun that starts the race. This reference time is $t = 0$; $t = 1$ sec is the instant one second after the closing of the switch; $t = -1$ sec refers to the instant of time one second before the closing of the switch.

Another set of names used in describing $v_1(t)$ are *dependent variable* for v_1 and *independent variable* for t. Time is the usual independent variable, but in some mathematical operations in circuit theory it is necessary to

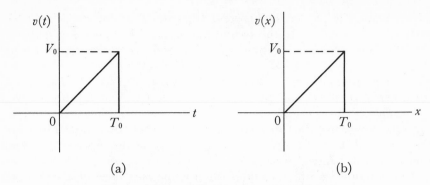

Figure 1.9 A particular signal waveform plotted as a function of t and also another variable, x.

replace t by another variable, say x. It is important that we understand that when t is replaced by x in the function $v(t)$, then $v(x)$ plotted against x looks exactly like $v(t)$ plotted against t. This statement is illustrated in Figure 1.9. All of this sounds ridiculously obvious,† but it may prove to be a stumbling block later.

To carry this discussion a bit further, let t be replaced by $x + T$ where T is a constant. Clearly, if $v(x + T)$ is plotted against $x + T$, we get one more plot identical to the two of Figure 1.9. But if $v(x + T)$ is plotted against x, then things become a little different. This results in a *shift* or *translation* of the graph with respect to the abscissa. To illustrate, consider the signal waveform of Figure 1.9(b) which is described by the equations

$$v(x) = \begin{cases} 0, & x < 0, \\ \dfrac{V_0}{T_0}x, & 0 \le x \le T_0, \\ 0, & x > T_0. \end{cases} \tag{1.3}$$

Replacing x by $x + T$, we have

$$v(x + T) = \begin{cases} 0, & x + T < 0, \\ \dfrac{V_0}{T_0}(x + T), & 0 \le x + T \le T_0, \\ 0, & x + T > T_0. \end{cases} \tag{1.4}$$

Rearranging the inequalities in the intervals of the piecewise description of $v(x + T)$, we find that

$$v(x + T) = \begin{cases} 0, & x < -T, \\ \dfrac{V_0}{T_0}(x + T), & -T \le x \le T_0 - T, \\ 0, & x > T_0 - T. \end{cases} \tag{1.5}$$

† Any fact is *obvious* once we understand it.

This equation is plotted in Figure 1.10(a) for T positive and in Figure 1.10(b) for T negative. In the second figure, note that since T is negative, $-T$ is positive. Such a shifting operation will occur frequently in our study.

Another common transformation on $v(t)$ is to replace t by Kx or Kt to form $v(Kx)$ or $v(Kt)$ and plot this with respect to x or t. This is called *time scaling*. It finds use in the selection of an appropriate time unit; for example, replacing time in seconds by time in microseconds. The effect on the graph is either stretching or compressing the abscissa. More on this in a later chapter.

An operation we will encounter often is the *integration* of a signal $v(t)$ to give another signal $f(t)$. From our discussion on change of variable, it is clear that

$$\int_{t_1}^{t_2} v(t) \; dt = \int_{t_1}^{t_2} v(x) \; dx. \tag{1.6}$$

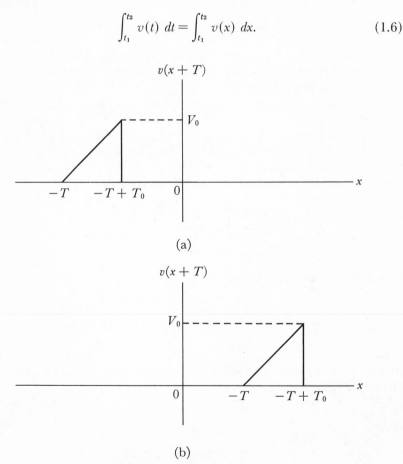

(a)

(b)

Figure 1.10   The signal waveform of Figure 1.9 is shown shifted as specified by Equation 1.5.

For that matter, we may use any other letter in the English, Greek, Russian, or any other alphabet. The value of the integral will be the same in all cases. Because of the invariance and independence of the value of the integral with respect to the choice for our independent variable, t or x in Equation 1.6 is called a *dummy variable*. To illustrate the use of a dummy variable, suppose that the signal

$$v(t) = Ke^{-at} \tag{1.7}$$

is to be integrated beginning at $t = 0$ to give the new signal $f(t)$. It is confusing to write

$$f(t) = \int_0^t v(t) \, dt \tag{1.8}$$

as the value of f at time t for t is *both* a variable and a limit of integration. Instead, we make use of the dummy variable x as

$$f(t) = \int_0^t v(x) \, dx. \tag{1.9}$$

Carrying out these operations, we have

$$f(t) = K \int_0^t e^{-ax} \, dx = \frac{-K}{a} e^{-ax} \Big|_0^t = \frac{K}{a} (1 - e^{-at}). \tag{1.10}$$

Another application of the dummy variable is used when writing an expression for the *energy* that a source has supplied between time t_1 and time t. If the voltage of the source is $v(t)$ and the current $i(t)$, then the *energy* is

$$w(t) = \int_{t_1}^t v(x)i(x) \, dx. \tag{1.11}$$

The time rate of energy transfer at time t is the *power*

$$p(t) = \frac{dw(t)}{dt} = v(t)i(t). \tag{1.12}$$

We shall often express the integrand by different functions which are valid in different ranges. For example, the waveform of Figure 1.11(a) is expressed by the equations

$$v_1(t) = \begin{cases} 0, & t < 0, \\ V_0, & 0 \le t \le T_0, \\ 0, & t > T_0. \end{cases} \tag{1.13}$$

Then depending on the value of t, the proper expression in this set of equations is selected for the range being considered. Let v_2 be related to the v_1 of Equation 1.13 by the equation

$$v_2(t) = \int_{-\infty}^t v_1(x) \, dx. \tag{1.14}$$

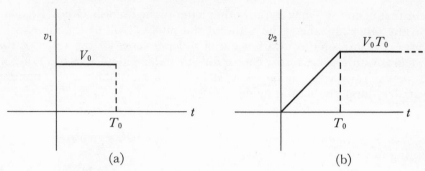

Figure 1.11   The integral of the signal of (a) is that shown in (b).

Substituting Equations 1.13 into this integral, we have

$$
v_2 = \begin{cases} 0, & \text{for} \quad t < 0, \\ \displaystyle\int_0^t V_0 \, dx = V_0 t, & \text{for} \quad 0 \le t < T_0, \\ \displaystyle\int_0^{T_0} V_0 \, dx + \int_{T_0}^t 0 \, dx = V_0 T_0, & \text{for} \quad t \ge T_0. \end{cases} \tag{1.15}
$$

The waveform for v_2 is shown in Figure 1.11(b). Integration is readily visualized as the adding of increments of area. In this example, we see that the area is zero for $t < 0$ and is a constant value for $t > T_0$ as shown in the figure.

● EXERCISES

1.2-1   If $f(t) = e^{-at} \sin bt$, write $f(x), f(\xi)$, and $f(\zeta + 1)$.

1.2-2   Consider the signal

$$
v(t) = \begin{cases} 0, & t < 0, \\ \sin t, & 0 \le t \le 2\pi, \\ 0, & t > 2\pi. \end{cases}
$$

Sketch $v(x + 2\pi)$ and $v(x - \pi)$ against x.

1.2-3   Let $v(t) = \sin t$ and $i(t) = \frac{1}{2} \sin t$. Find $w(t)$ using Equation 1.10 with $t_1 = 0$. What is the expression for $p(t)$?

1.2-4   If the signal $v(t)$ is that shown in Figure 1.9(a) with $V_0 = 5$ and $T_0 = 10$, sketch the following: (a) $v(x + 5)$ vs. x; (b) $v(t + 5)$ vs. t; (c) $v(x - 5)$ vs. x; (d) $v(t - 5)$ vs. t.

1.2-5   For $v(t)$ of Exercise 1.2-4, sketch the following: (a) $v(10x)$ vs. x; (b) $v(10t)$ vs. t; (c) $v(x/10)$ vs. x; (d) $v(t/10)$ vs. t.

1.2-6   For $v(t)$ of Exercise 1.2-4, sketch the following: (a) $v(10t - 5)$ vs. t; (b) $v(t/10 + 5)$ vs. t.

1.2-7   For $v(t)$ of Exercise 1.2-4, calculate the following integrals:

(a) $I_1 = \displaystyle\int_0^{10} v(t) \, dt,$

(b)　$I_2 = \int_0^{10} v(x)\ dx,$

(c)　$I_3 = \int_{-10}^0 v(x + 10)\ dx,$

(d)　$I_4 = \int_5^{15} v(x - 5)\ dx.$

Are these integrals expected to be equal to each other?

1.2-8　For $v(t)$ of Exercise 1.2-4, calculate

$$I = \int_0^t v(\tau)\ d\tau$$

and sketch I vs. t for $-1 \le t \le 20$.

1.2-9　The waveform shown in Figure 1.2(b) is observed on a cathode-ray oscilloscope connected to the output of the device described by Equation 1.14. With the oscilloscope leads reversed, draw the waveform that will be observed on the oscilloscope screen.

1.3　Nature of signal processing in networks

In a variety of applications it is desired to obtain signals with characteristics which are prescribed modifications of those pertaining to electric sources. This is usually done by imbedding the source in an appropriate interconnection of electric devices. The source signal may be a voltage or current time function. The source signal is usually called an *input signal* (or excitation), the desired signal is called the *output signal* (or response), and the interconnection of components or devices from which the output is obtained is called a *network*. Other signals in addition to the output may appear in the network. The network may be viewed as a processor which connects the input signal into another signal called the output signal. As an example, the input signal may be a time function $f(t)$, and the desired ideal output signal may be a constant K multiplied by the same time function $f(t)$.

For this example, the network is commonly called an *amplifier* for K greater than 1 and an *attenuator* for K less than 1. As another example, the input signal may be of the form $K_1 + K_2 \sin K_3 t$, where K_1, K_2, and K_3 are constants, and the desired output may be of the form $K_1 + K_4 K_2 \sin K_3 t$, where K_4 is very much less than 1. The network may be descriptively called a *filter*, since it tends to suppress and discriminate against a component of the input.

An engineer's primary function is to design. Aside from economic, social, and sometimes political considerations, an engineer must have sufficient technical understanding of the operation of the device, network, or system in order to carry out the design function wisely. In particular, he must be able to analyze the behavior of devices, networks, and systems. This book is devoted primarily to the basic network-analysis aspect of electrical engineering. In essence, the analysis problem reduces to the following: given a network and given an input signal, determine the output signal.

The interaction and interrelationships among various signals including the input and the output of a network are governed by two sets of fundamental constraints. One set is called Kirchhoff's laws to be studied in Chapter 5. In an axiomatic development of network theory, these laws are regarded as postulates. These "laws" may be verified experimentally. One of the laws pertains to the algebraic sum of certain voltages being zero. Another one pertains to the algebraic sum of certain currents being zero. These laws are analogous to Newton's laws in mechanics pertaining to the algebraic sum of certain forces being zero. Kirchhoff's laws govern equilibrium of voltage and current signals just as Newton's laws govern equilibrium of mechanical forces. The other set of fundamental constraints specify the relationships among the voltages and currents of individual devices or components. One of the most common of components called the resistor is specified by a functional relationship between the current and voltage at its terminals. These two sets of constraints lead to a set of equations involving voltage and current signals together with their integrals and derivatives. The output signal which is one of the unknowns in the system of equations may be obtained mathematically.

Before discussing the details of these two sets of fundamental constraints in Chapters 4 and 5, we find it convenient to develop simple concepts regarding signals in the following two chapters.

●   EXERCISES

1.3-1   An idealized version of a circuit known as a full-wave rectifier has the following equilibrium equations:

$$v_2(t) = \begin{cases} v_{\text{in}}(t), & \text{for} \quad v_{\text{in}}(t) \geq 0, \\ -v_{\text{in}}(t), & \text{for} \quad v_{\text{in}}(t) < 0, \end{cases}$$

$$v_{\text{out}}(t) = \frac{1}{T} \int_0^T v_2(\tau)\, d\tau, \qquad T = \text{const.}$$

Express the output signal in terms of the input signal.

1.3-2   A simple network is described by the following set of equations:

$$av_1(t) + bv_2(t) = v_3(t),$$
$$cv_1(t) + dv_2(t) = v_4(t).$$

Where $v_3(t)$ and $v_4(t)$ are input signals, $v_1(t)$ is the output signal, and a, b, c, and d are constants such that $ad - bc \neq 0$. Express the output signal in terms of the input signals.

1.3-3   The equations describing a network are as follows:

(a) $L\dfrac{d}{dt}i(t) + R\,i(t) + \dfrac{1}{C}\displaystyle\int_0^t i(\tau)\,d\tau = v_1(t),$

(b) $v_2(t) = \dfrac{1}{C}\displaystyle\int_0^t i(\tau)\,d\tau,$

where $v_1(t)$ is the input, and $v_2(t)$ is the output. Obtain a differential equation relating $v_1(t)$ to $v_2(t)$.

Problems

1-1   Suppose that the source labeled as v_1 in Figure 1.5(a) is such that $v_{kj}(t) = \cos 100t$. Determine v_1 at $t = 0$.

1-2   A system is characterized by the equations

$$v(t) = \int_0^t v_1(\tau)\,d\tau, \qquad v_2(t) = .02v(t).$$

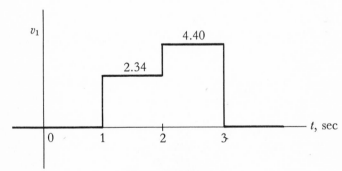

Figure Problem 1-2

If the input $v_1(t)$ is the staircase function shown in the figure, sketch the output waveform $v_2(t)$.

1-3   Repeat Problem 1-2 for the waveform of the accompanying figure.

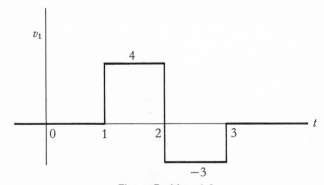

Figure Problem 1-3

1-4 If $v_1(t) = V_1 \sin \omega t$ is the signal passed through a device with an input-output characteristic like that of the figure, plot the output, $v_2(t)$. This model represents some rectifier devices.

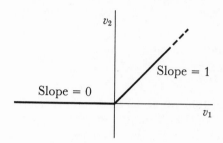

Figure Problem 1-4

1-5 Repeat Problem 1-4 for the different input-output characteristic of the figure.

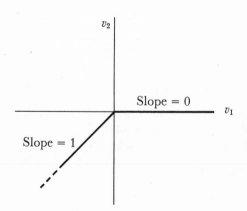

Figure Problem 1-5

1-6 Repeat Problem 1-4 for the different input-output characteristic of the figure.

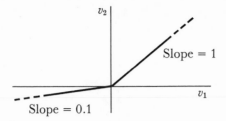

Figure Problem 1-6

1-7 Repeat Problem 1-4 for the different input-output characteristic of the figure.

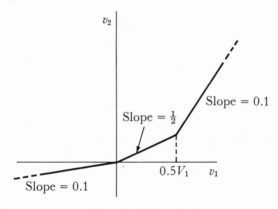

Figure Problem 1-7

1-8 If $i(t)$ is the integral in Exercise 1.2-8, calculate di/dt. Is di/dt equal to $v(t)$? The result of this exercise is an example of a more general rule for differentiating an integral with respect to the upper limit (check your calculus book). Thus we have

$$\frac{d}{dt} \int_0^t v(\tau) \, d\tau = v(t),$$

for *any* integrable $v(t)$. This result is important in circuit theory and will come up often in future discussions.

1-9 Let $v_1(t)$ be the signal in Figure 1.9(a) and define

$$v(t) = v_1(t) + v_1(2T_0 - t).$$

Calculate

$$v_0(t) = \int_{-\infty}^t v(x) \, dx.$$

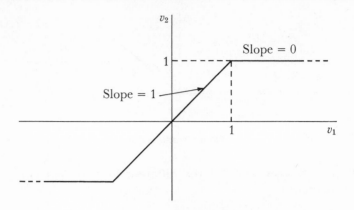

Figure Problem 1-10

1-10 A signal is passed through a limiter (which prevents the output
from exceeding a fixed value) and the output of the limiter is then
passed through an integrator. Compare this system to that where
the order of operations of limiting and integration are interchanged. Substantiate your comparison with appropriate equations.

1-11 Repeat Problem 1-10 if the limiter is replaced by a differentiator.

Signal Waveforms   **2**

For both analysis and design, it is necessary that waveforms produced by generators be represented by mathematical *abstractions* (formulas). These formulas are approximations to the actual waveforms in the same sense that models are idealizations of actual generators. In this chapter, we will study waveforms of importance in electrical engineering. As we will see, many of these waveforms may be expressed as linear combination of exponential functions such as†

$$v(t) = 3e^{-t} + 2e^{-3t} + 5e^{jt} + 5e^{-jt}. \tag{2.1}$$

This equation may be written in the compact form

$$v(t) = \sum_{k=0}^{n} a_k e^{s_k t}. \tag{2.2}$$

The $s_0, s_1, \ldots$ may be real, imaginary, or complex.

---

† The j in this equation is the same as the i used by mathematicians and is equal to $\sqrt{-1}$. This is to avoid confusion with i as a symbol for current.

2.1   The exponential function

The function

$$v(t) = Ke^{\sigma t} \tag{2.3}$$

with σ negative real is known as an *exponentially decreasing waveform* and an *exponentially increasing waveform* for σ positive real. The exponential waveform is shown in Figure 2.1. We define $T = 1/\sigma$ as the *time constant* of $v(t)$ in Equation 2.3. Observe from Equation 2.3 that for $\sigma < 0$, $v(T) = K/e$ which is approximately $0.37K$. Thus in one time constant, the exponential signal decays to 37 percent of its $t = 0$ or *initial value*. For $\sigma < 0$, σ is also known as *damping*.

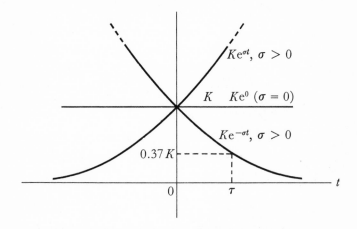

Figure 2.1   Exponential signal waveforms.

The exponential signal has a number of interesting properties. For example, the derivative of $v(t)$ in Equation 2.3 is

$$\frac{d}{dt} Ke^{\sigma t} = \sigma\, Ke^{\sigma t}, \tag{2.4}$$

which is the same waveform as v except for a scale factor. Similarly, if we integrate v from t_1 to t, we have

$$\int_{t_1}^{t} Ke^{\sigma \tau}\, d\tau = \frac{K}{\sigma} e^{\sigma t} + K_1. \tag{2.5}$$

Thus the passage of an exponential signal through an amplifier, integrator, or differentiator changes only the signal magnitude, except for a possible additional constant corresponding to the initial value of the integrator output. For example, if a system is characterized by the equation

$$v_3 = \frac{3dv_1}{dt} - 2v_1, \qquad (2.6)$$

where v_1 is the input and v_3 is the output, then for a signal $v_1 = e^{-t}$ at the input, the output is found to be

$$v_3 = -3e^{-t} - 2e^{-t} = -5e^{-t}. \qquad (2.7)$$

Consider next the equation

$$i = 3e^{-t} + 10e^{-2t}, \qquad t > 0, \qquad (2.8)$$

which is known as a *linear combination* of exponentials. Observe that the time constant of the first term is two times longer than that of the second term. A plot of the total signal has the characteristic shape shown in Figure 2.2. Such waveforms are encountered in the electronic recording of the radiation from radioactive materials in which two decay processes are present.

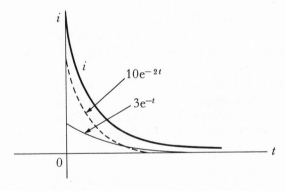

Figure 2.2 A signal waveform composed of two exponential terms.

Another linear combination of exponentials,

$$v_2 = \frac{1}{2} - e^{-t} + \frac{1}{2} e^{-0.1t}, \qquad t > 0, \qquad (2.9)$$

has a characteristic form illustrated by Figure 2.3. Observe that the signal waveform begins at zero value, rapidly assumes its maximum value, and then decays slowly. This slow decay, described by the colorful name *long tail*, is due to the third term in Equation 2.9, or the long duration component of the signal. The final value of the signal, $v_2(\infty)$, is $\frac{1}{2}$.

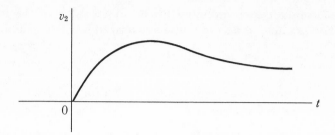

Figure 2.3   An exponential signal with a long tail.

● EXERCISES

2.1-1   A signal is described by the equation

$$v_1(t) = 5e^{-t} - 5e^{-3t}.$$

Does this signal have a long tail like Equation 2.9? Sketch v_1 for the range, $0 \le t \le 3$ sec.

2.1-2   The signal of Exercise 2.1-1 enters the system described by Equation 2.6. Determine the output of this system.

2.1-3   A signal of the form $v(t) = K(e^{-\alpha t} - e^{-\beta t})$ enters the limiter shown in Figure Problem 1-10 (p. 18). Find the largest value of K in terms of α and β for which the input and output waveforms will be identical.

2.1-4   (a) Show that the plot of an exponential function like $v(t) = Ke^{\sigma t}$ on semilogarithmic coordinates is a straight line for K positive and σ either positive or negative. (b) Show that derivatives of all order of $v(t)$ are straight lines parallel to $v(t)$ in this coordinate

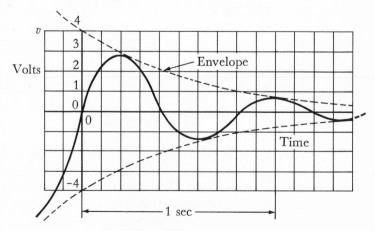

Figure Exercise 2.1-5

system. (c) Show that the spacing between the lines described in
(b) is constant and determine the value of the constant.

2.1-5   The signal in the given figure may be approximated by the equation $v(t) = Ke^{-\sigma t} \sin bt$. Determine appropriate numerical values for K, σ, and b.

2.2   The step, ramp, and impulse

At time $t = 0$, the reference time at which we usually begin our experiments, the switch shown in Figure 2.4 is thrown from position 1 to position 2. This ideal switch acts in zero time connecting a one-volt time-invariant source to an ideal recording meter (a model for instruments like the voltmeter, oscillograph, recording penmotor, etc.) which records or indicates instantaneous values. The waveform produced by the switching action is known as a *unit step function,* having been so named by the English engineer Oliver Heaviside (1850–1925). The *step* nature of the waveform is shown in Figure 2.5. We represent this step function by the symbol $u(t)$, where we have

$$u(t) = \begin{cases} 1, & \text{for} \quad t \geq 0, \\ 0, & \text{for} \quad t < 0. \end{cases} \qquad (2.10)$$

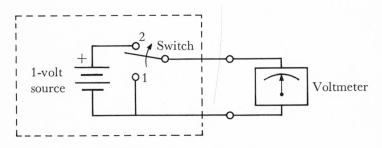

Figure 2.4   Step function generator.

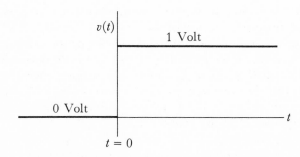

Figure 2.5   Waveform known as the unit step.

If the one-volt source is replaced by a source of K volts, then clearly the new voltage is $Ku(t)$.

Let the unit step voltage $u(t)$ be applied at the input of an ideal integrator. The output voltage v_2 is

$$v_2(t) = \int_0^t 1 \, dx + v_2(0), \qquad \text{for} \quad t \geq 0. \tag{2.11}$$

If the initial condition $v_2(0)$ at the integrator output is zero and if there is no other input before $t = 0$, then $v_2(t)$ is zero for negative time. The output waveform v_2 is described by the equation

$$v_2(t) = \begin{cases} t, & \text{for} \quad t \geq 0 \\ 0, & \text{for} \quad t < 0 \end{cases} \equiv r(t). \tag{2.12}$$

Because of the shape of this response, shown in Figure 2.6, $r(t)$ is known as a *ramp function*. When the ramp function has unit slope, it is known as a *unit ramp*. Should we both integrate and also multiply by a constant K, then for $t \geq 0$, $v_2 = Kt = Kr(t)$, which is described as a ramp of slope K. Observe that the slope of the ramp equals the magnitude of the step. In summary, we see that

$$\int_{-\infty}^t u(x) \, dx = r(t) \qquad \text{and} \qquad \frac{d}{dt} r(t) = u(t). \tag{2.13}$$

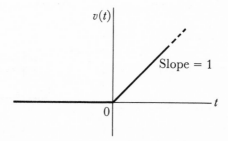

Figure 2.6   Waveform known as the unit ramp.

Notice that we are using the symbol $-\infty$ (minus infinity) to denote integration over the entire past history of the signal.

We next turn to a discussion of the derivative of the unit step function. The step function is discontinuous at $t = 0$, and the derivative is therefore not ordinarily defined at that point. A function generated by passing the unit step function through an ideal differentiator is known as a unit impulse function or a unit Dirac delta function, $\delta(t)$. To follow the philosophy of Equation 2.13, we require that

$$\frac{d}{dt} u(t) = \delta(t) \qquad \text{and} \qquad \int_{-\infty}^t \delta(x) \, dx = u(t), \tag{2.14}$$

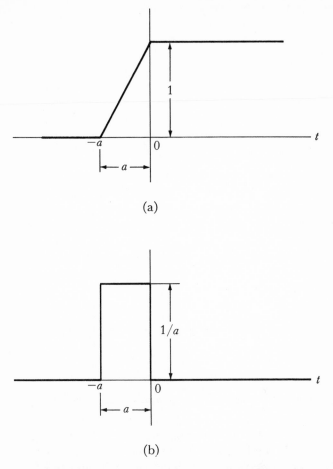

(a)

(b)

Figure 2.7   Figures used in describing the impulse function.

or simply that when we integrate and then differentiate that we get back
to where we started. The plausibility of the integration of Equation 2.14
being reasonable is suggested by Figure 2.7(a) which shows a waveform
similar to the step function but with a finite slope at its "leading edge."
The *pulse* waveform obtained by differentiating the modified step is
shown in Figure 2.7(b). This pulse has width a and height $1/a$ such that
the area of the pulse is $a \times 1/a = 1$. In the limit as a approaches zero, the
height of the pulse approaches infinity and the width approaches zero,
but the area remains equal to one.† Several steps in approaching this

† This heuristic argument is supported by reference to the properties of Schwarz distribu-
tions in advanced treatises. See, for example, S. Seshu and N. Balabanian, *Linear Network
Analysis*, John Wiley & Sons, Inc., New York, 1959, pp. 112-119.

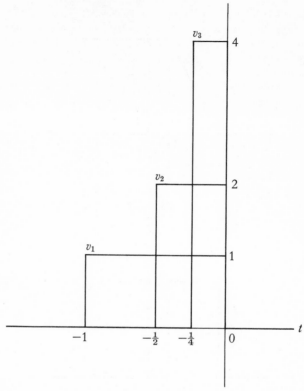

Figure 2.8   A set of pulse functions whose limit defines the impulse function.

limit are shown in Figure 2.8. Starting with the pulse v_1, we halve the width and double the height thus obtaining v_2, repeat to get v_3, and continue this process observing that as the width approaches zero, the height approaches an infinite value keeping the area under the pulse unity. Since the integral of Equation 2.14 is the area of $\delta(t)$, we see that a property of the unit impulse is

$$\int_{-\infty}^{t} \delta(x)\ dx = \begin{cases} 1, & t \geq 0, \\ 0, & t < 0. \end{cases} \tag{2.15}$$

More generally, $\delta(x)$ has the following defining properties:

(a) $\qquad\qquad\qquad \delta(x) = 0, \qquad \text{for} \quad x \neq 0; \tag{2.16}$

(b) for any function $f(x)$ which is continuous at $x = 0$, we have

$$\int_{b}^{a} f(x)\ \delta(x)\ dx = f(0), \qquad \text{for} \quad a \geq 0 \quad \text{and} \quad b < 0. \tag{2.17}$$

The sampling property expressed in Equation 2.17 states that if a continuous function $f(x)$ is multiplied by a delta function $\delta(x)$ and integrated over a range which includes $x = 0$, the value of the integral is $f(0)$, which is a sample of $f(x)$ at $x = 0$. For example, if $f(x)$ is $\sin(x + \pi/4)$, $a = -1$, and $b = 1$, then the value of the integral in Equation 2.16 is $\sin \pi/4 = 0.707$.

If we differentiate $Ku(t)$ rather than $u(t)$, then we obtain $K\delta(t)$, where K represents the area under the curve of the impulse function. In order to represent the impulse function and the corresponding value of K, the symbol shown in Figure 2.9 is used. The number beside the arrow and the arrow length represent K; a negatively directed arrow implies a negative value of K. Using this convention, we see that a number of impulses may be conveniently represented as shown in Figure 2.10. Impulses, steps, ramps, etc. may be shifted away from the origin. For the signal in Figure 2.10, the equation for $v(t)$ is

$$v(t) = 2\delta(t) + \delta(t-1) - 3\delta(t-2).$$

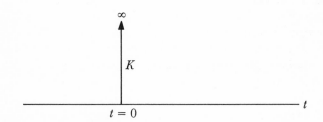

Figure 2.9 Representation of K times the unit impulse function, $\delta(t)$. It is usual to draw the arrow length proportional to K.

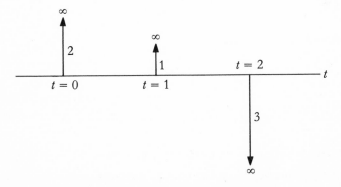

Figure 2.10 A train of impulse functions.

From the defining properties of the delta function we see that the integral of $\delta(x - T)$ is $u(x - T)$, that is, the integral of a delayed impulse is a delayed step with the same delay T. The height of the step is equal to the area of the impulse. For example, the integral of $K\delta(x-T)$ is $Ku(x-T)$ where K is an arbitrary real number. With this in mind, the integral of the signal in Figure 2.10 is

$$v_1(t) = 2u(t) + u(t-1) - 3u(t-2).$$

This integral is shown in Figure 2.11. Notice the jumps of height 2 at $t=0$, height 1 at $t = 1$ and height -3 at $t = 2$. If the signal in Figure 2.11 is passed through a differentiator, the signal in Figure 2.10 is obtained. At every jump discontinuity of $v_1(t)$, $v(t)$ has an impulse whose area equals the height of the jump of $v_1(t)$. This result is worth remembering, and it applies to the derivative of any function which has finite jump discontinuities but otherwise differentiable in the ordinary sense. The generalized derivative will contain an impulse at every point of discontinuity of the original function, and the area of the impulse will equal the height of the jump of the original function.

The step, ramp, and impulse are, of course, *abstractions* of signal waveforms produced by practical generators. The impulse function is an approximation for pulses of relatively short duration of large magnitude. The most common form of electronic ramp generator produces a repetitive ramp or a "sawtooth."

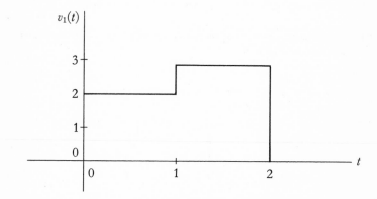

Figure 2.11   Integral of signal in Figure 2.10.

● EXERCISES

2.2-1   If the input v_1 has the dimension of volts and if t has the dimension time, what are the units of the output v_2 for each of the following: (a) ideal integrator; (b) ideal differentiator.

2.2-2 The ramp function shown in the figure is applied to an ideal differentiator. Find the resulting $v_2(t)$ in the form of a sketch.

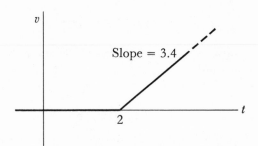

Figure Exercise 2.2-2

2.2-3 A step function of amplitude 3 volts as shown in the figure is applied to an ideal differentiator. Describe $v_2(t)$.

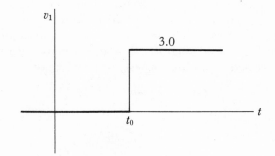

Figure Exercise 2.2-3

2.2-4 The signal shown in Figure 1.11(a) (p. 12) is the input v_1 for the system described by

$$v_2(t) = -v_1(t) + \int_0^t v_1(\tau)\, d\tau.$$

Draw the signal waveform of $v_2(t)$ indicating maximum and minimum signal values.

2.2-5 Figure 2.10 shows a *train* of impulses. Find the output that results when this impulse train is applied to an ideal integrator. Sketch $v_2(t)$.

2.2-6 The waveform shown in Figure Problem 1-2 (p. 15) is the input to an ideal differentiator. Find the corresponding output.

2.2-7 The American electrical engineer E. A. Guillemin (1898–   ) uses the symbol $u_0(t)$ for a unit impulse and then describes other singular functions through the recursion relationship

$$u_{n+1}(t) = \frac{du_n(t)}{dt}.$$

By this system, what symbol should be used to describe a unit step? A unit ramp?

2.3 The sinusoid

The circular functions, sine and cosine, are familiar from studies in trigonometry as the vertical and horizontal projections of a point on a unit circle as functions of the angular displacement of a line through this point and the origin. The corresponding sinusoidal time-varying signal is

$$v_1(t) = V_1 \sin \omega t, \tag{2.18}$$

where ω is the constant of proportionality between time displacement and angular displacement (a scale factor). This constant is defined as the frequency of $v_1(t)$. Here V_1 is a real, positive number which is the *maximum magnitude* of the sine wave. The sine wave is shown in Figure 2.12. If the sinusoidal signal is shifted such that it does not have zero value at $t = 0$, this shift is described by a *phase angle* ϕ in the equation

$$v_2(t) = V_2 \sin (\omega t + \phi_2), \tag{2.19}$$

or in the alternative representation

$$v_2(t) = V_c \cos (\omega t + \phi_3). \tag{2.20}$$

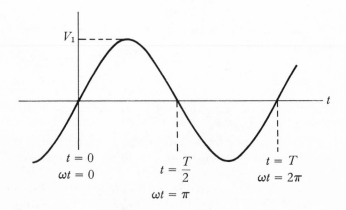

Figure 2.12 A sinusoidal signal.

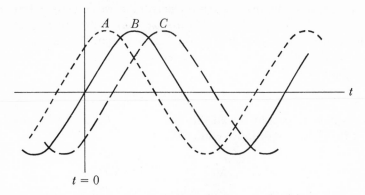

Figure 2.13 With sinusoid *B* as the reference, *A* leads *B* and *C* lags *B*.

In comparing Equation 2.19 with Equation 2.18, we say that v_2 *leads* v_1 if ϕ_2 is positive or *lags* v_1 for negative ϕ_2. Shifted sine waves are shown in Figure 2.13.

Since the sine and cosine are related by identities like

$$\cos\left(\theta - \tfrac{1}{2}\pi\right) = \sin\theta \tag{2.21}$$

and

$$\sin\left(\theta + \tfrac{1}{2}\pi\right) = \cos\theta, \tag{2.22}$$

it is evident that a sine function can be expressed by an equivalent cosine function with a different phase angle and *vice-versa*. We use the term sinusoid to mean a signal waveform which may be expressed as either a sine or cosine function with any phase angle.

Sinusoids may be expressed in exponential form. Thus† we have

$$\sin\omega t = \frac{1}{2j}\left(e^{j\omega t} - e^{-j\omega t}\right) \tag{2.23}$$

and

$$\cos\omega t = \tfrac{1}{2}\left(e^{j\omega t} + e^{-j\omega t}\right). \tag{2.24}$$

The unit of the quantity ωt in the equations of this section has the dimension of *radians*, although it is common in electrical engineering to use the older unit, the *degree* (which dates back to the Babylonians in 2000 B.C.). When ωt is in radians and t is in seconds, the unit for the frequency ω is the radian/sec.

We next seek the smallest positive number T such that

$$\sin\omega(t + T) = \sin\omega t. \tag{2.25}$$

---

† These two equations follow from the familiar *Euler formula* $e^{\pm jx} = \cos x \pm j \sin x$.

By an inspection of Figure 2.12, it is clear that if we shift the curve (either to the left or to the right) by an amount $\omega t = \omega T = 2\pi$, the new curve will coincide with the old. No amount of shift less than 2π will cause such a complete overlapping. Alternatively, we may expand the left-hand side of the Equation 2.25 to get

$$\sin \omega t \cos \omega T + \cos \omega t \sin \omega T = \sin \omega t. \tag{2.26}$$

For this equation to hold for all values of t, $\cos \omega T$ must be equal to 1 and $\sin \omega T = 0$. These conditions require that

$$T = \frac{2k\pi}{\omega}, \qquad k = \text{any integer.} \tag{2.27}$$

The smallest positive value of T corresponds to $k = 1$ which agrees with our previous discussion. This value is known as the *period* of the sine wave. During T seconds, *one cycle* of the sine wave $\sin(2\pi/T)t$ is described, and another cycle during the subsequent T seconds. The number of cycles of sine wave per second is seen to be $1/T$, and since $\omega T = 2\pi$, we have

$$\frac{1}{T} = \frac{\omega}{2\pi} \equiv f, \tag{2.28}$$

where f is the frequency in the unit of cycles/sec or Hertz. Other related units for f are kiloHertz, megaHertz, and kilomegaHertz. (10^3, 10^6, and 10^9 cycles/sec or Hertz.)

What happens to a sinusoidal signal when it passes through an ideal differentiator or ideal integrator? Since

$$\frac{d}{dt} \sin \omega t = \omega \cos \omega t = \omega \sin \left(\omega t + \frac{\pi}{2} \right) \tag{2.29}$$

and

$$\int_{t_1}^{t} \sin \omega \tau \, d\tau = -\frac{1}{\omega} \cos \omega t + \frac{1}{\omega} \cos \omega t_1 = \frac{1}{\omega} \sin \left(\omega t - \frac{\pi}{2} \right) + K, \tag{2.30}$$

we see that except for a possible integrator initial condition, these operations *change the magnitude and phase of the sinusoid but do not change its frequency*. We shall exploit this important conclusion in later chapters in the study of networks excited exclusively by sinusoidal signals.

Another signal waveform of importance is the *damped sinusoid* which is given by the equation

$$v_3(t) = Ae^{-\sigma t} \sin \omega t, \qquad \sigma > 0, \tag{2.31}$$

where A is a real, positive constant. Expressing the sine function in exponential form and combining with $e^{-\sigma t}$, we have

$$v_3(t) = \frac{A}{2j} \left[e^{(-\sigma + j\omega)t} - e^{(-\sigma - j\omega)t} \right]. \tag{2.32}$$

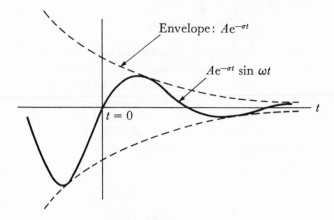

Figure 2.14   A damped sinusoidal signal.

From this form of the equation, we may interpret the damped sinusoid as a special linear combination of exponentials with *complex* time constants.

This waveform is shown in Figure 2.14. Observe that the function $\pm Ae^{-\sigma t}$ is the bound of the oscillations and is therefore known as the *envelope* of the waveform. The time constant of the envelope is $T = 1/\sigma$.

The product of two sine waves of different frequencies like

$$v_4(t) = A \sin \omega_1 t \sin \omega_2 t \tag{2.33}$$

is another signal waveform of interest which arises in the study of modulation. Using the identity

$$2 \sin \omega_1 t \sin \omega_2 t = \cos (\omega_1 - \omega_2)t - \cos (\omega_1 + \omega_2)t, \tag{2.34}$$

we see that v_4 is equivalent to the sum of two sinusoidal functions whose frequencies are the sum and difference of ω_1 and ω_2. A typical signal of this form is shown in Figure 2.15.

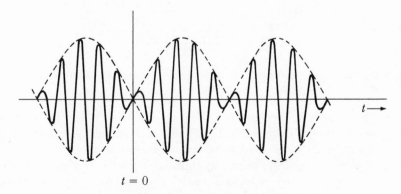

Figure 2.15   A modulated signal waveform.

● EXERCISES

2.3-1   The accompanying figure shows three sinusoidal waveforms which are recorded by means of an oscillograph for different voltages and currents in a given network. From these records, determine the following: (a) the frequency ω; (b) the period T; (c) the number of Hertz; (d) the phase relationship of the three waveforms; (e) write an equation for each waveform using the numerical values found previously. State any assumptions made in writing these equations.

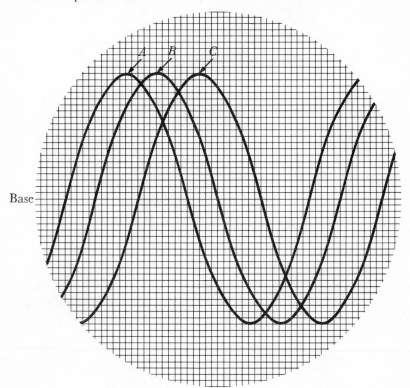

Figure Exercise 2.3-1   Horizontal sensitivity: 0.416 msec/sq. Vertical sensitivities: A, 0.38 amp/sq; B, 8.5 V/sq; C, 0.6 amp/sq.

2.3-2   A signal is known to be a damped sinusoid. When $t = \frac{1}{2}$ sec, the envelope has decayed to 37 percent of its initial value, and one full cycle of oscillation is completed. It is also known that $v_1(0) = 0$, and $v_1(\frac{1}{8}) = 2$ volts. Write an expression for the signal, $v_1(t)$, determining as many numerical values for the parameters as you can.

2.3-3   The inputs to a multiplier consist of two sine waves, one of maximum magnitude $V_1 = 2$ and frequency $\omega_1 = 3$, the other $V_2 = 1$ and $\omega_2 = 2$. Sketch the product waveform.

2.3-4   For the system represented by the equation $v_2(t) = (dv_1/dt) - v_1$, determine $v_2(t)$ when $v_1(t) = \sin 2t$. Write $v_2(t)$ in the form $V_2 \sin(\omega t + \phi_2)$ and determine numerical values for V_2, ω, and ϕ_2. [*Note:* V_2 should be chosen to be real and *positive.*]

2.4   Three-phase sinusoidal sources

Three voltage sources displaced in phase by 120° and described by the equations

$$v_1(t) = V_1 \sin \omega t,$$
$$v_2(t) = V_2 \sin(\omega t - 120°), \qquad (2.35)$$

and

$$v_3(t) = V_3 \sin(\omega t - 240°),$$

where $V_1 = V_2 = V_3$, constitute a set called a *balanced three-phase* voltage source. If the peak values are not equal or if the phase differences are not exactly 120° and 240°, the three-phase source is said to be *unbalanced.* The waveforms corresponding to Equations 2.35 for the balanced case are shown in Figure 2.16.

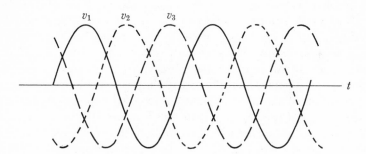

Figure 2.16   Balanced three-phase sinusoidal voltages.

The balanced three-phase voltages (similar definitions may be made for currents) are produced by commercial *alternators* and are of great importance in the power-generation and distribution field. In the alternator, these voltages are constrained to be of precisely the same frequency. The two common methods for connecting the three sources together are illustrated in Figure 2.17. These are the Y (or wye) and the Δ (delta) connections.

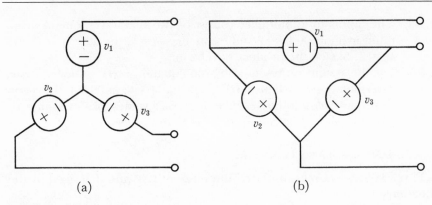

(a)   (b)

Figure 2.17 The two common methods of connecting three-phase sinusoidal sources together: (a) is known as a *Y* connection, and (b) as a delta.

2.5   Sampled signals and quantized signals

The operation of some systems containing a digital computer as one of the parts (an automatic control system in a high-speed aircraft or missile, for example) is based on *sampling* of a continuous input. In such a system, known as a *sampled data system*, the signal is not a continuous function of time but rather a train of sample values of the form shown in Figure 2.18. The sampling concept applies to waveforms like those studied earlier in this chapter and also to general signal waveforms like that of Figure 2.18.

The sampled output signal may be *restored* approximately from the train of signals to a continuous signal by employing an electronic device known as a *hold circuit* to *clamp* the signal at the last sampled value until the next sample arrives. An example of a partially restored waveform resulting from clamping is shown in Figure 2.19. Observe that a better approximation to a smooth curve is obtained if the sampling rate is high.

The operation of sampling is closely related to *quantizing*. In a *quantized signal*, the values of the signal at different instants of time are interpreted to be any one of a specified set of numbers. For example, a signal $v(t)$ may be sampled at $t = 0, 1, 2, 3, \ldots$ as in the second column of Table 2.1.

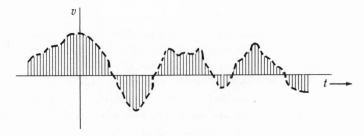

Figure 2.18 A sampled signal representation.

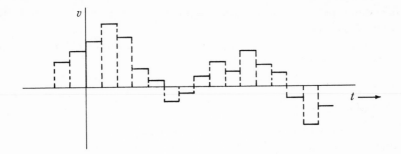

Figure 2.19 A partially restored sampled signal.

Table 2.1

t	Sampled value	Quantized value
0	0.45	0.50
1	1.20	1.00
2	1.60	1.50
3	1.40	1.50
4	1.35	1.50
5	2.10	2.00

Suppose that the quantized signal is allowed to have values among only the following set of numbers: 0, 0.5, 1, 1.5, 2, 2.5, 3.0. Then to produce the quantized signal, each sampled value is replaced or approximated by the closest available value allowable in the quantized signal. In this example, 0.45 is replaced by 0.50, 1.20 by 1.00, etc. as is shown in Table 2.1 and illustrated by Figure 2.20.

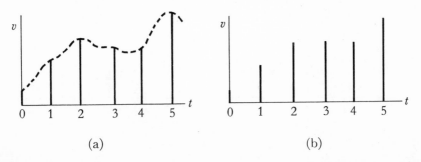

(a)   (b)

Figure 2.20 An illustration of the dual operations of first sampling a signal (a) and then quantizing it (rounding it off) as in (b).

In systems using sampling, quantizing is also usually used right after sampling. This is the case in a digital computer in a control system. Quantizing a sampled signal is analogous to the "rounding off" of empirical data. (See Problem 2-14.)

2.6 Signals with time delay

The notation which we shall use in describing signals which are shifted in time is easily described in terms of the operation of a magnetic tape recorder. We shall specify that our special tape recorder have two playback heads, identified as No. 1 and No. 2. With the tape moving forward at normal speed, there is a time interval t_1 in the passage of a given point on the tape through the two heads. Unless otherwise specified, assume that the two playback heads are set at the same gain level.

At the reference time $t = 0$, the tape begins to move with constant speed and head No. 1 plays back a recorded signal. Let $v_1(t)$ be the value of v_1 at time t having the waveform of Figure 2.21(a). The signal corresponding to head No. 2 is shown in Figure 2.21(b). How might we describe $v_2(t)$? Observe that the signal from the second head is *shifted* t_1 units of time to the right with respect to the signal from head No. 1. Clearly, the second signal waveform is described in terms of the first by the equation

$$v_2(t) = v_1(t - t_1). \tag{2.36}$$

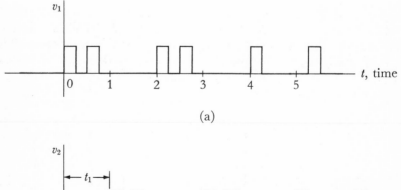

Figure 2.21 Signal waveform $v_2(t)$ is delayed by t_1 compared to $v_1(t)$.

The tape recorder is one example of a device capable of delaying a signal in time. Others are the transmission line and quartz crystal used as an acoustical delay line. All such devices may be represented by a model which will be identified as the *ideal delay line*. If the input signal to the ideal delay line is $v_1(t)$, then the output is $v_1(t-a)$, where a is the *delay*. For example, the application of a unit step signal, $u(t)$, at the input produces at the output a signal $u(t-a)$ as shown in Figure 2.22. The shifted step function, $u(t-a)$, is given by the equation

$$u(t-a) = \begin{cases} 1, & t \geq a, \\ 0, & t < a. \end{cases} \tag{2.37}$$

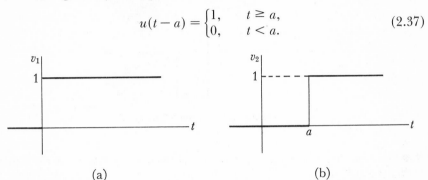

(a)   (b)

Figure 2.22 Input and output waveforms for a delay line.

Some waveforms for which we have frequent use can be regarded as having been generated by the use of delay lines. Figure 2.23 shows a rectangular pulse which may be written as

$$v_2(t) = u(t) - u(t-a), \tag{2.38}$$

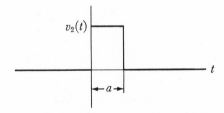

Figure 2.23 A rectangular pulse.

which is a pulse of width a. The linear combination of the two step functions, one positive, the other negative and delayed in time, together form a pulse. A model for a system which generates such a pulse may be represented by the set of equations

$$\begin{aligned} v_2(t) &= v_1(t) + v_3(t), \\ v_3(t) &= v_4(t-a), \\ v_4(t) &= -v_1(t), \end{aligned} \tag{2.39}$$

where $v_1(t)$ is the input, $v_2(t)$ is the output, and the pulse is obtained when the input is a unit step function.

A more complicated pulse is shown in Figure 2.24. This pulse may be represented by the equation

$$v_2(t) = u(t) - 2u(t-a) + u(t-2a). \tag{2.40}$$

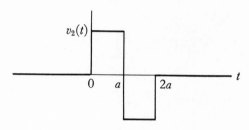

Figure 2.24   A double pulse.

This scheme for representing waveforms may be extended to describe a "square wave,"

$$v_2(t) = u(t) + \sum_{k=1}^{\infty} (-1)^k 2u(t-ka). \tag{2.41}$$

as shown in Figure 2.25.

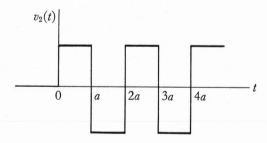

Figure 2.25   A square wave.

● EXERCISES

2.6-1   Let v_2 of Equation 2.36 be recorded from head No. 2 with $t_1 = 4$. Sketch $v_2(t)$ if v_1 has the waveform of Figure 2.21(a).

2.6-2   Let v_1 be the input to an ideal delay line of delay a, $v_1(t) = K_1 e^{-\sigma_1 t} \sin(\omega_1 t + \phi_1) u(t)$. Determine $v_2(t)$.

2.6-3   Repeat Exercise 2.6-2 for $v_1 = A_2 \sin(\omega_2 t + \phi_2)$. Show that the derivative of the negative of the phase shift caused by the passage of a sine wave through an ideal delay line with respect to the angular frequency ω_2 is the time delay.

2.6-4   A system is described by the equation $v_2(t) = v_1(t) - 2v_1[t - (a/2)]$. Determine the output $v_2(t)$ when the input is a rectangular pulse of duration a. Sketch the waveform of the output signal.

2.6-5   Repeat Exercise 2.6-4 for the system described by $v_2(t) = v_1(t) - v_1(t - a)$.

2.6-6   A system is described by

$$v_2(t) = \int_0^t v_1(\tau)\, d\tau - v_1(t - 1)$$

as schematically represented in the figure. Sketch the output for the given input.

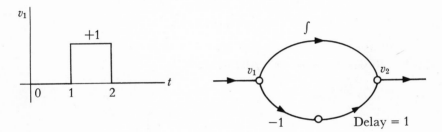

Figure Exercise 2.6-6

2.6-7   A system is described by $v_2(t) = 2v_1(t) + v_1[t - (\pi/2)]$. Sketch $v_2(t)$ for $v_1(t) = \sin 2t$.

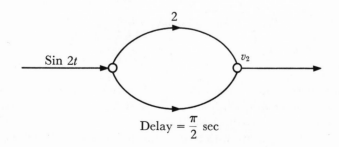

Figure Exercise 2.6-7

2.6-8 Given the following signal

$$v_1(t) = \begin{cases} 0, & \text{for} \quad t < 0, \\ v_0 t, & \text{for} \quad 0 \le t \le 1, \\ 0, & \text{for} \quad t > 1, \end{cases}$$

sketch $v_2(t) = v_1(t - 2) + v_1(t - 3)$.

2.6-9 The output of a system is the sweep voltage shown in the figure. Express the output in terms of delayed functions.

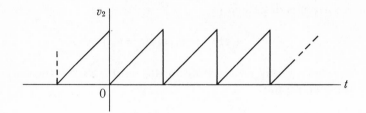

Figure Exercise 2.6-9

2.6-10 Repeat for $v_2(t)$ as in the figure.

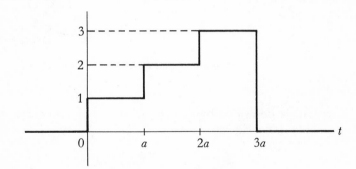

Figure Exercise 2.6-10

Problems

2-1 One of the most interesting signals is that which propagates along a nerve fiber in the human body when a neuron is properly excited (say by a sock on the jaw). This signal is in the form of a pulse as shown in the figure with a time duration of about 1 millisecond and an amplitude of about 200 millivolts. Write an equation, a mathematical abstraction, of this signal waveform, evaluating all constants in your equation.

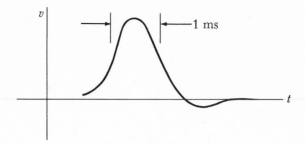

Figure Problem 2-1

2-2 (a) Sketch the function

$$f(t) = \begin{cases} \dfrac{1}{\sigma} e^{-t/\sigma}, & t \geq 0, \\ 0, & t < 0, \end{cases}$$

as a function of t for $\sigma = 1, 0.5, 0.1$.

(b) Calculate the area under the curve for this function.

(c) The limit of $f(t)$ as σ approaches zero may be used as a definition for the delta function. Does this definition have advantages over the definition based on a pulse?

2-3 Repeat Problem 2-2 for the function

$$f(t) = \frac{1}{\sqrt{2\pi}} e^{-t^2/2}.$$

Calculate the integral† of this function from $-\infty$ to $+\infty$. This function is known as a Gaussian or normal distribution.

2-4 Repeat Problem 2-3 if t is replaced by $t - T_0$ where T_0 is a constant.

2-5 Sketch the function

$$v(t) = \begin{cases} \dfrac{\pi}{2\epsilon} \sin \dfrac{\pi}{\epsilon} (t + \epsilon) & -\epsilon \leq t \leq 0, \\ 0, & t < -\epsilon \quad \text{and} \quad t > 0. \end{cases}$$

Show that the integral of $v(t)$ approaches a unit step as $\epsilon \to 0$.

2-6 A new function is defined by the equation

$$\int_{-\infty}^{t} r(\tau) \, d\tau = p(t),$$

where $r(t)$ is the unit ramp. Sketch $p(t)$. What name for $p(t)$ do you think is appropriate?

† See Dwight, *Table of Integrals and Other Mathematical Data*, The Macmillan Company, New York, 1957, Integral 861.3.

2-7   A waveform is approximated by a number of straight line segments in the accompanying figure. For this "piecewise linear" waveform, plot dv/dt and d^2v/dt^2.

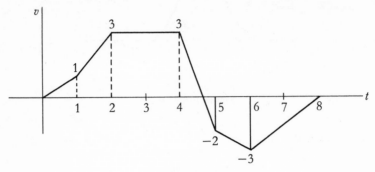

Figure Problem 2-7

2-8   The impulse train shown in the accompanying figure represents the second derivative of a function, $f(t)$. Determine $f(t)$. State any assumptions made in arriving at your answer.

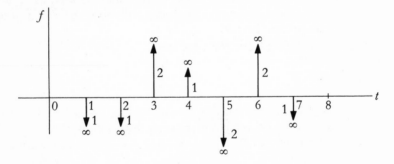

Figure Problem 2-8

2-9   The input signal to the system represented by the signal-flow schematic of the figure or the equation $v_2(t) = v_1(t) + dv_1(t)\ dt$ is $v_1 = 2 \sin 2t$. Show that the output signal, $v_2(t)$, has the form $v_2 = A \sin (2t + \phi)$ and determine A and ϕ.

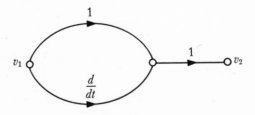

Figure Problem 2-9

2-10 (a) Express the waveform in Figure Problem 2-10(a) in terms of steps, ramps, delayed steps, delayed ramps, etc.
(b) Repeat (a) for the waveform in Figure Problem 2-10(b).
(c) Specify a system (by means of its equations) where input is a unit step and where output is the waveform in Figure Problem 2-10(a).
(d) Repeat (c) for the waveform in Figure Problem 2-10(b).

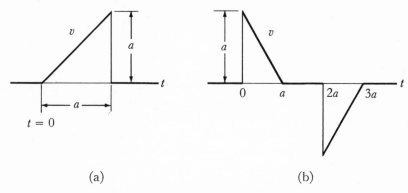

(a)   (b)

Figure Problem 2-10

2-11 Prepare sketches of the waveforms described by the following equations:
(a) $r(t-3)$,
(b) $\sum_{n=0}^{10} \delta(t-nT)$,   for $T=1$,
(c) $u(t) \sin \frac{2\pi t}{T}$, $u(t-T/2) \sin \frac{2\pi t}{T}$, $u(t-T) \sin \frac{2\pi t}{T}$,
(d) $r(t)u(t-1)$, $r(t) - r(t-1) - u(t-1)$.

2-12 Sketch the function

$$g(t) = \int_{-\infty}^{t} f(x)\, dx$$

vs. t, where $f(t)$ is given in Problem 2-2 for $\sigma = 1, 0.5, 0.1$. Discuss the limiting plot for $\sigma \to 0$.

2-13 Sketch the function

$$r_1(t) = \int_{-\infty}^{t} g(x)\, dx$$

vs. t, where $g(t)$ is given in Problem 2-12 for $\sigma = 1, 0.5, 0.1$. The limit of $r_1(t)$ as σ approaches zero may be used as a definition for a unit ramp.

2-14 In this and the previous chapter, we have introduced two similarly related descriptions: (1) devices and models; and (2) device wave-

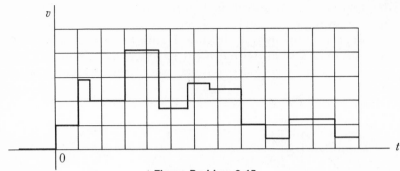

Figure Problem 2-15

forms and their mathematical abstractions. In working problems and in equipment design, we make use of *exact numbers* and *approximate numbers*. In distinguishing these two kinds of numbers, the following expressions are useful: (a) roundoff of a number, roundoff error; (b) number of significant digits; and (c) margin of error.†
Discuss the meaning of these expressions with respect to the actual and idealized quantities listed under (1) and (2).

2-15 (a) Show that any staircase signal such as that shown in the figure can be represented as a sum of step functions of various magnitudes and delays, that is

$$v(t) = \sum_{k=0}^{N} a_k u(t - \tau_k).$$

2-16 Specify the equations of a system where input is a unit impulse and where output is as shown in Figure Problem 2-7. Your system may contain amplifiers, integrators, ideal delay lines, and adders.

2-17 A special tape recorder (No. 1) contains a tape with a recorded signal $v_1(t)$ on it, while another similar recorder (No. 2) is loaded with a blank tape. The output from No. 1 is to be recorded on No. 2. Both recorders are turned on simultaneously with the tapes beginning to travel in the same forward direction. After t_a seconds, the tapes are stopped. A switch for reversing the direction of travel of tape No. 1 is closed. The tapes are started again, with tape No. 2 traveling forward and tape No. 1 backward, for a period of t_b seconds. After t_b seconds, the tapes are stopped and the switch is thrown so that tape No. 1 may run forward again. The tapes are then started and are permitted to run forward until they run out completely. Determine an equation for the signal $v_2(t)$ in terms of $v_1(t)$.

† For a good review of these topics, see Virginia L. Senders, *Measurement and Statistics*, Oxford University Press, New York, 1958, pp. 3-32.

Partial Signal Specifications   **3**

In Chapters 1 and 2, we discussed signals that were specified either in equation form or by tabular or graphical display. For many purposes, it is not necessary to give such *complete* specification of a signal. If, for example, we are interested in knowing if a device or component such as a capacitor will fail due to overvoltage, then we need know only the maximum or peak value of the magnitude of the signal voltage. For other purposes, we find frequent use for such specifications as average value, root-mean-square value, rise time, overshoot, and settling time. These quantities are *partial specifications* of a waveform; they represent digested information about some interesting property of a signal. These characterizing partial specifications are considered in this chapter.

3.1 Average value of a signal

The average (or arithmetic mean) of n numbers is found from the familiar relationship

$$\bar{a} = \frac{a_1 + a_2 + \cdots + a_n}{n}.$$
$$(3.1)$$

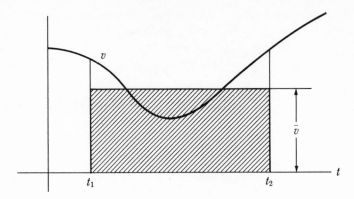

Figure 3.1 Here $\bar{v}$ is the average or mean value of $v(t)$ over the interval from t_1 to t_2.

What do we mean by the average or mean value of a continuous function rather than n numbers? If the function $v(t)$ can be integrated over an interval from t_1 to t_2, then the average value $\bar{v}$ multiplied by the interval is equal to the area under $v(t)$ from t_1 to t_2 as shown in Figure 3.1. Thus we have

$$(t_2 - t_1)\bar{v} = \int_{t_1}^{t_2} v(t)\ dt. \tag{3.2}$$

In other words, the *average value* of $v(t)$ over the range t_1 to t_2 is

$$\bar{v} = \frac{1}{t_2 - t_1} \int_{t_1}^{t_2} v(t)\ dt. \tag{3.3}$$

We consider now an important class of signals, the set of periodic signals, meaning that the signal waveform repeats itself. More precisely, $v(t)$ is periodic if there is a quantity T such that

$$v(t) = v(t + T) \tag{3.4}$$

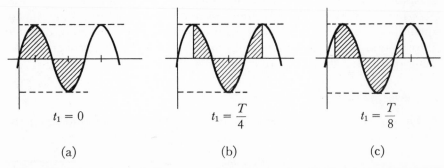

Figure 3.2 Area under periodic curve over a range $t_2 - t_1 = T$ is the same regardless of the value of t_1.

for all t. The smallest T that satisfies the condition in Equation 3.4 is called the *period* as defined in the previous chapter for sinusoidal signals. If $t_2 - t_1 = T$, then the average value $\bar{v}$ is

$$\bar{v} = \frac{1}{T} \int_{t_1}^{t_1+T} v(t) \, dt. \tag{3.5}$$

Notice that the area under a periodic curve over a range $t_2 - t_1 = T$ is the same for all t_1. This is illustrated in Figure 3.2. We should always choose t_1 for the most convenient numerical evaluation in a specific situation. If $t_2 - t_1 = 2T$, we see that the total area under the curve will be twice that if $t_2 - t_1$ were just T. Hence the average value $\bar{v}$ is the same as that for $t_2 - t_1 = T$. It is easy to see that the average value of a periodic signal over an integral multiple of a complete period is equal to the average value over one complete period.

Suppose however that $t_2 - t_1$ is not an integral multiple of T, that is, $t_2 = t_1 + nT + \tau$, where n is 0 or any integer 1, 2, 3, . . . and τ is a positive quantity less than T. If we denote the area under the periodic curve over a period by A_1 and the area under the curve from $t_1 + nT$ to $t_1 + nT + \tau$ by A_0, then we have

$$\bar{v} = \frac{1}{nT + \tau} \int_{t_1}^{t_1 + nT + \tau} v(t) \, dt = \frac{1}{nT + \tau} [nA_1 + A_0]. \tag{3.6}$$

We see that provided A_0 is finite, then as n becomes large, $\bar{v}$ becomes almost equal to A_1/T. In practical devices for measuring average value, $t_2 - t_1$ is often not an integral multiple of T, but $t_2 - t_1$ is often relatively much larger than T and A_0 is finite in all practical cases so that the error involved in assuming that it is the value given in Equation 3.5 is small. We shall then take the average value of a periodic signal as that which corresponds to one complete period.

An interesting special case of Equation 3.5 occurs when the periodic function of period T has symmetry. This leads to simplification in the calculation of the area under the curve.

EXAMPLE 3.1-1. For the periodic signal shown in Figure 3.3, we see

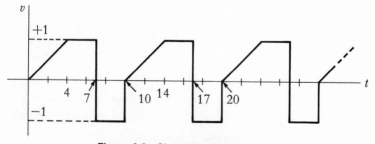

Figure 3.3 Signal for Example 3.1-1.

that the waveform repeats itself after every 10 seconds so that $T = 10$. The average value is seen by inspection to be

$$\bar{v} = \frac{1}{10}\left(\frac{1 \times 4}{2} + 1 \times 3 - 1 \times 3\right) = 0.2. \ \square \qquad (3.7)$$

EXAMPLE 3.1-2.   For the sine wave $v(t) = V \sin(2\pi/T)t$, the area under the curve from 0 to $T/2$ is the negative of the area under the curve from $T/2$ to T. Hence the average value of a sine wave over any number of periods is zero. $\square$

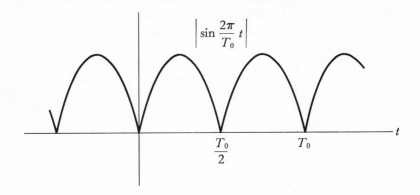

Figure 3.4   Full-wave rectified sine wave.

EXAMPLE 3.1-3.   Consider the periodic waveform of Figure 3.4 which is the magnitude of a sine function,

$$v(t) = \left|\sin\frac{2\pi}{T_0}t\right|. \qquad (3.8)$$

This wave is known as a *full-wave rectified sine wave*. By inspection of the waveform, we see that the period is $T_0/2$. Note also that the area under the curve from 0 to $T_0/4$ is equal to that from $T_0/4$ to $T_0/2$. This symmetry allows us to write

$$\bar{v} = \frac{1}{(T_0/2)} \cdot 2 \cdot \int_0^{T_0/4} \sin\frac{2\pi}{T_0}t \ dt = \frac{2}{\pi} \cdot \square\dagger \qquad (3.9)$$

● EXERCISES

3.1-1   What is the period of the signal $v(t)$ in Figure Exercise 3.1-1? This waveform is known as a half-wave rectified sine wave.

† The symbol $\square$ is used to indicate the end of an example.

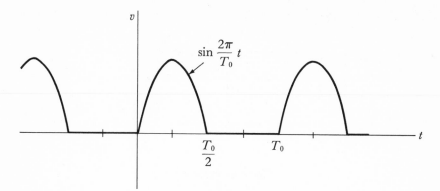

Figure Exercise 3.1-1

3.1-2   What is the average value of $v(t)$ for Exercise 3.1-1?

3.1-3   Is the waveform shown in the figure periodic? Give a reason or reasons for your answer.

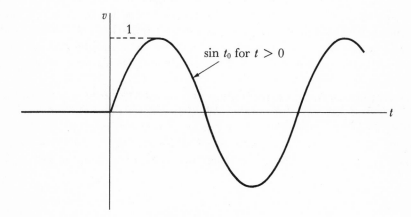

Figure Exercise 3.1-3

3.1-4   What is the average value of the signal of Figure Exercise 3.3-10? The waveshape is shown for one cycle.

3.1-5   Determine the average value of the waveform of the figure as a function of a and K.

3.1-6   If the average value of a periodic signal $v_{12}(t)$ is V_0, what is the average value of $v_{21}(t)$?

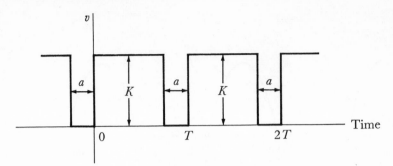

Figure Exercise 3.1-5

3.2   Peak value of a signal

The *peak value* of a signal is its maximum absolute value. This definition is general, applying to both periodic and aperiodic (nonperiodic) signal waveforms. Applying this definition to the waveforms of Figures 3.3 and 3.4, we see that each has a peak value of one. For periodic signals, especially sinusoidal signals, we will use capital letters with the subscript m or max. Thus, if $v(t)$ is sinusoidal, we designate its peak value V_m or V_{max} in the equation, $v(t) = V_m \sin(\omega t + \phi)$. In the introduction to the chapter, we mentioned that peak values of current are similarly important in establishing the rating of many electric devices. In vacuum-tube and semiconductor diodes, the allowable peak inverse voltage is a critical design and operating quantity.

A quantity useful in the calibration and use of a cathode ray oscillograph is the *peak-to-peak* value of a signal. We define this value to be the algebraic difference of the maximum signal value and the minimum signal value. In the case of a sinusoidal signal of maximum value V_m, the peak-to-peak value is clearly $2V_m$. For a general signal, it is as represented in Figure 3.5.

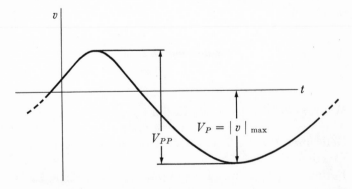

Figure 3.5   The identification of peak value and peak-to-peak value for an arbitrary signal.

● EXERCISES

3.2-1 Find the peak value and the peak-to-peak value of the signal wave-forms shown in Figure Exercise 3.2-1.

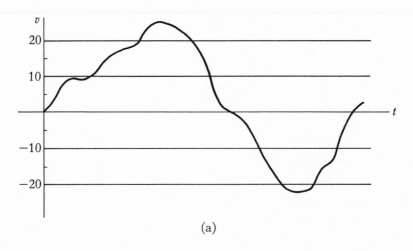

(a)

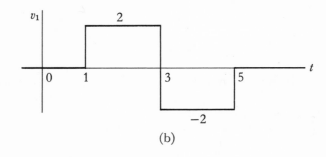

(b)

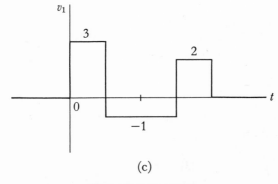

(c)

Figure Exercise 3.2-1

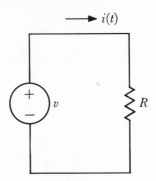

Figure 3.6   Periodic voltage source connected to *R* for definition of rms value.

3.3   Root-mean-square value of a signal

A periodic voltage $v(t)$ is impressed across the resistor shown in Figure 3.6. The current through the resistor is related to this voltage by Ohm's law,

$$i(t) = \frac{1}{R} v(t). \tag{3.10}$$

The instantaneous power is

$$p(t) = v(t)i(t) = \frac{1}{R} v^2(t). \tag{3.11}$$

Our objective is to characterize $v(t)$ under the constraint that the energy delivered to the resistor is equal to that of an equivalent time-invariant voltage source. Since power is the time rate of energy transfer, the total energy delivered to the resistor over the time interval from 0 to T is

$$W = \int_0^T p(t) \ dt = \int_0^T \frac{1}{R} v^2(t) \ dt. \tag{3.12}$$

Suppose now that instead of the periodic voltage $v(t)$, we have the constant voltage of an ideal battery V connected to the resistor. From Equation 3.11, the corresponding instantaneous power is

$$p = VI = \frac{1}{R} V^2. \tag{3.13}$$

Since p is constant if V is constant, the energy delivered to the resistor over the interval from 0 to T is

$$W = pT = \frac{1}{R} V^2 T. \tag{3.14}$$

Equating Equations 3.12 and 3.14 gives

$$\frac{1}{R} V^2 T = \frac{1}{R} \int_0^T v^2(t)\ dt, \tag{3.15}$$

$$V = \sqrt{\frac{1}{T} \int_0^T v^2(t)\ dt}. \tag{3.16}$$

This characteristic value is known as the *effective* value or *root-mean-square* (abbreviated rms) value of the periodic voltage $v(t)$. The rms value concept applies only to *periodic* signals. It is the effective voltage in the sense that it results in the same heating of the resistor (heat and energy being proportional) as would result from a time-invariant source of the same value. This quantity will be distinguished by the subscripts *eff* or *rms*. This same definition applies to a periodic current and to other physical quantities. As for the average value studied in the first section of this chapter, the integration may be performed starting at any time t_a and continuing for one period to $t_a + T$. Thus, Equation 3.16 becomes

$$V_{\mathrm{rms}} = \sqrt{\frac{1}{T} \int_{t_a}^{t_a + T} v^2(t)\ dt}. \tag{3.17}$$

In any given situation, t_a may be chosen to make computation easy.

EXAMPLE 3.3-1. Consider the sine wave $v(t) = V_m \sin \omega t$. The effective value of this signal is

$$V_{\mathrm{rms}} = \sqrt{\frac{1}{T} \int_{t_a}^{t_a + T} V_m^2 \sin^2 \omega t\ dt} \tag{3.18}$$

$$= \sqrt{\frac{V_m^2}{T} \int_0^T \frac{1 - \cos 2\omega t}{2} dt} \tag{3.19}$$

$$= \sqrt{\frac{V_m^2}{T} \left(\frac{1}{2} t - \frac{1}{4\omega} \sin 2\omega t \right) \Big|_0^T} \tag{3.20}$$

$$= \sqrt{\frac{V_m^2}{T} \left(\frac{1}{2} T - \frac{1}{4\omega} \sin 2\omega T \right)}. \tag{3.21}$$

Now, since $\omega T = 2\pi$, $\sin 2\omega T = 0$, and we have

$$v_{\mathrm{rms}} = \frac{V_m}{\sqrt{2}} \approx 0.707\ V_m. \tag{3.22}$$

This result will be used repeatedly in working with sinusoidal signals. You should memorize it.

●   **EXERCISES**

3.3-1   Calculate the rms value of the signal shown in the figure.

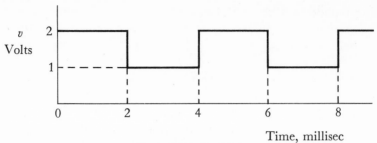

Figure Exercise 3.3-1

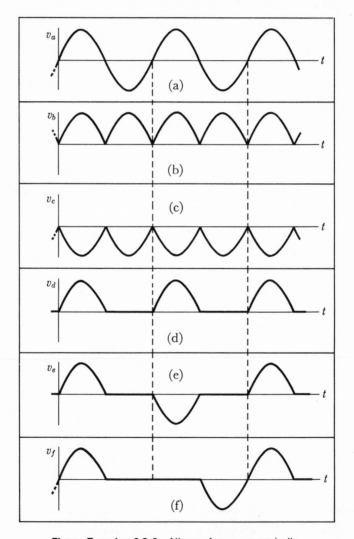

Figure Exercise 3.3-2   All waveforms are periodic.

3.3-2 The sine waves or parts of sine waves shown in the figure all have the same maximum amplitude. If the rms value of the signal shown as (a) is 0.648 volts, find the rms value of the other signals.

3.3-3 The periodic waveform shown in (a) of the figure causes a power dissipation of one watt in a resistor. Find the power dissipation in the same resistor produced by the other voltage waveforms of the figure.

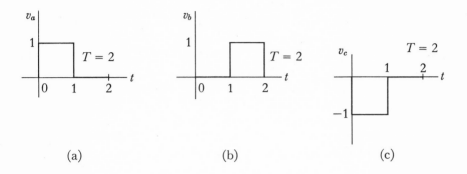

(a)   (b)   (c)

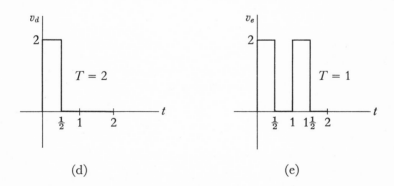

(d)   (e)

Figure Exercise 3.3-3

3.3-4 Determine the rms value of the signal given in Figure 3.3 (p. 49).

3.3-5 Repeat Exercise 3.3-4 for the signal of Figure 3.4 (p. 50).

3.3-6 Calculate the rms value of the signal $v(t) = V_m \cos (\omega t + \phi)$.

3.3-7 Find the rms value of the signal represented by the equation $v(t) = 5 + 2 \sin 3t$.

3.3-8 Determine the rms value of the signal $v(t) = 5 \sin \omega t + 4 \cos (\omega t + \pi/6)$.

3.3-9 If the rms value of $v_{12}(t)$ is V, what is the rms value of $v_{21}(t)$?

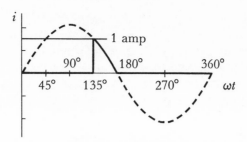

Figure Exercise 3.3-10

3.3-10   The portion of a sine wave shown in the figure represents the
current in a grid-controlled Thyratron. In one cycle, the current
is sinusoidal from $\omega t = 135°$ to $180°$ but otherwise zero. If the
signal has a maximum amplitude of one ampere, find the rms
value of the current.

3.4   Specification of the response to a step input

The step function described in Chapter 2 is an important signal in the
testing of a network or a system. With a step applied at the input, the output or response of many systems has the waveform similar to that shown in
Figure 3.7. In comparison to the input step, the output overshoots, under-
shoots, and continues to oscillate with decreasing amplitude. The overshoot is one characteristic by which the response may be described. If the
steady-state value of the response $v(t)$ is $v(\infty)$ and if $v(\infty)$ is not zero, then
the *overshoot* is

$$\text{overshoot} = v_{\max} - v(\infty), \tag{3.23}$$

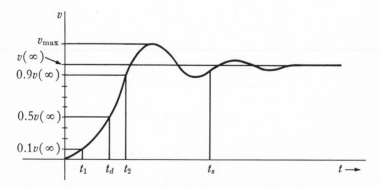

Figure 3.7   The form of response for which overshoot, rise time, time delay, and settling
time are defined.

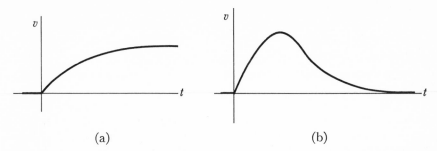

Figure 3.8 Signal waveform in (a) has zero overshoot. In (b), overshoot is not defined.

where v_{max} is the peak value. We sometimes speak of *percent overshoot* by which we mean

$$\text{percent overshoot} = \frac{v_{max} - v(\infty)}{v(\infty)} \times 100\%. \qquad (3.24)$$

Overshoot is not defined when $v(\infty) = 0$. The signals of Figure 3.8, for example, are such that overshoot is zero and undefined respectively.

Rise time is defined for the same response signal as overshoot. Referring to Figure 3.7, we find that the rise time is defined as

$$\text{rise time} = t_2 - t_1, \qquad (3.25)$$

where t_1 is the time at which $v(t) = 0.1 \, v(\infty)$ and t_2 is the time at which $v(t) = 0.9 \, v(\infty)$ as shown in the figure. The numbers 0.1 and 0.9 are most commonly used but other conventions are in existence. Rise time is an important specification when speed of response is important and thus applies to components of digital computers, nuclear counters, pulse generators and test equipment like cathode-ray oscillographs. Rise times range from fractions of a nanosecond† in electronic equipment to several seconds in the case of large electromechanical servomechanisms.

Rise time gives one measure of the speed of a system in reacting to a step input. Another is *time delay* (which we must distinguish from delay time in a delay line as studied in Chapter 2). For some responses, the time elapsed from the value $t = 0$ to the time at which $v(t) = 0.1 \, v(\infty)$ may be large compared to the rise time. For such a situation, an additional specification is useful. The *time delay* is defined as the time interval from $t = 0$ until the time at which $v(t) = 0.5 \, v(\infty)$. Roughly speaking, it is the time required for an "appreciable" response to appear. Knowing both the rise time and the time delay gives a more accurate description of the response waveform than either of the two specifications alone.

† 1 nanosecond = 10^{-9} second.

The signal $v(t)$ of Figure 3.7 has an oscillatory behavior as it approaches its steady value $v(\infty)$. A rough measure of the decay of the oscillation is called the *settling time*. It is defined as the time elapsed between the application of the step input ($t = 0$) and the time at which the oscillation is "negligible." By negligible, we usually mean that $[v(t) - v(\infty)]$ is not greater than five percent of the steady value $v(\infty)$.

The four characteristics, overshoot, rise time, time delay, and settling time, together describe a step response in sufficient detail for many purposes. The student will find in working the exercises that he can construct the response waveform from the four specifications with reasonable accuracy.

● EXERCISES

3.4-1 Determine the overshoot and the percent overshoot for the waveform given in the figure.

3.4-2 A response signal is given by the equation $v_1(t) = 1 - e^{-t} \cos \omega t$. Find an expression for the overshoot of this signal.

3.4-3 Given the response signal

$$v(t) = K(1 - e^{-\sigma_1 t}), \qquad t \geq 0 \qquad \text{and} \qquad \sigma_1 > 0,$$

show that the rise time is approximately $2.2/\sigma_1$.

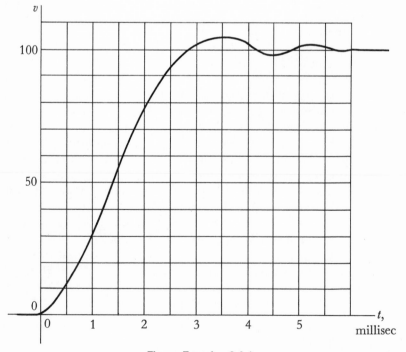

Figure Exercise 3.4-1

3.4-4 Determine the rise time and time delay of the waveform shown in the figure of Exercise 3.4-1.

3.4-5 For the signal described in Exercise 3.4-3, find an expression for the time delay in terms of σ_1.

3.4-6 Find the settling time for the signal of Exercise 3.4-2 with $\omega = 1$.

3.5 The measurement of signal characteristics

Practical meters and instruments measure many of the characteristics described in this chapter. For example, D'Arsonval-type meters measure average values of current and voltage, dynamometer- and thermocouple-type meters measure effective or root-mean-square values of voltage and current. Other instruments have been designed to measure peak values of voltage or current.

The step-response characteristics described in Section 3.4 are not ordinarily directly measured by an instrument. From a recording of such a waveform or the waveform displayed on a cathode ray oscillograph, it is an easy matter to measure the four quantities that have been described.

Problems

3-1 This problem is concerned with the properties of periodic functions. (a) Is the product of two sine waves, $v(t) = \sin \omega_1 t \sin \omega_2 t$, always periodic? (b) Is $v(t) = \sin \omega t + \sin 2\omega t$ periodic? How about $v_1(t) = \sin \omega t + \sin \sqrt{2}\omega t$? In general, is the sum of any number of sine waves always periodic? Explain. (d) Is the product of two periodic functions always periodic? Explain.

3-2 Show that the average value of the sum of N periodic functions with identical periods is equal to the sum of the average values of the N periodic functions.

3-3 A sinusoidal signal is passed through a limiter which clips off the top and bottom of the sinusoid. The clipping level is set at one half the peak value of the signal. Calculate the rms value of the clipped signal. Assume an arbitrary peak value V_0 and frequency ω.

3-4 Show that if $v_1(t)$ and $v_2(t)$ are periodic and if their periods are harmonically related ($nT_1 = mT_2$, where T_1 and T_2 are the periods and n and m are integers), then the rms value of $v(t) = v_1(t) + v_2(t)$ is given by

$$V_{\text{rms}}^2 = V_{1\text{rms}}^2 + V_{2\text{rms}}^2,$$

provided further that

$$\int_0^T v_1(t)v_2(t) = 0,$$

where T is the period of $v(t)$.

3-5   Extend the result in Problem 3.4 to the sum of N functions.

3-6   Show that in general the rms value of the sum of periodic waves is not equal to the sum of the rms values of the periodic waves.

3-7   For the signal response resulting from a unit-step input $v_1(t) = K_1(1 - e^{-\sigma_1 t} \cos \omega t)$, determine an expression for the rise time, the time delay, and the overshoot. Let $\sigma_1 = \frac{1}{2}\omega$.

3-8   If $v(t)$ is a periodic signal with an average value V_{av} and an rms value of V_{rms}, show that $V_{av} \leq V_{rms}$. [*Hint:* Let $v(t) = V_{av} + v(t) - V_{av}$.]

3-9   If $\bar{v}_1$ is the average value of a periodic signal $v_1(t)$, what is the average value of $v_2(t) = v_1(t + \tau)$, where τ is a constant? How about the average value of $v_3(t) = K v_1(t + \tau)$, where K and τ are constants?

3-10 If V_1 is the rms value of a periodic signal $v_1(t)$, what is the rms value of $v_2(t) = v_1(t + \tau)$, where τ is a constant? How about the rms value of $v_3(t) = K v_1(t + \tau)$, where K and τ are constants.

3-11 If V_m is the peak value of a signal $v_1(t)$, what is the peak value of $v_1(t + \tau)$, where τ is a constant?

3-12 Show that if $v(t) = V_0 + v_1(t)$, where $v_1(t)$ is periodic with zero average value and V_0 is constant, then

$$V_{rms} = \sqrt{V_0^2 + V_{1rms}^2},$$

where V_{1rms} is the rms value of v_1.

Network Models for Devices   **4**

In the preceding chapters, we have introduced idealized operations such as differentiation, integration, addition, and multiplication for the processing of signals. In this chapter we shall associate some of these operations with models for the physical components or devices. An interconnection of these components constitutes a *network*. The word *circuit* is sometimes used interchangeably for network, but usually, circuit refers to a relatively simple (perhaps one-loop) network consisting of a few components. Another term which we have used frequently in the preceding chapters is *system*. The meaning we attach to it is a set of things or parts forming a whole. Thus a network may or may not be a system depending on whether it is the whole or simply a part. A physical system may contain components which are electrical, mechanical, hydraulic, pneumatic, etc. In this chapter, we shall describe the most commonly used models for electrical and mechanical components. These models are called *network elements*.

4.1 Terminal properties of *R*, *L*, and *C* elements

A complete understanding of the electric behavior of electric components and devices requires an understanding of the interaction of materials
with electric, magnetic, and electromagnetic fields. However, in studying
the total behavior of networks—interconnections of components—it is
often times sufficient to characterize the components by their external
behavior. For example, the effect of a component on the overall behavior
of an interconnection of components may be adequately assessed by knowing *what* the terminal voltage–terminal current relationship is for the
particular component, rather than knowing *how* or *why* such a component
exhibits its characteristics. The main concern of network analysis is to
determine not only *what* but *how* and *why* a total network characteristic is
caused by individual component behaviors and characteristics. The components are represented by models whose external behaviors approximate
those of the actual components.

The first model we consider is that of a *resistor*, a two-terminal component or device which has relatively negligible electric or magnetic-field
energy-storage capability. Its external behavior is approximately described
by a function relationship between voltage and current at the terminals.
The relationship may be given graphically rather than analytically. An
example of such a relationship is shown in Figure 4.1. The graph specifies
what the current will be for any voltage *v* across the resistor model. Suppose that the resistor model of Figure 4.1 is connected to a voltage source
such as an ideal battery as shown in Figure 4.2. Since the battery voltage

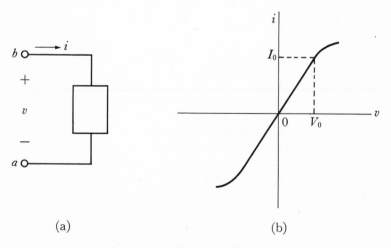

(a)   (b)

Figure 4.1 An example of the terminal characteristics of a resistor model.

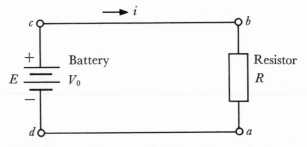

Figure 4.2   A series connection of a resistor and a battery.

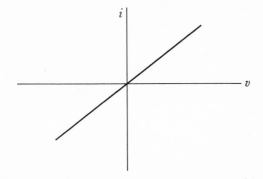

Figure 4.3   The *v-i* characteristic for a constant linear resistor model.

$v_{cd} = V_0$ is impressed across terminals b and a, we see that $v_{ba} = V_0$. Then according to Figure 4.1(b), the resulting current will be I_0. A simpler model is shown in Figure 4.3. In the latter case, v and i are linearly related by

$$v = Ri, \qquad (4.1)$$

where R is a *constant*. The quantity R is called the *resistance* of the model and $1/R$ is called *conductance*. The symbol for the resistor model is shown in Figure 4.4. If v and i are in volts and amperes, respectively, then R is in

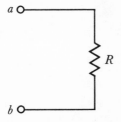

Figure 4.4   Symbol for the resistor model.

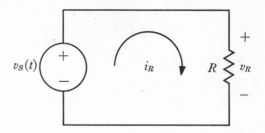

Figure 4.5 A general voltage source connected to a resistor.

ohms, and *G* is in *mhos*, named after the German scientist Georg Ohm, who postulated Equation 4.1. Equation 4.1 is also known as Ohm's law. Instead of a battery, suppose we connect a general voltage source with time-varying magnitude and polarity, as in Figure 4.5. If the reference direction for the current is taken in the clockwise direction shown in Figure 4.5 and the voltage polarity marks are such that the plus terminals of the source and resistor are superimposed, then comparison with the situation of Figures 4.1 and 4.2 shows that this circuit is described by Ohm's law in the form

$$v_R(t) = Ri_R(t). \tag{4.2}$$

If either the current reference or the voltage reference is reversed, then Ohm's law becomes

$$v_R(t) = -Ri_R(t). \tag{4.3}$$

For the reference possibilities of Figure 4.6, we see that (a) and (b) are described by Equation 4.2, while those of (c) and (d) require the use of Equation 4.3.

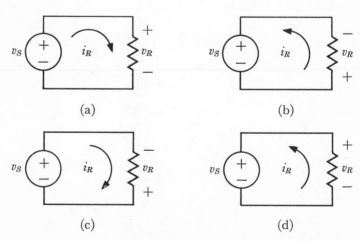

Figure 4.6 For (a) and (b), Ohm's law is Equation 4.2; for (c) and (d), it is Equation 4.3.

The resistor R is said to be linear and constant (or time-invariant) whenever v and i are related by a linear equation such as in Equation 4.2 and where R is not a function of time. If R is an explicit function of time, the resistor is said to be time-varying. If R in Equation 4.1 depends on i or v, then the resistor is described as nonlinear. Thus a resistor represented by the equation

$$v(t) = 22i(t) \tag{4.4}$$

is linear time-invariant; one represented by

$$v(t) = 33(1 + \tfrac{1}{2}e^{-t})i(t) \tag{4.5}$$

is linear time-varying; one represented by

$$v(t) = 47i^2(t) = [47i(t)]i(t) \tag{4.6}$$

is nonlinear; and one represented by

$$v(t) = (100 + 10 \sin t)\,\sqrt{i(t)} \tag{4.7}$$

is nonlinear. For nonlinear resistors, resistance may be defined either as the ratio v/i or the slope dv/di, depending on the application. For linear resistors, the two definitions yield the same quantity. For nonlinear resistors, the voltage corresponding to a given current or the current corresponding to a given voltage may not be unique. For instance, in Figure 4.7, there are some current values for which there are three possible voltage values. In Figure 4.8, for $v = 1$, there correspond infinitely many possible values between $i = 1$ and $i = 2$ for the current. However, in Figure 4.7, v uniquely defines i, that is to say, for any given v there is only one i. This characteristic is said to be *voltage-controlled.* Similarly in Figure 4.8, i uniquely defines v and the characteristic is said to be *current-controlled.* Thus we speak of a current-controlled resistor or a voltage-controlled resistor. The characteristic in Figure 4.1 is both voltage-controlled and current-controlled. Linear resistors are always current-controlled as well as voltage-controlled.

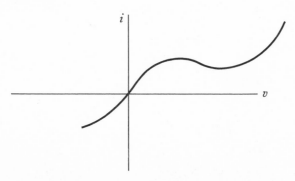

Figure 4.7 A voltage-controlled resistor characteristic.

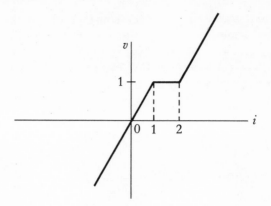

Figure 4.8 A current-controlled resistor characteristic.

For the nonlinear resistor, the equation relating v and i is nonlinear. Considering only voltage-controlled or current-controlled resistors, if the relationship between v and i does not contain time t explicitly, the resistor is said to be time-invariant. Otherwise, it is time-varying. For example, the relation expressed by Equation 4.6 does not involve t explicitly so that the nonlinear resistor is time-invariant; the resistor associated with Equation 4.7 is time-varying as well as nonlinear because time t appears explicitly.

The second network element we consider is the model for a component known as a *capacitor*. It is a component or device which has relatively negligible magnetic-field storage capability, negligible dissipation of energy, and so behaves as an electric-field energy-storage device. The capacitor device is approximated by a capacitor model and associated equation which relates the charge and voltage across the two terminals. Charge is the time integral of current, or current is the time rate of charge transfer. Figure 4.9 shows the symbol for the capacitor model, and Figures 4.10

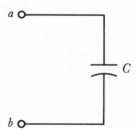

Figure 4.9 Symbol for the capacitor model.

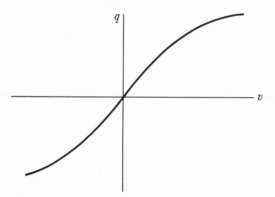

Figure 4.10   Example of charge-voltage relationship for a capacitor model.

and 4.11 show possible q–v characteristics. As in the discussion of the resistor model, we have linear, nonlinear, time-invariant, and time-varying capacitor models. If q and v are linearly related as in Figure 4.11, then we may write q as

$$q = Cv, \tag{4.8}$$

where the proportionality factor C is defined as the *capacitance* corresponding to the capacitor model. If q is in coulombs (integral of current in amperes with respect to time in seconds), and v is in volts, then C is in *farads* (F). In Equation 4.8, C does not depend on v but it may depend on time t. If C is also independent of t, then C is said to be time-invariant. In this case, C is simply a constant. Otherwise it is time-varying. For the linear time-invariant case, a differentiation of Equation 4.8 yields

$$i(t) = \frac{dq(t)}{dt} = C\,\frac{dv(t)}{dt}, \tag{4.9}$$

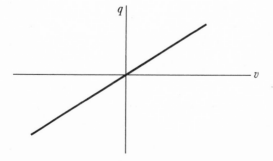

Figure 4.11   Charge-voltage relationship for a linear capacitor model.

which is sometimes taken as the defining equation for a linear time-invariant capacitor model. Integrating Equation 4.9 from 0 to t, we have

$$\int_0^t i(\tau)\, d\tau = C[v(t) - v(0)] \tag{4.10}$$

or

$$\int_0^t i(\tau)\, d\tau + Cv(0) = Cv(t). \tag{4.11}$$

The integral may be interpreted as the net change in charge between 0 and t, and $Cv(0)$ may be interpreted as the initial charge at $t = 0$, giving an algebraic sum which is the total charge at time t. This is, of course, equivalent to Equation 4.8. Equations 4.8 and 4.9 are forms of Coulomb's law.

Analogous to the situation in resistor models, we may have a *charge-controlled* capacitor model or a *voltage-controlled* capacitor model or both. Again, linear models are always both charge-controlled and voltage-controlled.

A third network element model is the *inductor*. The inductor is used to represent a magnetic-field energy-storage device in which other effects may be neglected. The model used to idealize the inductor assumes that the time-integral of voltage, called *magnetic flux*, or simply *flux*, is related to the current by means of a function. We shall denote flux by the symbol $\psi(t)$ so that we have

$$v(t) = \frac{d}{dt}\psi(t). \tag{4.12}$$

Figures 4.12 and 4.13 show possible ψ–i characteristics for an inductor and Figure 4.14 shows the symbol for the model. When ψ is directly pro-

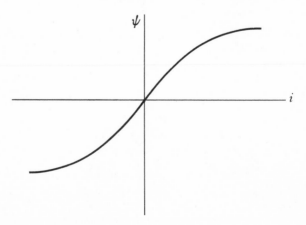

Figure 4.12   Flux-current relationship for an inductor model.

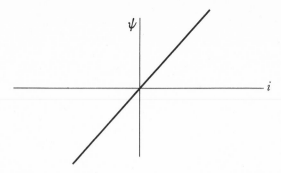

Figure 4.13   Flux-current relationship for a linear inductor model.

portional to i as in Figure 4.13, the model is said to be linear and ψ may be written as

$$\psi = Li, \qquad (4.13)$$

where L, the proportionality factor, is called the *inductance* corresponding to the linear inductor model. Inductance is in *henrys* (H) (after Joseph Henry, American scientist) when current is in amperes, and ψ is in volt-seconds. If L is explicitly independent of time, L is said to be time-invariant. For the linear time-invariant case, Equation 4.13 may be differentiated to give

$$v(t) = L\frac{di(t)}{dt}. \qquad (4.14)$$

Analogous to Equation 4.9, we may integrate Equation 4.14 and obtain

$$\int_0^t v(\tau)\ d\tau + Li(0) = Li(t). \qquad (4.15)$$

The left-hand side of Equation 4.15 is, of course, the total flux at time t, the integral is the net change in flux from 0 to t, and $Li(0)$ is the initial flux at time $t = 0$.

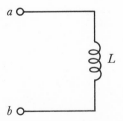

Figure 4.14   Symbol for inductor model.

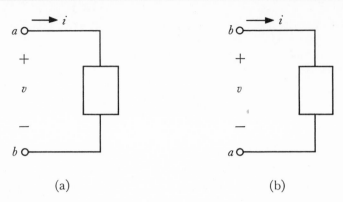

(a)   (b)

Figure 4.15 If terminal characteristics are unchanged when terminals are interchanged, the element is bilateral.

For the nonlinear inductor model, the meaning of a current-controlled and flux-controlled inductor should be evident. Again, the linear model is always flux-controlled as well as current-controlled.

It is conceivable that for any of the three models, the terminal characteristics remain unchanged even if the terminals are interchanged, as in Figure 4.15. Note that in Figure 4.15 the voltage and current reference directions are maintained, but the terminals are physically interchanged. Where network behavior is not affected by interchanges in terminal connections of the elements, the elements are defined as *bilateral*. It is readily seen that linear elements are always bilateral. Nonlinear elements are bilateral if the terminal equations ($v-i$ for resistor, $q-v$ for capacitor, and $\psi-i$ for inductor) are of the form $y = f(x)$, where $f(x)$ is an odd function. A function $y = f(x)$ is *odd* if for every x

$$-y = f(-x). \tag{4.16}$$

For example, a voltage-controlled capacitor represented by the terminal or branch equation

$$q = v^3 \tag{4.17}$$

is a bilateral element. A current-controlled resistor represented by the branch equation

$$v = 3i + 5i^3 \tag{4.18}$$

is bilateral.

If the equation relating flux and current associated with an inductor does not involve time t explicitly, the inductor is said to be time-invariant. Otherwise it is time-varying. For example, if the flux-current relationship is $\psi = i^3$, then the associated inductor model is said to be time-invariant. Of course it is nonlinear. Likewise, a capacitor is said to be time-invariant if the charge–voltage relationship does not involve time t explicitly. For example, the charge–voltage relationship in Equation 4.17 is associated with a time-invariant but nonlinear capacitor.

A summary of the description of the three network elements discussed in this section is given in Table 4.1 for reference.

Table 4.1   Summary of R, L, C description.

Element and principal unit	Symbol and reference directions for variables in equations	Terminal characteristics		
		Linear	*Time-invariant*	*General*
Resistor, ohm (Ω)		$v = Ri$ or $i = Gv$ If time-invariant R is constant	$v =$ function of i only (current-controlled) or $i =$ function of v only (voltage-controlled)	$v =$ function of i and t (current-controlled) or $i =$ function of v and t (voltage-controlled)
Capacitor, farad (F)		$q = Cv$ or $v = \dfrac{1}{C} q$ $i = \dfrac{dq}{dt}$ If time-invariant also, C is constant	$q =$ function of v only (v-controlled) or $v =$ function of q only (q-controlled)	$q =$ function of v and t (v-controlled) or $v =$ function of q and t (q-controlled)
Inductor, henry (H)		$\psi = Li$ or $i = \dfrac{1}{L} \psi$ $v = \dfrac{d\psi}{dt}$ If time-invariant also, L is constant	$\psi =$ function of i only (i-controlled) or $i =$ function of ψ only (ψ-controlled)	$\psi =$ function of i and t (i-controlled) or $i =$ function of ψ and t (ψ-controlled)

All the above elements are called *lumped* elements. This is because in the applications for which the above models are useful, it is reasonable to assume that the electrical properties of the elements are concentrated or "lumped" at points in space. Such an assumption leads to total derivatives in the defining equations. In applications where space variables must be considered, the defining equations for the elements involve partial derivatives. These latter elements are called *distributed* elements.†

---

† Lumped elements and distributed elements are both mathematical models and hence represent approximations to the actual devices and components. The lumped models are cruder approximations compared to the distributed models but the resulting theory for lumped models is also much simpler. The lumped approximation is useful for signals with frequency components up to that which has a wavelength of the same order of magnitude as the physical dimensions of the components. Typically, this is up to several megahertz.

● EXERCISES

4.1-1   In most physics textbooks, the relationship of v_L and i_L for the inductor is given as $v_L = -L(di_L/dt)$. Reconcile the form of this equation with Equation 4.14. (Check with a physics textbook to find the meaning of the minus sign.)

4.1-2   A component (or part) in a radio set is marked 1 μF (1 μF $= 10^{-6}$ farad). What significance does the word *model* have with respect to this component? What are the meanings of the words *capacitor* and *capacitance* in terms of this component?

4.1-3   Give an example of a resistor model which is not bilateral.

4.1-4   Give an example of an inductor model which is nonlinear but bilateral.

4.1-5   Suppose that a nonlinear resistor as described by Equation 4.18 is connected across a constant current source I. Draw the network and label the terminals of the current source a and b. Show that the voltage v_{ab} remains the same regardless of how the resistor is connected to the current source, i.e., verify that the resistor model is bilateral.

4.1-6   Give an example of a charge-controlled capacitor which is not voltage-controlled.

4.1-7   Give an example of a voltage-controlled capacitor which is not charge-controlled.

4.1-8   Give an example of a nonlinear capacitor which is both charge-controlled and voltage-controlled.

4.1-9   Give an example of a linear but time-varying inductor.

4.1-10   Obtain a differential equation describing a linear time-varying capacitor.

4.2 Voltage-current relationships for magnetically coupled coils

The lumped circuit idealizations considered in this section and the next differ from the resistor, inductor, and capacitor of Section 4.1 in that two pairs of terminals are involved rather than one. We first consider coils which are magnetically coupled as shown by Figure 4.16; the magnetic

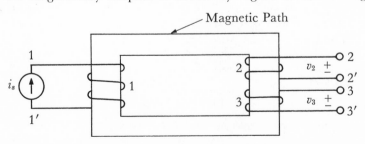

Figure 4.16 A system of coupled coils.

path may be air or it may be some ferro-magnetic material. For a linear time-invariant model, the voltage induced in the windings marked 2–2′ and 3–3′ due to the time rate of change of current in winding 1–1′ is related by a constant known as the coefficient of mutual inductance, M_{jk} and has a polarity which depends on the winding sense of the coil. Thus, in the magnetic system of Figure 4.16, the polarity of the voltage induced in winding 2–2′ with the terminal 2′ as the reference is opposite that of the voltage induced in winding 3–3′ with terminal 3′ as the reference. The voltage–current relationships for coupled coils depend on both the coefficient M_{jk} and on the winding sense of the coils.

It is conventional in circuit theory to indicate winding sense by a pair of dots or polarity marks placed near one of the terminals for each coil. These polarity marks may be established by a procedure which will be described with reference to Figure 4.17. There a battery is connected to coil 1 by the closing of a switch. The polarity mark of coil 1 is chosen to be that terminal which is connected to the plus terminal of the battery. Now the closing of the switch will cause the current in coil 1 to increase so that di_1/dt is positive. The polarity mark for coil 2 is assigned to the terminal which is positive as indicated by a positive deflection of a voltmeter with the plus reference terminal of the voltmeter connected to that terminal.

When both polarity marks and the coefficient M_{jk} are given, the voltage–current relationships are easily written. If the plus reference mark for the voltage v_2 coincides with the dotted terminal, the situation depicted in Figure 4.18(a), then we have

$$v_2(t) = M_{12}\frac{di_1(t)}{dt}, \qquad M_{12} > 0. \qquad (4.19)$$

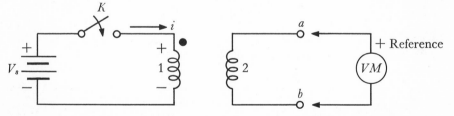

Figure 4.17 The arrangement employed to establish polarity marks for two coupled coils.

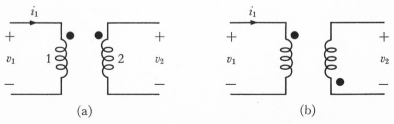

(a)   (b)

Figure 4.18 Equation 4.19 applies for (a), Equation 4.20 for (b).

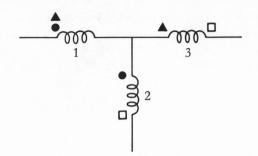

Figure 4.19 For more complicated magnetic systems,
several kinds of polarity marks are used.

If the plus reference mark for v_2 is at the undotted terminal as shown in
Figure 4.18(b), then we have

$$v_2(t) = -M_{12}\frac{di_1(t)}{dt}, \qquad M_{12} > 0. \tag{4.20}$$

With current in L_2, the expression for v_2 will contain an additional term
$L_2(di_2/dt)$. For instance, if in Figure 4.18(a) the reference direction for i_2
is towards the dotted terminal (from right to left in the top lead), then the
total $v_2(t)$ is

$$v_2(t) = L_2\frac{di_2(t)}{dt} + M_{12}\frac{di_1(t)}{dt}. \tag{4.21}$$

In Figure 4.18(b), if the reference direction for i_2 is also towards the dotted
terminal (from right to left on the bottom lead), then the total $v_2(t)$ is

$$v_2(t) = -L_2\frac{di_2(t)}{dt} - M_{12}\frac{di_1(t)}{dt}. \tag{4.22}$$

Similarly, for the assigned reference directions of i_2 in both figures, the
total voltage $v_1(t)$ for Figure 4.18(a) is

$$v_1(t) = L_i\frac{di_1(t)}{dt} + M_{21}\frac{di_2(t)}{dt}, \tag{4.23}$$

and for Figure 4.18(b) is

$$v_1(t) = L_1\frac{di_1(t)}{dt} + M_{21}\frac{di_2(t)}{dt}. \tag{4.24}$$

We postulate here that $M_{12} = M_{21}$. That such is the case can be proved
using energy considerations.†

For complicated magnetic coupling situations, it is sometimes necessary
to use a number of pairs of dots. It is conventional to choose the sets of
dots to have different identifying shapes as is illustrated in Figure 4.19. The

† See N. Balabanian, *Fundamentals of Circuit Theory*, Allyn and Bacon, Boston, 1961.

circular symbols specify the coupling between coils 1 and 2, the triangular symbols specify the coupling between coils 1 and 3 and the square symbols specify the coupling between coils 2 and 3.

For nonlinear models, the fluxes and currents are no longer related by linear equations. For instance, for current-controlled nonlinear coupled coils, the terminal relationships have the general form

$$\psi_1 = f_1(i_1, i_2), \tag{4.25}$$

$$\psi_2 = f_2(i_1, i_2), \tag{4.26}$$

where ψ_1 and ψ_2 are the fluxes at the two-terminal pairs. Of course, for the time-varying case, the functions f_1 and f_2 also depend explicitly on time t.

● EXERCISES

4.2-1   For the magnetic circuit of Figure 4.16, establish a system of polarity marks using Lenz's law (after Lenz, German scientist). (Consult your physics textbook for Lenz's law.)

4.2-2   For the circuit shown in Figure Exercise 4.2-2(a), write an equation for the part of $v_2(t)$ due to the current in coil 1.

4.2-3   Repeat Exercise 4.2-2 for the circuit of Figure Exercise 4.2-2(b).

4.2-4   Repeat Exercise 4.2-3 for Figure 4.16.

4.2-5   For the circuit in Figure 4.18(a), replace $i_1(t)$ by $i_a(t)$ which is opposite to i_1, and assume i_b as the current in coil 2 directed towards the dot. Write the equations for v_1 and v_2 in terms of L_1, L_2, M, i_a, and i_b.

4.2-6   Replace v_1 in Figure 4.18(a) by v_a which has a reference mark opposite to that of v_1. Write the equations for v_a and v_2 in terms of L_1, L_2, M, i_1, and i_2, where i_2 is directed towards the dotted terminal.

4.2-7   Repeat Exercise 4.2-6 for Figure 4.18(b) where i_2 is directed towards the undotted terminal.

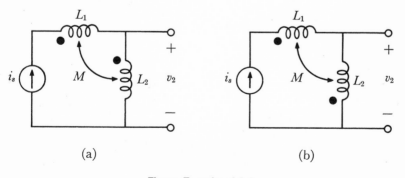

(a)   (b)

Figure Exercise 4.2-2

4.3 Ideal convertors

The ideal convertors to be discussed in this section are lumped models of electrical devices which have two terminal pairs. The *ideal transformer* represented in Figure 4.20(a) is a model useful in connection with the study of actual transformers which are used in power and communications applications, and is also used often to accomplish isolation in electronic circuits. The two voltages and two currents for the ideal transformer are related by the equations

$$v_2 = nv_1 \tag{4.27}$$

and

$$i_2 = \frac{-1}{n} i_1 , \tag{4.28}$$

where n is a real number. This idealization is useful not only because it is accurate for some purposes but also because it may be combined with ideal R, L, C elements to represent practical transformers.

If a linear (possibly time-varying) resistor is connected to terminals 2–2′, then v_2 and i_2 are related by Ohm's law as follows:

$$v_2 = -Ri_2 . \tag{4.29}$$

Substituting this equation into Equations 4.27 and 4.28 and solving for v_1 in terms of i_1, we have

$$v_1 = \frac{1}{n} v_2 = \frac{-1}{n} Ri_2 = \frac{1}{n^2} Ri_1 . \tag{4.30}$$

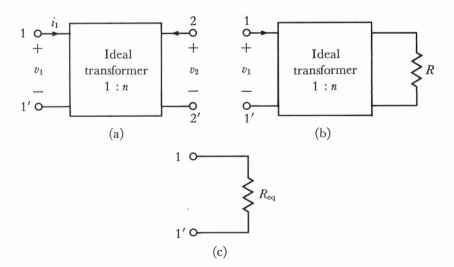

Figure 4.20 Schematics of the ideal transformer.

Indeed, Equation 4.30 is the defining characteristic of a linear resistor. At terminals 1–1′, the network appears as a resistor of value

$$R_{\mathrm{eq}} = \frac{1}{n^2} R, \tag{4.31}$$

and an equivalent representation of the network of Figure 4.20(b) is that shown in (c) of the figure. Thus the ideal transformer acts to adjust the magnitude of resistance in terms of measurements made at the input terminals of the ideal transformer.

Another useful converter model is the *gyrator* first introduced by Tellegen (Dutch engineer, 1900–   ) in 1948. The gyrator is a model for a number of physical devices including *Hall-effect* semiconductor devices and also certain microwave structures. It is represented by the special symbol shown in Figure 4.21. For the voltages and currents of the figure, it is required that

$$v_1 = K i_2 \tag{4.32}$$

and

$$v_2 = -K i_1, \tag{4.33}$$

where K is a real constant which may be either positive or negative. Thus the gyrator relates the current corresponding to a terminal pair to the voltage corresponding to another terminal pair. (In Hall-effect devices, electric-field effects are transformed into equivalent magnetic-field effects.)

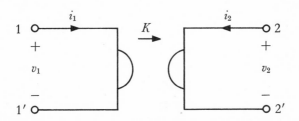

Figure 4.21   Conventional representation of the Tellegen gyrator.

An interesting behavior of the gyrator is exhibited by studying the two-terminal equivalent of the gyrator terminated in a linear (possibly time-varying) capacitor as shown in Figure 4.22(a). For this network, we have

$$v_1 = K i_2 = K\left(-\frac{d}{dt} C v_2\right). \tag{4.34}$$

Now, since $v_2 = -K i_1$, this equation becomes

$$v_1 = K \frac{d}{dt} C K i_1 = \frac{d}{dt} (K^2 C i_1) = \frac{d}{dt} (L_{\mathrm{eq}} i_1), \tag{4.35}$$

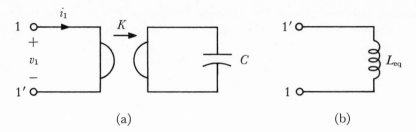

Figure 4.22   A gyrator terminated in a capacitor (a) is the equivalent of an inductor (b).

where the equivalent inductance has the value $L_{eq} = K^2 C$. By this demonstration, we see that a gyrator together with a linear capacitor is equivalent to a linear inductor. Hence, if we have resistors, linear capacitors, and gyrators, we can always construct (in theory) networks which are equivalent to those containing resistors, linear inductors, and linear capacitors.

Another useful convertor is the *negative convertor* which is a model for devices employing transistors or vacuum tubes which are common in the telephone industry. For the negative convertor as shown in Figure 4.23, we have either

$$v_1 = -K v_2 \tag{4.36}$$

and

$$i_1 = i_2 , \tag{4.37}$$

or

$$i_1 = -K i_2 \tag{4.38}$$

and

$$v_1 = v_2 , \tag{4.39}$$

where K is a positive real constant. Equations 4.36 and 4.37 define a *voltage-inversion* type of negative convertor. Equations 4.38 and 4.39 define

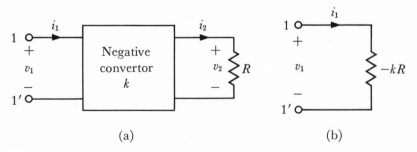

Figure 4.23   The negative convertor terminated in R is equivalent to $-R$ when $k = 1$.

a *current-inversion* type of negative convertor. The negative convertor has the property that when it is terminated in a resistor (possible nonlinear) at terminals 2–2′, the two-terminal behavior at 1–1′ is that of a resistor which is the negative of that at 2–2′. Similar statements apply to the inductor and the capacitor. Practical realizations of negative convertors of high precision have been manufactured by the Bell Telephone Laboratories.†

● EXERCISES

4.3-1 Find the two-terminal equivalent of an ideal transformer terminated in (a) a linear inductor, (b) a linear capacitor.

4.3-2 Find the two-terminal equivalent of a gyrator terminated at 2–2′ in (a) linear R, and (b) linear L. Repeat for the R or L termination (linear) at terminals 1–1′ and find the two-terminal equivalent network at 2–2′.

4.3-3 Show that the two-terminal equivalent of a negative convertor terminated in a linear L is $-L$ when $k = 1$. Show also that when the termination is a linear C, the equivalent network is $-C$ when $k = 1$.

4.3-4 A new device is constructed by connecting two gyrators in cascade (or tandem). Show that this device is equivalent to an ideal transformer.

4.4 Linear models for mechanical elements

As in electrical networks, the analysis and design of mechanical systems or networks are often based on simple and idealized models for components. We shall present here the three simplest and most common linear mechanical elements which are mass, compliance (spring), and damping (dashpot). The physical quantities that are related by these elements are force and velocity. We assume that the elements are *lumped* or concentrated. If a force f acts on a lumped mass or point *mass*, Newton's law states that the mass will undergo a change in velocity. Specifically, we have

$$f = M \frac{dv}{dt}, \qquad (4.40)$$

where M is a proportionality constant and v is velocity. The time derivative of velocity is called acceleration, and the integral of velocity is position or

† J. G. Linvill, "Transistor Negative Impedance Converters," *Proc. IRE*, **41**, pp. 725-729, June, 1953; see also F. H. Blecher, "Application of Synthesis Techniques to Electronic Circuit Design," *IRE Trans. on Circuit Theory*, **CT-7**, Special Supplement, August, 1960, pp. 79-91. Negative convertors used in industry operate up to about 1 megahertz (MHz).

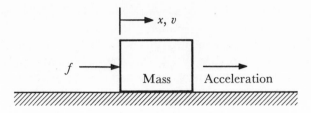

Figure 4.24   Force on a mass causing acceleration.

displacement. The acceleration is in the same direction as the force as shown in Figure 4.24. The motion of the mass is with respect to the inertial reference frame. Notice that if the force variable is thought of as a current variable in an electrical element, and velocity thought of as voltage, then Equation 4.40 is like the defining equation for the linear time-invariant capacitor. On the other hand, if we think of force as voltage and velocity as current, then Equation 4.40 is like the defining equation for the linear time-invariant inductor. The similar character of electrical and mechanical networks can be exploited to advantage. To facilitate the analogies, we will adopt symbols for the mechanical elements mass, spring, and damper which emphasize their two-terminal nature.

Figure 4.25 shows the symbol for mass, with a rectangle connected to a terminal point, and an L to another terminal point. The L is tied to the reference frame for displacement or motion. The reference directions on the variables f and v (force and velocity) in Figure 4.25 have the same significance as those for current and voltage in electrical elements. The arrow direction for f indicates the direction for positive force. The plus (+) reference mark for velocity denotes positive velocity reference with respect to the minus (−) terminal.

The defining relation in Equation 4.40 assumes that the mass is linear and time-invariant. For time-varying mass, we write force equal to the time

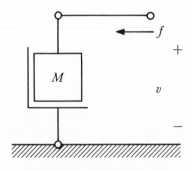

Figure 4.25   Symbol for mass.

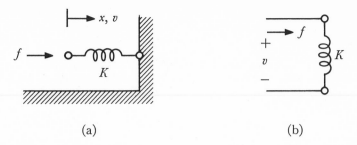

(a)   (b)

Figure 4.26   (a) Force on a spring causing displacement. (b) Symbol for spring.

rate of Mv. Here Mv is known as *momentum*. In the *MKS* system of units, if force is in newtons, and velocity in meters per second, then M is in kilograms.

The second lumped two-terminal linear time-invariant mechanical element we define is the *spring* shown in Figure 4.26. The spring constant K called *compliance* relates force and velocity as

$$v = K\frac{df}{dt} \tag{4.41}$$

or, assuming force to be zero at $t = 0$,

$$f(t) = \frac{1}{K}\int_0^t v(\tau)\,d\tau = \frac{1}{K}\int_0^t \frac{dx}{d\tau}\,d\tau = \frac{x(t) - x(0)}{K}. \tag{4.42}$$

That is, the net displacement $x(t) - x(0)$ at any time t is proportional to the force at time t.†

The third linear mechanical element, *damper*, symbolized by the dashpot in Figure 4.27, relates force and velocity by

$$f = Dv, \tag{4.43}$$

where D is the *damping coefficient* which is assumed to be a constant. The dashpot is similar to the shock absorber in an automobile, and, in our linear model, the force is linearly proportional to the velocity of the piston. This mechanical model is analogous to the resistor for electrical networks.

For the three mechanical elements defined above, force and velocity play analogous roles as voltage and current for electric elements. *Force* and *velocity sources* are defined in exactly analogous manner as voltage and current source. Mechanical systems involving M, K, D, velocity, and force sources are called *translational* mechanical networks or systems, and M, K,

† This is based on Hooke's law.

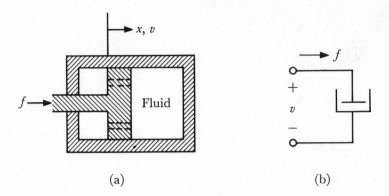

Figure 4.27   (a) Force on a dashpot causing velocity. (b) Symbol for damper or dashpot.

and D are translational mechanical elements. Table 4.2 summarizes the mechanical–electrical analogies.

Let us consider a very simple numerical example for obtaining the parameter for a mechanical model. Suppose that on a linear track we have a vehicle to which a constant force of 100 lbs is applied. Measurements are taken on the position of the vehicle as a function of time, and it is found that the position can be described approximately by the equation

$$x = 0.1t^2 \qquad (4.44)$$

where x is the position in meters, and t is the time instant in seconds. Since the second time-derivative of the displacement x is a constant, and since the applied force is a constant, the vehicle may be modeled by a simple mass element. Since for a mass Equation 4.40 applies, all we have to do to obtain M is to convert the given force and displacement data into a common system of units. If we choose the *MKS*, we have to convert the 100-lb force into newtons. But 1 newton (*MKS*) = 0.2248 lb of force. So 100 lbs of force equals (100/.2248) newtons, and applying Equation 4.40, we obtain

$$\frac{100}{0.2248} = M\frac{d^2x}{dt^2} = M(2)(0.1). \qquad (4.45)$$

Hence the mass is

$$M = \frac{100}{(0.2248)(2)(0.1)} = 2224 \text{ kilograms.} \qquad (4.46)$$

Table 4.2 Mechanical elements and their electrical analogies.

Element	Equation	Electric Analogy (force ~ current)	Electrical Analogy (force ~ voltage)
Mass M	$f = M\dfrac{dv}{dt}$	$M \sim C$	$M \sim L$
Spring K	$f = K\int v\,dt$	$K \sim \dfrac{1}{L}$	$K \sim \dfrac{1}{C}$
Dashpot D	$f = Dv$	$D \sim \dfrac{1}{R}$	$D \sim R$

● **EXERCISES**

4.4-1   A one-pound weight is resting on a helical spring. When the weight is removed, the spring elongates by 0.1 inch. What is the compliance K of the spring in *MKS* units?

4.4-2   A mass in Figure 4.24 is initially at rest. A force of one newton is applied at $t = 0$ and removed at the end of one second. What is the displacement at $t = 2$ sec if $M = 1$ kilogram?

Problems

4-1   Find the corresponding $i(t)$ or $v(t)$ for the linear time-invariant positive elements and signal waveforms shown in the figure.

4-2   Find the two-terminal equivalent of a gyrator terminated in (a) a voltage source, and (b) a current source.

4-3   For the two cascade connections of ideal convertors shown in the figure, each one terminated in a linear capacitor C_2, find the single element equivalent at terminals 1–1'.

4-4   For the circuits in Figure Exercise 4.2-2, write equations for v_2 in terms of i_s. [*Hint:* Both the time rate of change of the current through L_1 and that of the current through L_2 affect v_2.]

4-5   Suppose the signal waveforms shown in Figure Problem 4-1 represent forces on the mass as shown in Figure 4.24. Compute the displacement in each case, assuming that $x(0) = 0$, $M = 1$.

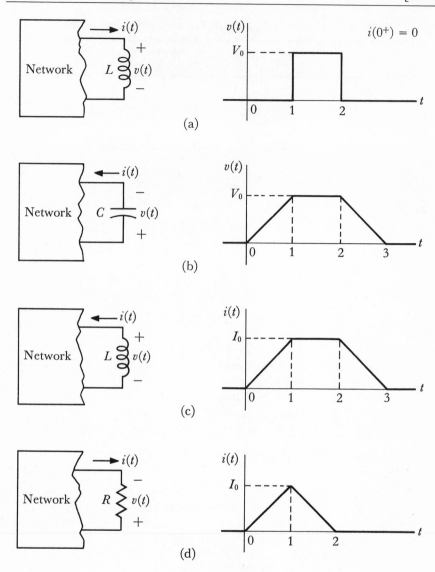

Figure Problem 4-1

4-6   Suppose the signal waveform shown in Figure Problem 4-1(b) represents a velocity plot vs. time. (a) If the velocity corresponds to a
moving mass M, plot the force acting on the mass. (b) If the velocity
corresponds to the end of a spring K, plot the force acting on the
spring.

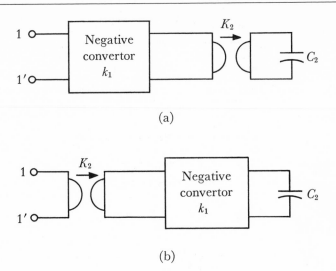

(a)

(b)

Figure Problem 4-3

4-7   The simple network shown in the figure contains a voltage-controlled voltage source. Show that it is equivalent to a voltage inversion-type negative convertor, with $K = 1$.

4-8   The simple network shown in the figure contains a current-controlled current source. Show that it is equivalent to a current inversion-type negative convertor, with $K = 1$.

4-9   The simple network shown in the figure contains two current-controlled voltage sources. Show that it is equivalent to a gyrator.

4-10   Suppose that a voltage-controlled resistor with v and i conventions as in Figure 4.1(a) is described by $i = 3v + v^2$. The resistor is connected to a voltage source as in Figure 4.6(a) whose terminal b is on top. If $v_s = 10$ volts, compute i. Suppose the resistor connection is re-

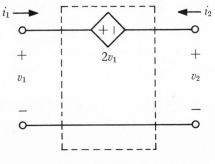

Figure Problem 4-7

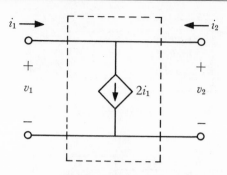

Figure Problem 4-8

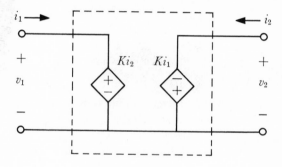

Figure Problem 4-9

versed so that b is at the bottom. Compute i, for the same v_s. Is the resistor bilateral?

4-11   A nonlinear voltage-controlled capacitor has a model described by $q = 3v^3$. Compute the current if a voltage source with a waveform as in Figure Problem 4.1(b) is impressed across it.

4-12   Repeat Problem 4-11 for the waveform in Figure Problem 4-1(a).

4-13   Repeat Exercise 4.3-1 for (a) a nonlinear inductor $\psi = i^2$, reference convention as in Table 4.1, and for (b) a nonlinear capacitor $v = q^{1/2}$, reference convention as in Table 4.1.

4-14   Repeat Exercise 4.3-3 for a nonlinear current-controlled inductor as a termination.

4-15   Repeat Exercise 4.3-3 for a nonlinear flux-controlled inductor as a termination.

4-16   Repeat Exercise 4.3-3 for (a) a voltage-controlled nonlinear capacitor as a termination, and for (b) a charge-controlled nonlinear capacitor as a termination.

Kirchhoff's Laws **5**

5.1 Network terminology

We have already introduced the words *element, network,* and *terminal* in previous chapters. We shall have need for additional definitions to describe certain aspects of a network. The word *branch* is used synonymously with two-terminal *element.* In the literature, however, *branch* is sometimes used in a wider sense to mean a string of elements joined end to end or even a two-terminal subnetwork. In the network of Figure 5.1, elements *c* and *d* may be considered separate branches or they may be considered parts of a single branch *cd.* Usually, the precise meaning will be clear from the context. The junction of two or more branches is called a *node.* In Figure 5.1, node 5 joins branches *d, e, f,* and *g.* If only two branches are involved, the node is called *simple.* Thus, in Figure 5.1 node 4 is a *simple node.* A *terminal* of a network is a node to which an input source may be connected, or from which an output signal may be observed, or to which another network terminal may be connected. An end-to-end connection of branches such as *c* and *d* in Figure 5.1 is called a series connection. Other series con-

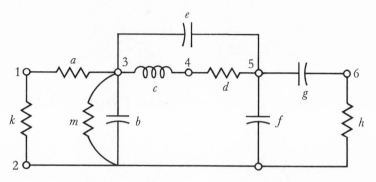

Figure 5.1   Network for illustrating definitions for branches, nodes, paths, and circuits.

nections in the figure are *ak* and *gh*. A parallel connection of branches implies the joining of one terminal from each branch to form a node, and the remaining terminals joining to form another node. Thus branches *b* and *m* are in parallel. Branch *f* is also in parallel with branch *gh*. The word *path* implies a specified train of branches. There are several kinds of paths. One path in Figure 5.1 starts at node 3, continues to node 4, and thence to node 5. Such a path is called an *open path*. Note that for an open path there is a starting node to which only one branch is connected, and an ending node to which only one branch is connected. If the starting and ending are one and the same, we have a *closed path*. One closed path is *cdfb*. Another is *ambefk*. If each node in the closed path connects exactly two branches, then the closed path is called *simple*. Simple closed paths are also called *topological circuits* or *loops*. In Figure 5.1, *cde* is an example of a loop.

●   EXERCISES

5.1-1   (a) Find all paths between nodes 1 and 3 in Figure Exercise 5.1-1, and (b) between nodes 1 and 5 in Figure 5.1.

5.1-2   Find as many loops as you can in Figure Exercise 5.1-1 and in Figure 5.1. Identify these loops in terms of the node or element labels.

5.2   Kirchhoff's current law

The first of Kirchhoff's laws is known as *Kirchhoff's current law* (abbreviated KCL). It states that the sum of the currents entering a node must be equal to the sum of the currents leaving the node. If this were not true, then charge could accumulate at a node! If currents entering and leaving are distinguished by positive and negative signs, respectively, then we say that the sum of currents entering a node is zero. For example, in Figure 5.2, consider node 1 and the three branches connected to it to be a portion

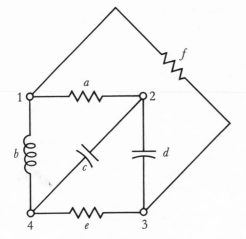

Figure Exercise 5.1-1

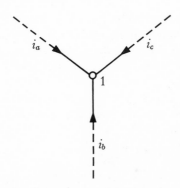

Figure 5.2 Illustration for Kirchhoff's current law.

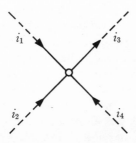

Figure 5.3 A node for illustration of Kirchhoff's current law.

of a complete network. For the given reference directions, Kirchhoff's current law requires that

$$i_a + i_b + i_c = 0. \tag{5.1}$$

Thus, if $i_a = 5$ and $i_b = 2$, KCL requires that i_c be -7. As a second example, consider Figure 5.3. Applying KCL, we get $i_1 + i_2 - i_3 + i_4 = 0$. Thus, if $i_1 = 5 \sin \omega t$, $i_2 = 3 \sin \omega t$, $i_3 = 6 \cos \omega t$, then i_4 must be

$$i_4 = -i_1 - i_2 + i_3 = -8 \sin \omega t + 6 \cos \omega t = 10 \sin \left(\omega t + \tan^{-1} \frac{6}{-8} \right). \tag{5.2}$$

The last step is accomplished by letting $-8 = A \cos \theta$ and $6 = A \sin \theta$, and then using the double angle relationship

$$A \sin \omega t \cos \theta + A \cos \omega t \sin \theta = A \sin (\omega t + \theta).$$

A and θ are thus determined. The current law of Kirchhoff may be thought of as a consequence of some other assumption or postulate such as the conservation of charge. The latter states that the net charge flowing into a node is equal to the net charge flowing out of a node. The current law then follows directly by differentiation with respect to time.

In applying KCL to a given node, all branch currents with the reference arrows pointing toward the node in question, have the same sign. The reference arrows out of the node require the opposite sign for these corresponding terms in the KCL equation.

In general, if there are N_v nodes and N_b branches, then Kirchhoff's current law may be written in the very compact form

$$\sum_{j=1}^{N_b} a_{kj} i_j = 0, \qquad k = 1, \ldots, N_v, \tag{5.3}$$

where $a_{kj} = +1$ if branch j is connected to node k and the current reference for i_j is away from node k; $a_{kj} = -1$ if branch j is connected to node k and the current reference for i_j is toward node k; and $a_{kj} = 0$ if branch j is not connected to node k.

The current law may be applied to several nodes and the resulting KCL equations added. This simple addition of KCL equations leads to a generalized KCL as follows. Consider a network as in Figure 5.4 which is arbitrarily pulled apart so as to expose the connections. Also the pulling apart is such that if all the exposed connections were to be cut, the network would be completely separated into two parts. Now apply KCL to each node of one part labeled Network 2 in Figure 5.4. Each branch current in each KCL equation for Network 2 is either one of the currents in the exposed wires $(i_1, i_2, \ldots, i_n)$ or a current for a branch connecting two nodes inside Network 2. Let j and k be any two of the nodes inside Network 2. Then, for

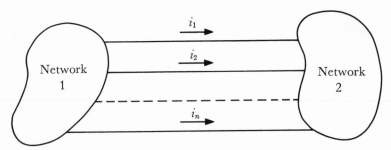

Figure 5.4 Generalized Kirchhoff's current law: the algebraic sum of currents flowing from Network 1 to Network 2 is zero.

KCL at node j, we have i_{kj} entering the node and, for KCL at node k, we have i_{jk} entering the node. If we add the KCL equations for all the nodes in Network 2, $i_{jk} + i_{kj}$ will appear in the expression. Since $i_{jk} = -i_{kj}$, we see that $i_{jk} + i_{kj} = 0$. Each such branch will be involved in exactly two node equations resulting in a cancellation. Hence, the only currents that are left are the ones pertaining to the exposed wires. Therefore, we have

$$i_1 + i_2 + \cdots + i_n = 0. \tag{5.4}$$

The above conclusion may be restated as a generalized Kirchhoff's current law: The sum of the currents entering minus the sum of the currents leaving one side of a hypothetical plane dividing a network into two parts is zero. The wires cut by the plane constitute a *cut set*.

It should be emphasized that Kirchhoff's current law is a topological constraint on the currents at a node (or through a hypothetical plane). Nothing is said about the branch characteristics. The law holds for networks containing nonlinear as well as linear elements. Regardless of how the currents come about, they have to satisfy Kirchhoff's current law at each instant of time.

● EXERCISES

5.2-1   For the network of Figure Exercise 5.2-1, apply KCL at nodes 1, 2, 3, and 4, using single-subscription notation and the reference directions shown.

5.2-2   Repeat Exercises 5.2-1 using double-subscription notation.

5.2-3   In the network of Figure Exercise 5.2-1, suppose that nodes 1 and 2 are grouped together for Subnetwork 1 and nodes 3 and 4 for Subnetwork 2. Verify that $i_f + i_b - i_c + i_d = 0$ by applying KCL to nodes only.

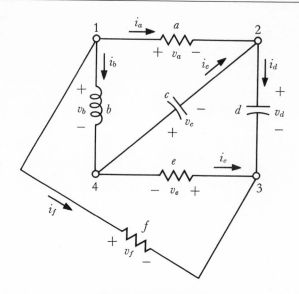

Figure Exercise 5.2-1

5.2-4 Suppose nodes 1 and 3 of the network in Figure Exercise 5.2-1 are in Subnetwork 1, nodes 2 and 4 in Subnetwork 2, and the subnetworks pulled apart, what branch currents correspond to the exposed connecting wires? Apply KCL to the hypothetical separating plane.

5.2-5 Repeat Exercise 5.2-4 for nodes 1 and 4 in Network 1 and nodes 2 and 3 in Network 2.

5.2-6 Show that for the network in Figure Exercise 5.2-1 the KCL equation at node 1 is obtainable from the sum of the KCL equations at the remaining nodes.

5.2-7 Repeat Exercise 5.2-6 for the KCL at node 2.

5.2-8 Repeat Exercise 5.2-6 for the KCL at node 3.

5.2-9 Repeat Exercise 5.2-6 for the KCL at node 4.

5.3 Kirchhoff's voltage law

The second law of Kirchhoff is concerned with the summation of voltages in a closed path or loop. Figure 5.5 shows a portion of a network which contains a loop. An arbitrary orientation is assigned to a loop, say clockwise, such as the loop 12341. In tracing around the loop with its specified orientation or direction which in our example is clockwise, we enter branch b at its + reference terminal and leave it at its (−) reference terminal. We say that in going from node 1 to node 2, we have a *voltage drop* of v_b. The variable v_b may or may not be positive, so that the drop in

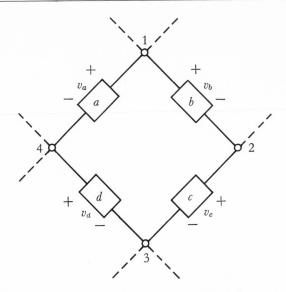

Figure 5.5 A loop for illustration of Kirchhoff's voltage law.

voltage refers to the reference polarity of the voltage only. Similarly, in going from node 3 to node 4, we enter branch d at the $(-)$ reference terminal and leave it at the $+$ reference terminal. We say that in tracing through branch d from 3 to 4, we have a *voltage rise* of v_d. Again the rise in voltage refers to the reference polarity of the voltage v_d whose value may or may not be positive.

Kirchhoff's voltage law (abbreviated KVL) states that in tracing around a loop with a specified orientation, the sum of the voltage drops must exactly equal the sum of the voltage rises. If different signs are assigned to rise and drop, then we may say that the sum of voltages around a loop is zero. Thus, for the clockwise loop in Figure 5.5, KVL yields

$$v_b + v_c - v_d - v_a = 0. \tag{5.5}$$

Instead of the $+$ and $(-)$ reference convention for voltage, we may use the double-subscript notation. The portion of the network in Figure 5.5 is shown again in Figure 5.6 without the $+$ and $(-)$ references. If we choose a clockwise orientation, then in going from 1 to 2, we encounter a voltage drop v_{12}. This is also equivalent to saying that in going from 1 to 2, we encounter a voltage rise of v_{21} since v_{21} is the negative of v_{12}. So applying KVL to the loop 12341 of Figure 5.6, using double-subscript notation, we have

$$v_{12} + v_{23} + v_{34} + v_{41} = 0. \tag{5.6}$$

If $v_{12} = 2$, $v_{23} = -3$, and $v_{34} = 5$, then v_{41} must be equal to -4.

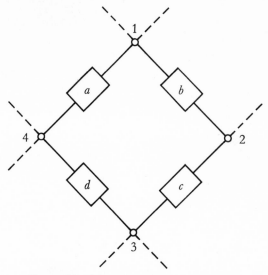

Figure 5.6   A loop imbedded in a network.

We note that if we are using the double-subscript notation for voltages, the application of KVL around a circuit yields positive signs for the terms of the summation if the second subscript of every term is the first subscript of the succeeding term. Equation 5.6 may, of course, be rewritten as

$$v_{12} - v_{32} + v_{34} - v_{14} = 0. \qquad (5.7)$$

If the reference convention for the voltages is the polarity mark reference, we may adopt the following convenient rule: In tracing through a loop, if we enter a branch at its + reference node, the sign of the corresponding term in the KVL equation is positive. Otherwise, the corresponding term in the KVL equation is negative. Equation 5.5 is obtained this way be tracing the loop in Figure 5.5 in the clockwise direction. Reversing the direction by which we trace a circuit changes the sign of each term in the equation formulated from KVL. In the network of Figure 5.5, tracing the loop in the counterclockwise direction, we obtain

$$-v_b + v_a + v_d - v_c = 0. \qquad (5.8)$$

This equation reduces to Equation 5.5 when multiplied by -1. The above discussion leads to the following general statement of Kirchhoff's voltage law in compact form:

$$\sum_{j=1}^{N_b} b_{kj}v_j = 0, \qquad k = 1, \ldots, N_l, \qquad (5.9)$$

where N_b is the number of branches and N_l is the number of loops. In tracing around a loop (the choice of direction is arbitrary), say loop k, if branch j is not in loop k, then $b_{kj} = 0$. If branch j is in loop k and in tracing through branch j the $+$ reference of branch j is encountered first, then $b_{kj} = +1$. Otherwise $b_{kj} = -1$. Simple.

Like Kirchhoff's current law, Kirchhoff's voltage law holds for networks containing nonlinear as well as time-varying elements. KVL constrains the voltage in all loops to sum to zero for all instants of time.

● **EXERCISES**

5.3-1 For Figure Exercise 5.2-1, apply KVL to the following loops: (a) 12341, (b) 1241, (c) 2342, (d) 1431. Use single-subscript notation as indicated on the figure.

5.3-2 Repeat Exercise 5.3-1 using double-subscript notation.

5.3-3 For Figure 5.1, apply KVL to the following loops: (a) 1321, (b) 3453, (c) 34523, (d) 5625. Use double-subscript notation.

5.3-4 Suppose in Figure 5.5, $v_a = -5$, $v_b = 3$, $v_d = -6$, determine v_c.

5.3-5 Suppose in Figure 5.6, $v_{13} = 6$, $v_{42} = 5$, and $v_{12} = 2$, determine v_{14}, v_{43}, and v_{32}.

5.4 Applications to simple networks

Consider the series-connected network in Figure 5.7. By a straightforward application of KCL, we see that $i_{12} = i_{23} = i_{34} = i_{45}$. Thus the branch

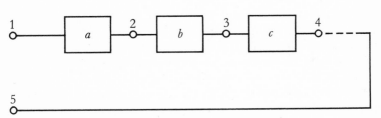

Figure 5.7 A series-connected network.

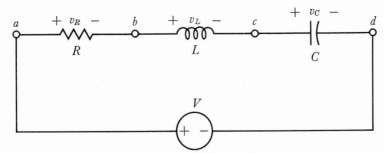

Figure 5.8 A series *RLC* network.

currents in a series network are equal. A specific example of a series network is shown in Figure 5.8. Application of KVL gives

$$v_R + v_L + v_C - v = 0$$

or

$$v_R + v_L + v_C = v. \qquad (5.10)$$

If the elements are both linear and time-invariant, we know that for the voltage reference conventions indicated in the figure we have

$$v_R = Ri_{ab}, \qquad v_L = L\frac{di_{bc}}{dt}, \qquad v_c = v_C(t_1) + \frac{1}{C}\int_{t_1}^{t} i_{cd}(\tau)\ d\tau. \qquad (5.11)$$

Since the currents in series-connected branches are equal, that is,

$$i_{ab} = i_{bc} = i_{cd}, \qquad (5.12)$$

then from Equations 5.11 and 5.12, Equation 5.10 can be written as

$$v = Ri + L\frac{di}{dt} + v_C(t_1) + \frac{1}{C}\int_{t_1}^{t} i(\tau)\ d\tau, \qquad (5.13)$$

where t_1 is an arbitrary instant of time and i is the common current. If t_1 is our reference time, $v_C(t_1)$ is called the *initial voltage* across the capacitor. Usually, $t_1 = 0$ and Equation 5.13 becomes

$$v = Ri + L\frac{di}{dt} + \frac{1}{C}\int_{0}^{t} i(\tau)\ d\tau + v_C(0). \qquad (5.14)$$

Equation 5.13 or 5.14 is the *integro-differential equation* relating the current i to the voltage v of the RLC series circuit in Figure 5.8. The right-hand side of Equation 5.14 specifies the processing of i necessary to obtain the left-hand side v.

Instead of the current $i(t)$, we may use the charge variable $q(t)$ which is related to $i(t)$ by

$$q(t) = \int_{0}^{t} i(\tau)\ d\tau + q(0). \qquad (5.15)$$

Since $q(0) = Cv(0)$, Equation 5.14 may be rewritten as

$$v(t) = L\frac{d^2q(t)}{dt^2} + R\frac{dq(t)}{dt} + \frac{1}{C}q(t). \qquad (5.16)$$

Equation 5.16 is the differential equation that relates the charge $q(t)$ to the voltage $v(t)$ if the elements in the network of Figure 5.8 are linear and time-invariant.

Suppose that instead of the linear branch constraints of Equation 5.11 we have the nonlinear characteristics

$$v_R = f_R(i_{ab}), \qquad \psi_L = f_L(i_{bc}), \qquad v_C = f_C(q), \qquad (5.17)$$

where f_R, f_L, and f_C are nonlinear functions. Recalling that $v_L(t)$ is the time derivative of the flux ψ_L and since the series branch currents are all equal and equal to the time derivative of charge $q(t)$, Equation 5.10 becomes

$$f_R\left[\frac{dq(t)}{dt}\right] + \frac{d}{dt}f_L\left[\frac{dq(t)}{dt}\right] + f_C[q(t)] = v(t). \tag{5.18}$$

Equation 5.18 is a nonlinear differential equation relating charge $q(t)$ to voltage $v(t)$ written for the nonlinear branch characteristics of Equation 5.17.

Consider now a network with parallel branches as in Figure 5.9. A simple application of KVL shows that $v_{12} + v_{43} = 0$ or $v_{12} = v_{34}$. Similarly, $v_{34} + v_{65} = 0$ or $v_{34} = v_{56}$. In other words, the branch voltages of branches in parallel are all equal. A specific simple network consisting entirely of branches in parallel is shown in Figure 5.10. Applying KCL at node a, we have

$$i - i_R - i_L - i_C = 0 \tag{5.19}$$

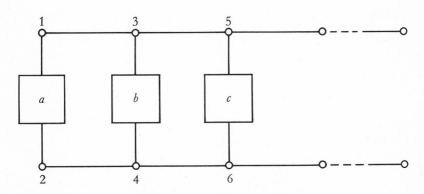

Figure 5.9 Branches in parallel.

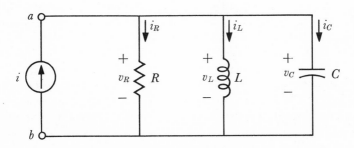

Figure 5.10 A parallel *RLC* network.

or

$$i = i_R + i_L + i_C .$$ (5.20)

Assuming linear time-invariant branch characteristics for the R, L, and C elements, we may write Equation 5.20 as

$$i = \frac{1}{R} v + \left[\frac{1}{L} \int_{t_1}^{t} v(\tau) \, d\tau + i_L(t_1) \right] + C \frac{dv}{dt} .$$ (5.21)

At this point, we note the similarity of this equation and Equation 5.14. If in Equation 5.14, v is replaced by i, i by v, R by G, L by C and C by L, we obtain Equation 5.21. Insofar as the mathematical problem is concerned, the two are identical and the same type of integro-differential equation is involved in both cases. The only difference is the physical significance of the variables and the constants involved. These two networks are said to be *topological duals*. If the corresponding coefficients are numerically equal, then the solution of the mathematical problem is the same.

Equation 5.21 may be rewritten in terms of flux $\psi(t)$. Since $v = d\psi/dt$, Equation 5.21 becomes

$$i = \frac{1}{R} \frac{d\psi(t)}{dt} + \frac{1}{L} \psi(t) + C \frac{d^2\psi(t)}{dt^2} .$$ (5.22)

This equation is similar to Equation 5.16 so that $q(t)$ and $\psi(t)$ are dual variables also. Furthermore, if the branches have the nonlinear characteristics

$$i_R = f_R(v_R), \qquad i_L = f_L(\psi), \qquad q_C = f_C(v_C),$$ (5.23)

then Equation 5.20 may be rewritten as

$$i = f_R \left[\frac{d\psi(t)}{dt} \right] + f_L [\psi(t)] + \frac{d}{dt} f_C \left[\frac{d\psi(t)}{dt} \right] .$$ (5.24)

If the nonlinear functions in Equation 5.23 are equal to the corresponding ones in Equation 5.17 (note that f_C in Equation 5.23 corresponds to f_L in Equation 5.17), then Equation 5.24 is essentially the same differential equation as in Equation 5.18. The only difference is the use of the function $i(t)$ instead of $v(t)$ and $\psi(t)$ instead of $q(t)$.

In general, the mathematical analysis of networks is based on the solution of simultaneous equations found from KCL and KVL. The KCL equations relate currents at a node, and the KVL equations related voltages around loops. The other equations needed specify relationships of voltage and current for the network elements, as discussed in the previous chapter. These equations are called branch equations. The topological equations and the branch equations together completely describe any network.

● EXERCISES

5.4-1 For the network in Figure 5.8, assume that R, L and C are all equal
to unity for simplicity. If $v_R(t)$ has the waveform as in Figure
Exercise 5.4-1A, verify that the waveform for $i(t)$ is as shown in
Figure Exercise 5.4-1B, and that the waveform for $v_L(t)$ is as shown
in Figure Exercise 5.4-1C. The reference direction of i is from a
to b through R.

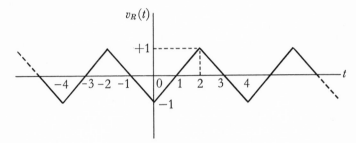

Figure Exercise 5.4-1A

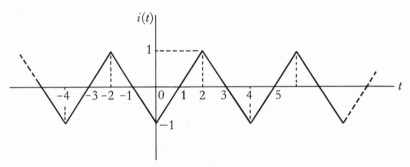

Figure Exercise 5.4-1B

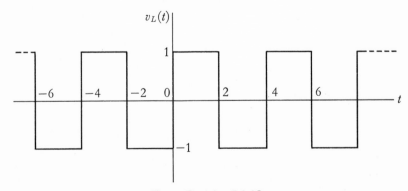

Figure Exercise 5.4-1C

5.4-2   Given the data in Exercise 5.4-1, and $v_C(0) = 0$, show that $v_C(t)$
has the waveform as in Figure Exercise 5.4-2A for t between 0 and
2. Determine the equation for $v_C(t)$ in the interval 0 to 2. Similarly,
show that $v_C(t)$ has the waveform as in Figure Exercise 5.4-2B for
$2 \leq t \leq 4$ and determine the equation for $v_C(t)$ in the interval. Also,
since $v_C(4) = 0 = v_C(0)$ and since the wave shape of $i(t)$ in $4 \leq t \leq 8$
is the same as that in $0 \leq t \leq 4$, what can you say of the wave shape
of $v_C(t)$ in $4 \leq t \leq 8$? Can you conclude that the complete waveform for $v_C(t)$ is as in Figure Exercise 5.4-2C? Give reasons.

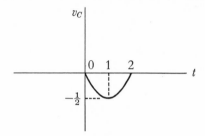

Figure Exercise 5.4-2A

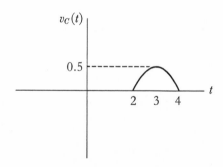

Figure Exercise 5.4-2B

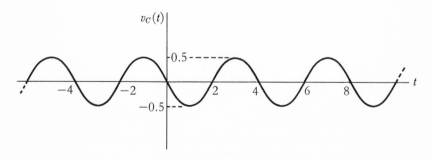

Figure Exercise 5.4-2C

5.4-3 For the network in Figure 5.8, the waveforms for $v_R(t)$, $v_L(t)$, and $v_C(t)$ are shown in Figure Exercises 5.4-1A, 5.4-1C, and 5.4-2C, respectively. Verify that the waveform for $v(t)$ is as shown in Figure Exercise 5.4-3.

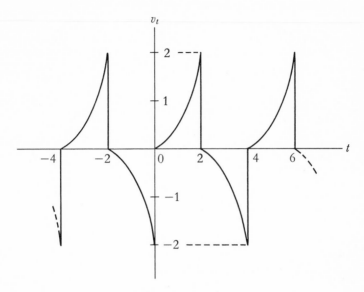

Figure Exercise 5.4-3

5.4-4 If $v_C(t)$ of Figure 5.8 is defined as

$$v_C(t) = \begin{cases} 1 - \cos 5t, & 0 \le t \le \dfrac{2\pi}{5}, \\ 0, & \text{elsewhere,} \end{cases}$$

as shown in Figure Exercise 5.4-4, find $v_R(t)$, $v_L(t)$, and $v(t)$. Assume that R, L, and C are all equal to unity for simplicity.

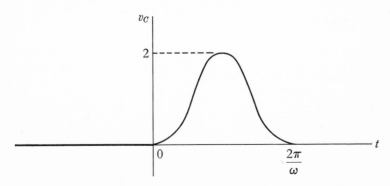

Figure Exercise 5.4-4

5.4-5   For the network in Figure 5.10 with $R = 1$ ohm, $L = 0.1$ henry, $C = \frac{1}{2}$ farad, and $v_{ab}(t) = u(t) \sin 10t$ volts as shown in Figure Exercise 5.4-5, plot $i(t)$, given that $i_L(0) = 0$.

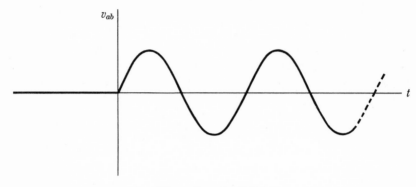

Figure Exercise 5.4-5

5.4-6   Repeat 5.4-5 if $v_{ab}(t)$ is as shown in Figure Exercise 5.4-6. The initial current $i_L(0)$ is also zero.

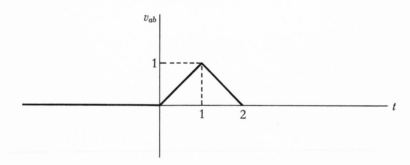

Figure Exercise 5.4-6

5.5 Equilibrium equations for mechanical networks

For electric networks, Kirchhoff's laws govern voltage and current equilibrium throughout a network. In addition, the individual differential equations defining the various elements relate the voltages with the currents. Likewise, the equations of motion of a mechanical network or system are governed by an equilibrium law called *D'Alembert's principle*. The principle states that the sum of the net instantaneous external forces acting on a body in a given direction and the body's reaction force in that direction due to inertia is zero. Thus, if $f(t)$ is the total force acting on a mass M in the x direction, $-M[d^2x(t)/dt^2]$ is the reaction force in the x direction and

$$f(t) - M\frac{d^2x(t)}{dt^2} = 0. \tag{5.25}$$

In electric networks, the terminals of elements which are joined together have a common voltage with respect to some reference. Likewise, in drawing a mechanical network, the terminals which move together are connected at a common junction. All terminals that remain stationary with respect to the reference frame are also connected together. Just as it is necessary to assign a reference polarity for voltages, it is also necessary to assign a reference direction of motion for each moving junction. The force and velocity sources must, of course, have reference directions too.

EXAMPLE 5.5-1.   The body represented by the constant mass M in Figure 5.11 is restrained by a spring K, one end of which is tied to the reference frame. The motion of the mass is also restrained by the damping represented by D. The mechanical network is shown in Figure 5.12. Re-

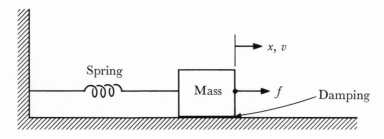

Figure 5.11   A simple mechanical translational system.

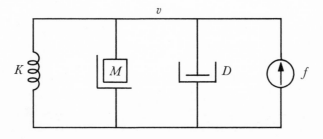

Figure 5.12   Mechanical network diagram for system in Figure 5.11.

ferring to Figure 5.11, we see that as the mass moves to the right, the spring stretches, and the spring exerts a positive force on the mass which is directed to the left. Likewise, the damper force is directed to the left if motion is to the right. Acceleration is also to the right so that the reaction force is to the left. Hence we have

$$f(t) - f_K(t) - f_B(t) - f_M(t) = 0 \qquad (5.26)$$

or

$$f(t) - \frac{1}{K}x - D\frac{dx}{dt} - M\frac{d^2x}{dt^2} = 0. \qquad (5.27)$$

Equation 5.27 is analogous to that for a parallel *RLC* circuit with a current excitation. The analogous quantities are force and current, velocity and voltage, mass and capacitance, damper and electric conductance, and compliance and inductance. It is also possible to compare Equation 5.27 with that for a series *RLC* circuit excited by a voltage source. In the latter case, force is analogous to voltage, velocity is analogous to current, mass is analogous to inductance, damping is analogous to electric resistance, and stiffness is analogous to capacitance.   □

EXAMPLE 5.5-2.   The two masses labeled M_1 and M_2 in Figure 5.13 are restrained by two springs with stiffness coefficients K_1 and K_2. Mass M_1 moves on rollers which are assumed to be frictionless, and M_2 slides on the inertial reference surface with a damping coefficient D. A force f is applied as shown. Assign position references to the masses as x_1 and x_2 which are indicated in Figure 5.13. The arrow directions signify the positive reference directions. Choose the coordinate origins for x_1 and x_2 to be the equilibrium positions with the springs neither extended nor compressed (the force f is not applied). So for $x_1 = 0$ and $x_2 = 0$ there is no force on the springs.

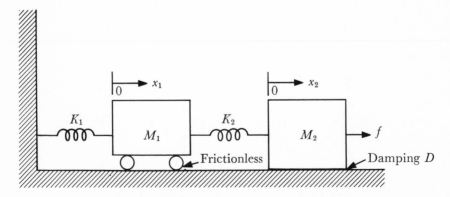

Figure 5.13   Mechanical system for Example 5.5-2.

Let us examine the forces acting on the masses. For M_1 we have a spring force K_1x_1 acting on M_1 with positive reference to the left. Also acting on M_1 is the spring force $K_2(x_1 - x_2)$ with positive reference to the left. This is because $x_1 - x_2$ is a compression on the spring K_2 which results in a force on M_1 with positive reference to the left. Finally, the acceleration force on M_1 is $M_1(d^2x_1/dt^2)$ with positive reference to the right. Hence the reaction force of M_1 is $M_1(d^2x_1/dt^2)$ with positive reference to the left. Applying D'Alembert's principle to forces acting on M_1 we have

$$M_1 \frac{d^2x_1}{dt^2} + K_1x_1 + K_2(x_1 - x_2) = 0. \tag{5.28}$$

In terms of velocity v_1 defined as

$$v_1 = \frac{dx_1}{dt}, \tag{5.29}$$

Equation 5.28 becomes

$$M_1 \frac{dv_1}{dt} + K_1 \int v_1 dt + K_2 \int (v_1 - v_2) dt = 0. \tag{5.30}$$

Similarly, the forces acting on M_2 are: the given force f, positive reference to the right; the damping force $-Ddx_2/dt$, positive reference to the right; the spring force $K_2(x_1 - x_2)$, positive reference to the right; and reaction force $-M_2(d^2x_2/dt^2)$, positive reference to the right. D'Alembert's principle, applied to M_2 yields

$$f - D \frac{dx_2}{dt} + K_2(x_1 - x_2) - M_2 \frac{d^2x_2}{dt^2} = 0. \tag{5.31}$$

In terms of velocity v_1 and velocity v_2, which is defined as

$$v_2 = \frac{dx_2}{dt}, \tag{5.32}$$

Equation 5.31 may be rewritten as

$$M_2 \frac{dv_2}{dt} + K_2 \int (v_2 - v_1) dt + Dv_2 = f. \tag{5.33}$$

Equations 5.30 and 5.33 describe the mechanical system in terms of the velocity variables v_1 and v_2. For MKS units, force is in newtons, velocity in meters per second, time in seconds, mass in kilograms, spring stiffness in newtons per meter, and damping coefficient in newtons per meter per second. □

EXAMPLE 5.5-3. Let us draw a mechanical network diagram for the mechanical system in Figure 5.13. The important point to remember is that mechanical parts which do not move relative to each other are repre-

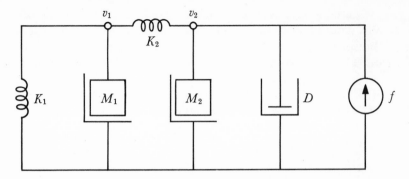

Figure 5.14 Network diagram for the mechanical system in Figure 5.13.

sented by a common node. For example one end of K_1, one end of K_2, and the whole mass M_1 move together and the velocity v_1 is represented by a node in Figure 5.14. Similarly, one end of K_2, one end of M_2, one end of D, and one end of f are joined at node v_2. The inertial reference is also represented by a node.

D'Alembert's principle is applied to the various nodes in exactly the same way as Kirchhoff's current law is applied to nodes of an electrical network, treating force as analogous to current. Let us illustrate this by first drawing an electrical network, replacing each mechanical element by its electrical counterpart as summarized in Table 4.2 for the force–current analogy, and using the same topology or manner of interconnection. From Table 4.2, we see that we have to replace M by C, K by $1/L$, D by $1/R$, and f by i, and velocity by voltage. The resulting network is shown in Figure 5.15. If we apply Kirchhoff's current law to the two top nodes corresponding to voltages v_1 and v_2 we have

$$C_1 \frac{dv_1}{dt} + \frac{1}{L_1} \int v_1 dt + \frac{1}{L_2} \int (v_1 - v_2) dt = 0 \qquad (5.34)$$

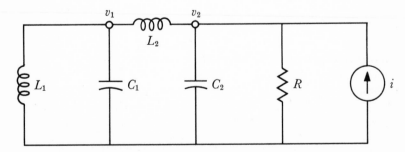

Figure 5.15 Electrical dual of the mechanical network in Figure 5.14, where force is analogous to current.

and

$$C_2 \frac{dv_2}{dt} + \frac{1}{L_2} \int (v_2 - v_1)dt + \frac{1}{R} v_2 = i. \qquad (5.35)$$

With the appropriate substitution of parameters as mentioned above, Equations 5.30 and 5.33 are immediately obtained. If desired, D'Alembert's principle may be applied directly to Figure 5.14, using it in much the same way as Kirchhoff's current law and treating force in the same way as current.

The electrical analogy based on a force-to-voltage substitution is not as neat as that for a force to current substitution. The electrical network for the force-voltage analogy is the topological dual of the network for force-current analogy.

The mechanical-electrical analogy depicted in the above example shows that mechanical systems may be analyzed by treating the electrical analogs. The electrical analogs are very simply obtained from the mechanical network diagrams. In the case of a force-current analogy, the mechanical and electrical networks have identical topologies. ☐

● **EXERCISES**

5.5-1 At time $t = 0$, a constant force F is applied to the mass shown in Figure Exercise 5.5-1. This mass is initially at rest at $x = 0$. Obtain the differential equation for the position $x(t)$.

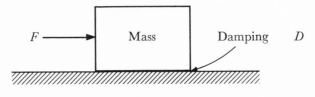

Figure Exercise 5.5-1

5.5-2 Draw an electric analog for the mechanical system of Exercise 5.5-1, making voltage analogous to force.

5.5-3 Repeat Exercise 5.5-2 for current analogous to force.

Problems

5-1 Write the differential equation relating $i(t)$ to $v(t)$ for the network in Figure Problem 5.1(a). Assume that the elements are linear and time-invariant. If the current is

$$i(t) = K_1(1 - e^{-(R/L)t})u(t)$$

as shown in Figure Problem 5.1(b), where K_1 is a positive constant and $u(t)$ is the unit step function, determine $v(t)$. Repeat the above for

$$i(t) = K_2 e^{-(R/L)t} u(t), \qquad K_2 > 0,$$

as shown in Figure Problem 5-1(c).

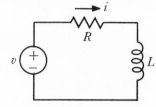

Figure Problem 5-1(a)

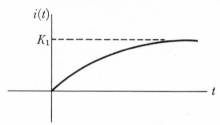

Figure Problem 5-1(b)

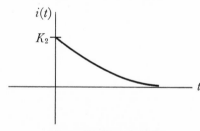

Figure Problem 5-1(c)

5-2   For the network in Figure Problem 5-2, if R and C are constant and

$$i(t) = K_1 e^{-t/RC} u(t), \qquad K_1 > 0,$$

sketch $v_C(t)$ if $v_C(0) = 0$. Determine $v(t)$.

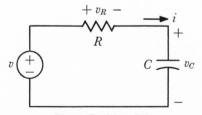

Figure Problem 5-2

5-3 Write the differential equation relating $i(t)$ to $v(t)$ for the network in Figure Problem 5-3, if L and C are linear but time-varying.

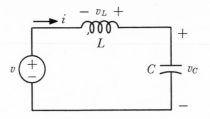

Figure Problem 5-3

5-4 For the network in Figure Problem 5-2, solve for $v(t)$ if $R=8$ ohms, $C = \frac{1}{3}$ farad, and $i(t)$ is the triangular pulse shown in Figure Problem 5-4. The initial voltage $v_C(0)$ is zero.

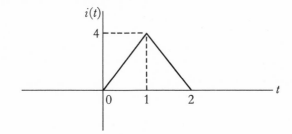

Figure Problem 5-4

5-5 Repeat Problem 5-4 for the current waveform as shown in Figure Problem 5-5.

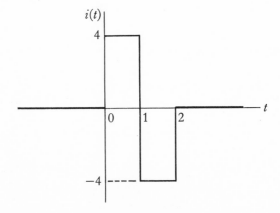

Figure Problem 5-5

5-6   In the network of Figure Problem 5-6, K is closed at $t = 0$, and the current is

$$i(t) = \begin{cases} 2e^{-t}, & t \geq 0, \\ 0, & t < 0. \end{cases}$$

Capacitor C_1 is initially charged corresponding to a voltage V_0 with polarity as shown in the figure, and C_2 is initially uncharged. Determine the voltages across the two capacitors as a function of time using numerical values where possible. Determine the final values of the two capacitor voltages, i.e., the values for $t \to \infty$.

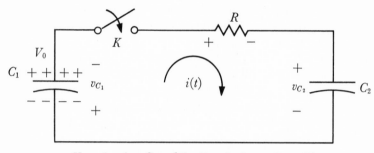

$V_0 = 6$ volts, $C_1 = \frac{1}{2}$F., $R = 3$ ohms, $C_2 = 1$F.

Figure Problem 5-6

5-7   In the network shown in Figure Problem 5-7, the switch is moved from a to b at $t = 0$. Find the differential equation for $i(t)$ for $t > 0$, if R_1 and R_2 are positive constants and L is nonlinear described by $\psi = Ki^2$, where K is a positive constant.

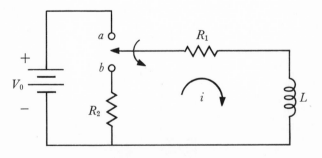

Figure Problem 5-7

5-8 Two nonlinear current-controlled resistors are connected in series with a voltage source as shown in Figure Problem 5-8. If the resistor characteristics are described by $v_{R_1} = K_1 f(i_{R_1})$ and $v_{R_2} = K_2 f(i_{R_2})$, where f is a specified function and K_1 and K_2 are constants, show that the resulting v_{R_1} and v_{R_2} in the network do not depend on the function f.

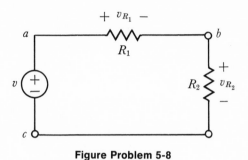

Figure Problem 5-8

5-9 In the network of (a) in the figure, four currents and one voltage are identified. In (b) is shown a signal waveform.

(1) If i_R has the waveform of (b), find the waveform for all other voltages and currents.

(2) Repeat (1) if i_L instead of i_R has the waveform of (b).

(3) Repeat (1) if i_C instead of i_R has the waveform of (b).

(4) Repeat (1) if v instead of i_R has the waveform of (b).

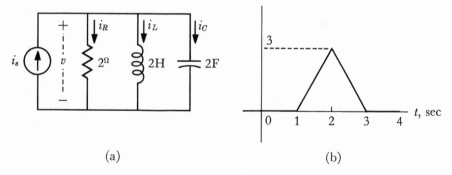

(a)   (b)

Figure Problem 5-9

5-10 The waveform of the voltage across the capacitor of the given network is shown in the figure. Determine the voltage generated by the source. Repeat if $v_C(t) = 100\sqrt{2} \sin 2\pi(60)t$, writing the result in the form $v_s(t) = V_{sm} \sin[(2\pi(60)t + \phi)]$.

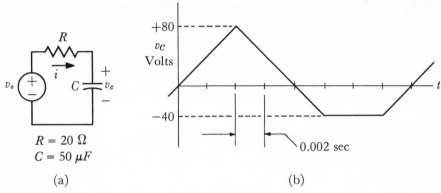

$$R = 20 \ \Omega$$
$$C = 50 \ \mu F$$

(a)   (b)

Figure Problem 5.10

5-11   For the waveform shown in the figure for $v_2(t)$, find the source
       voltage waveform, $v_1(t)$, using numerical values for maximum and
       minimum values, slopes, etc.

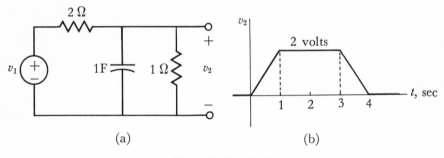

(a)   (b)

Figure Problem 5-11

5-12   (a) For the network shown, write a differential equation relating
       the node-to-datum voltage, v_a, to the driving voltage, v_S.
       (b) If $v_a(t)$ is a unit ramp, and the capacitors are initially uncharged,
       determine $v_S(t)$.

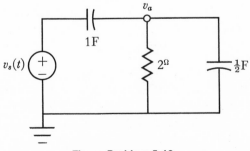

Figure Problem 5-12

5-13   Suppose that the nonlinear resistors in Figure Problem 5-8 have
characteristics as shown in Figure Problem 5-13. For $v = 2$ volts,
determine i. [*Hint:* Obtain a composite $v–i$ characteristic for the
two series resistors first.]

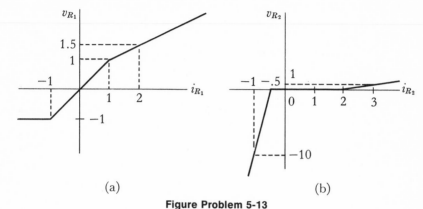

(a)   (b)

Figure Problem 5-13

5-14   Determine a composite $v–i$ characteristic for the two resistors in
parallel in Figure Problem 5-14, if the individual characteristics are
as shown in Figure Problem 5-13. If $i = 2$, find v.

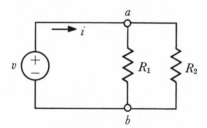

Figure Problem 5-14

5-15   For the network in Figure Problem 5-15(a), sketch the characteristic
for v vs. i, for E and R_1 positive constants. Suppose the resistor R is
connected in series with E and R_1, where R has the characteristic
shown in Figure Problem 5-15(b). Relate i to i_R and v to v_R by means
of Kirchhoff's laws. How would you determine the actual v and the
actual i?

5-16   Suppose that for the mechanical system of Figure 5.11 the velocity
has the waveshape as in Figure Problem 5-9(b). Assuming $M = 1$
kilogram, $K = 1$ meter per newton, and $D = 2$ newtons per meter
per second, determine the force $f(t)$.

5-17   Repeat Problem 5-16 if the waveform in Figure Problem 5-9(b) is
acceleration rather than velocity.

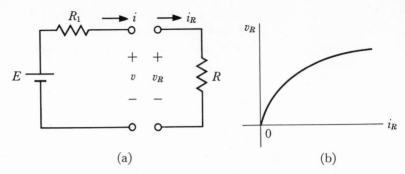

Figure Problem 5-15

5-18   Suppose the reference direction for f in Figure 5.11 is reversed and suppose the reference direction for x is also reversed. Write the force equation, using D'Alembert's principle.

5-19   Using force-to-current analogy, draw the electrical analog for the mechanical system in Figure 5.11. Write the node equation for the network and, using the appropriate substitution of parameters from Table 4.2, verify the mechanical equation describing the mechanical system (see Equation 5.27).

Energy and Power   **6**

6.1   Energy dissipation and energy storage in network elements

It was mentioned in Chapter 1 that the *instantaneous power* or time rate of energy flow associated with a two-terminal or 1-port network is the product vi, where v and i are the terminal voltage and current, respectively. Unless indicated to the contrary, the energy flow that is considered is the flow *into* the network. For such an energy flow direction, the power p is equal to vi if v and i have references as shown in Figure 6.1(a). In Figure 6.1(b), $p = -vi$. Thus the reference sign for p depends entirely on the relative references chosen for v and i. If in Figure 6.1(a) v and i are both positive or both negative at a given instant of time t_1, then $p(t_1)$ is positive, and the energy flow into the network is increasing. On the other hand if at a given instant of time t_2, v and i in Figure 6.1(a) have opposite signs, then $p(t_2)$ is negative, and energy flow into the network is decreasing or energy flow from the network is increasing. The same situation is true for the case in Figure 6.1(b). The energy flow into the network of Figure 6.1(a) from the instant t_1 to the instant t_2 is the time integral of $p(t)$ from t_1 to t_2.

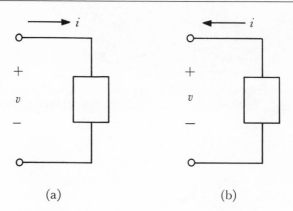

(a)   (b)

Figure 6.1 In (a), *vi* is the instantaneous time rate of energy flow *into* the network. In (b), *vi* is the instantaneous time rate of energy flow *from* the network.

For a linear resistor, with references as in Figure 6.1(a), the instantaneous power of R is

$$p(t) = v(t)\, i(t) = R(t)\, i^2(t). \tag{6.1}$$

If the resistor is time-invariant, $R(t)$ becomes a constant. We see that so long as $R(t)$ is not negative, $p(t)$ is not negative, and energy flows into R. For $R(t) \neq 0$, we may write Equation 6.1 as

$$p(t) = v(t)\, \frac{1}{R(t)}\, v(t) = \frac{1}{R(t)}\, v^2(t) = G(t)\, v^2(t), \tag{6.2}$$

where $G(t)$, the conductance, is the reciprocal of $R(t)$. For a current-controlled nonlinear resistor characteristic such as a current-controlled one as in Figure 6.2(a), with reference directions as in Figure 6.1(a), the power of R is

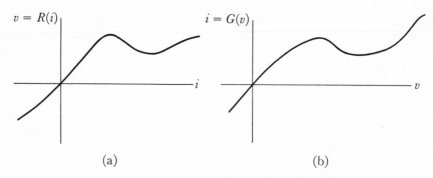

(a)   (b)

Figure 6.2 (a) Current-controlled resistance characteristic: *v* is a function of *i*. (b) Voltage-controlled characteristic: *i* is a function of *v*.

$$p(t) = vi = R(i)\, i, \tag{6.3}$$

where $R(i)$ is the function of i representing v. Similarly, for a voltage-controlled resistor characteristic as in Figure 6.2(b), p for the network is

$$p = vi = vG(v). \tag{6.4}$$

If the characteristic is neither voltage controlled nor current controlled, it is no longer possible to express v as an ordinary function of i nor i as an ordinary function of v. This situation will not be treated in this book.

EXAMPLE 6.1-1.   Suppose that at a certain instant t_1, the voltage and current associated with a network, with reference direction shown in Figure 6.1(a), are 5 volts and 3 amperes. Then the power is

$$p = vi = 5(3) = 15 \text{ watts.} \tag{6.5}$$

This means that the energy flow into the network is increasing at the rate of 15 watts. If the reference directions for voltage and current for the same network are as shown in Figure 6.1(b), then v would be the same as before but i would be -3 amperes. The power is

$$p = -vi = -(5)(-3) = 15 \text{ watts,} \tag{6.6}$$

which is the same as before, as it should be. $\square$

EXAMPLE 6.1-2.   Consider another network, with reference directions as in Figure 6.1(b), for which $v = 100 \sin 377t$ and $i = 2 \sin(377t + 3\pi/4)$. Then the power is

$$p = -vi = -200[\sin 377t][\sin(377t + 3\pi/4)] \tag{6.7}$$

for any instant t. $\square$

● EXERCISES

6.1-1   Suppose that in Figure 6.1(b), the reference polarity for v is reversed so that the plus reference mark is at the bottom. Write the expression for the instantaneous power of the network.

6.1-2   Repeat Exercise 6.1-1 for Figure 6.1(a).

6.1-3   Suppose that the reference directions for both v and i are reversed in Figure 6.1(a). Write the expression for the instantaneous power of the network.

6.1-4   Repeat Exercise 6.1-3 for Figure 6.1(b).

6.2 Average power for periodic signals

When $v(t)$ and $i(t)$ are periodic and of the same period, then $v(t)i(t)$ will be periodic, and if T is the period of $v(t)$ and $i(t)$, then $p(t) = p(t+T)$ for all t. However $T_1 = T$ may not be the smallest value satisfying $p(t) =$

$p(t + T_1)$ for all t. For example, suppose $v(t) = V_0 \sin \omega_0 t$, and suppose we wish to examine the instantaneous power into a constant positive resistor R. Then $i(t) = (V_0/R) \sin \omega_0 t$. So

$$p(t) = \frac{V_0^2}{R} \sin^2 \omega_0 t = \frac{V_0^2}{2R} [1 - \cos 2\omega_0 t]. \tag{6.8}$$

Thus the period of $p(t)$ is π/ω_0, but the period of $v(t)$ is $2\pi/\omega_0$. Recalling the definition for average value of Equation 3.5, we have the average power

$$P_{av} = \frac{1}{T_1} \int_{t_1}^{t_1 + T_1} p(t) dt, \tag{6.9}$$

where T_1 is the period of $p(t)$ and t_1 is arbitrary, and it is chosen for convenience. For the example above,

$$P_{av} = \frac{1}{\pi/\omega_0} \int_0^{\pi/\omega_0} \frac{V_0^2}{2R} [1 - \cos 2\omega_0 t] dt = \frac{V_0^2}{2R} = \frac{V_{rms}^2}{R} = I_{rms}^2 R, \quad (6.10)$$

where V_{rms} is the rms value of $v(t)$ and I_{rms} is the rms value of $i(t)$. The result in Equation 6.10 applies to any constant resistor and for any periodic $v(t)$. In general, for a time-varying current-controlled resistor we have

$$P_{av} = \frac{1}{T_1} \int_0^{T_1} i(t) \, v[i(t), t] dt, \tag{6.11}$$

and for a time-varying voltage-controlled resistor we have

$$P_{av} = \frac{1}{T_1} \int_0^{T_1} v(t) \, i[v(t), t] dt, \tag{6.12}$$

provided $p(t)$ is periodic with period T_1. For a linear time-invariant capacitor, let us show that the average power is zero. Recall that for a linear time-invariant capacitor, v and i are related by

$$i = C \frac{dv}{dt}. \tag{6.13}$$

In Equation 6.13, it is assumed that i and v have relative references as in Figure 6.1(a). Using Equation 6.13 in the definition of Equation 6.9 we have

$$P_{av} = \frac{1}{T_1} \int_{t_1}^{t_1 + T_1} \left[C \frac{dv}{dt} \right] v \, dt = \frac{1}{T_1} \left[\int_{v(t_1)}^{v(t_1 + T_1)} Cv \, dv \right]$$
$$= \frac{1}{2T_1} Cv^2 \Big|_{v(t_1)}^{v(t_1 + T_1)} = \frac{C}{2T_1} [v^2(t_1 + T_1) - v^2(t_1)]. \tag{6.14}$$

Since v is periodic of period T, then $v(t_1 + T_1) = v(t_1)$ so that $P_{av} = 0$.

It is equally straightforward to demonstrate that the average power of a linear time-invariant inductor is zero. Instead of Equation 6.13 we have

$$v = L\frac{di}{dt} \tag{6.15}$$

for the reference conventions in Figure 6.1(a). Using Equation 6.15 in Equation 6.9 we have

$$P_{av} = \frac{1}{T_1}\int_{t_1}^{t_1+T}\left[L\frac{di}{dt}\right]i\,dt = \frac{1}{T_1}\left[\frac{1}{2}Li^2\Big|_{i(t_1)}^{i(t_1+T_1)}\right]. \tag{6.16}$$

Since $i(t_1) = i(t_1 + T_1)$ because i is periodic of period T_1, then $P_{av} = 0$.

It will be demonstrated in Section 6.6 that even for nonlinear inductors and capacitors, provided these are time-invariant and they satisfy some mild restrictions on the type of nonlinearities, the average power is zero. For now, let us simply verify a specific example. Let the charge-voltage characteristic of a charge-controlled capacitor be given by

$$v = q^3. \tag{6.17}$$

Note that since time does not appear explicitly, the capacitor is time-invariant. However, it is nonlinear. The average power is

$$P_{av} = \frac{1}{T_1}\int_{t_1}^{t_1+T_1}vi\,dt = \frac{1}{T_1}\int_{q(t_1)}^{q(t_1+T_1)}v\,dq. \tag{6.18}$$

Substituting Equation 6.17 into Equation 6.18, we obtain

$$P_{av} = \frac{1}{T_1}\left[\frac{1}{4}q^4\Big|_{q(t_1)}^{q(t_1+T_1)}\right]. \tag{6.19}$$

Since v and i (and, therefore, q) are periodic of period T_1, then $q(t_1) = q(t_1 + T_1)$ so that $P_{av} = 0$.

● EXERCISES

6.2-1   For a linear time-invariant inductor of L henrys, and $i(t) = I_0 \sin \omega_0 t$, verify that the average power is 0 by solving for $v(t)$, and taking the time average of $v(t)i(t)$.

6.2-2   For a nonlinear time-invariant capacitor described by $q(t) = v^3(t)$ and $v(t) = V_0 \sin \omega_0 t$, verify that P_{av} is zero by solving for $i(t)$ and taking the average of $v(t)i(t)$.

6.2-3   For a time-varying linear inductor described by $\psi = (2 + \sin \omega_0 t)i$, compute the average power P_{av} into L if $i(t) = I_0 \cos \omega_0 t$. Is the inductor dissipating, generating or simply storing energy?

6.2-4   Repeat Exercise 6.2-3 for $\psi = (2 - \sin \omega_0 t)i$.

6.2-5   Suppose we have a time-varying voltage-controlled resistor. For a periodic $v(t)$, will $p(t)$ be necessarily periodic?

6.2-6   Suppose we have a time-varying current-controlled inductor. For a periodic current, will the instantaneous power into L be necessarily periodic?

6.2-7   For a linear time-invariant resistor $R = 10$ ohms, compute the average power if $i(t) = I_1 \sin(\omega_0 t + \alpha_1) + I_2 \sin(\omega_0 t + \alpha_2)$.

6.3   Passive, active, and lossless networks

We begin this section by considering an arbitrary network with n pairs of terminals, called an *n-port* network, as shown in Figure 6.3. We connect the n-ports to n sources as shown. Suppose that at the instant t_1 when the sources are connected the initial charges on capacitors are all zero and the initial fluxes in inductors are all zero. Then the energy flow into the network between t_1 and t is

$$W(t) = \sum_{k=1}^{n} \int_{t_1}^{t} v_k(\tau) i_k(\tau) \, d\tau. \tag{6.20}$$

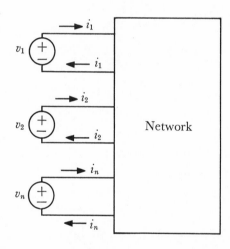

Figure 6.3   An *n*-port or *n* terminal-pair network.

If for any t and t_1 (t greater than t_1) and for any set of arbitrary sources, $W(t)$ is nonnegative, then the n-port is said to be *passive*. Otherwise, if $W(t)$ is negative for some value of t and some set of sources, then the n-port is said to be *active*. The definitions just given apply not only to arbitrary n-ports but, of course, to simple elements as well. We now consider a number of special cases and reserve Equation 6.20 for later use.

First consider the resistor. The energy flow into R is

$$W(t) = \int_{t_1}^{t} v(\tau) i(\tau) \, d\tau, \tag{6.21}$$

where either v is expressed in terms of i or i is expressed in terms of v. Since $W(t)$ must be positive or zero for arbitrary values of t, $v(t)i(t)$ must never be negative for any time interval. For if it were, then by choosing either i or v to be zero outside the interval, we would be left with the integral of a negative quantity which would be negative. Hence, it is necessary as well as sufficient for $v(t)i(t)$ to be nonnegative in order for $W(t)$ to be nonnegative. That is, the v-i characteristic must lie in the first and third quadrant in order for a resistor to be passive.

For a linear time-invariant positive capacitor or inductor, $W(t)$ is

$$W(t) = \tfrac{1}{2}Cv^2(t) \tag{6.22}$$

for a capacitor and

$$W(t) = \tfrac{1}{2}Li^2(t) \tag{6.23}$$

for an inductor, and since $C > 0$ and $L > 0$, $W(t)$ is nonnegative and hence the element is passive. Similarly, a linear time-invariant negative C or L is found to be an active element.

We have already seen that linear time-invariant capacitors and inductors are conservative elements in the sense that the integral of the periodic signal W_C or W_L over one period is zero. Conservative elements are also called *lossless* elements. In general, a time-invariant n-port is lossless if for periodic signals which are otherwise arbitrary the average power into the n-port is zero. We shall not define the lossless concept for time-varying networks. Note that a lossless n-port or element is not necessarily passive. For instance, a negative linear time-invariant capacitor is active but also lossless.

It is possible that a passive n-port may contain active elements. That is, although some elements may not be passive, the network viewed from the n-ports may be passive. Likewise, a lossless n-port may contain lossy elements. We define a *passive network* as a network all of whose elements are passive. Likewise we define a *lossless network* as a network containing only lossless elements. If a network is passive, then for any choice and number of ports, the resulting n-port is a passive n-port. A network is said to be an *active network* if it contains at least one active element. Similarly, a network is said to be a *lossy network* if it contains at least one lossy element.

● EXERCISES

6.3-1   Show that a time-invariant charge-controlled capacitor is necessarily passive if its v-q characteristic is in the first and third quadrant.

6.3-2   Give an example of a time-invariant charge-controlled passive capacitor whose characteristic is not restricted to the first and third quadrant.

6.3-3   Show that a time-invariant flux-controlled inductor is active if its i-ψ characteristic lies in the second and fourth quadrant.

6.3-4   Determine whether the ideal transformer as defined in Chapter 4 is lossless.

6.3-5   Determine whether the ideal transformer as defined in Chapter 4 is passive or active.

6.3-6   Is it possible for a network comprising a passive n-port to be an active network? Explain briefly if it is not possible or give an example if it is possible.

6.4   Conservation of energy

Conservation of energy is a universal physical law which may be stated in various ways. One way is as follows: Given a system or network, the total energy at any instant t_2 is equal to the sum of the total energy at any previous instant t_1 and the energy added to the system during the time interval between t_1 and t_2. The energy added to the system may be negative, i.e., positive energy may have been taken out of the system resulting in a decrease of energy at t_2. In applications where nuclear reactions may be involved, total energy must be interpreted to include the equivalent energy of mass in accordance with Einstein's mass-energy equation. In an ordinary electric network where no such mass-to-energy conversion takes place, the net electric energy added to the network is equal to the net increase in the electric energy stored plus the net energy converted to other forms of energy such as heat. That is,

$$\text{Net energy added} = \text{Net increase in stored energy}$$
$$+ \text{ net increase in energy converted.} \quad (6.24)$$

Of course, any of these terms may be negative, but the equality will hold. The energy in any network or system is equal to the algebraic sum of the energies in all the parts of the network or system. Thus it is possible to determine total energy by adding the energies corresponding to all the branches. In some problems it may be convenient to partition a network into several subnetworks in which case the total energy is equal to the algebraic sum of energies in the various subnetworks.

For periodic signals, we may consider average power instead of energy so that the total average power into a network is equal to the algebraic sum of the average powers in all the subnetworks. In particular, we note that in a time-invariant network, the average power into time-invariant capacitors and inductors is zero. Hence, the total average power in this case is equal to the algebraic sum of the average powers into all the other elements.

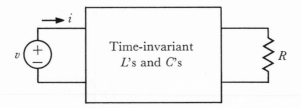

Figure 6.4 By the conservation-of-energy principle, average power into the network from the source is equal to the average power into *R*.

For example, for the special network in Figure 6.4, the average power from the source is equal to the average power into *R*.

Similarly, since Equation 6.24 holds for all t, differentiating both sides of the equation with respect to t yields a principle which may be called conservation of instantaneous power. By this we mean that the instantaneous power to the network equals the sum of the instantaneous rate of energy dissipation and the instantaneous rate of stored energy increase in all the elements. Alternatively, we may say that the instantaneous power input to the entire network is equal to the sum of the instantaneous power inputs to all the individual elements.

In a general network represented as the n-port network in Figure 6.3, the total energy into the n-port is the sum of the energies from the individual sources as in Equation 6.20. The sources do not have to be as simple as those shown in Figure 6.3. To illustrate this statement, the n-port labeled Network 1 in Figure 6.5 is connected to a set of networks. It is clear that the energy flow into Network 1 is given by Equation 6.20. When the ports are not identifiable, the situation is slightly different.

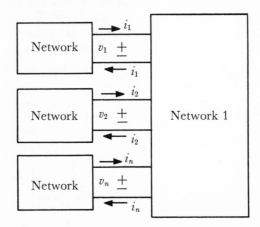

Figure 6.5 Energy flow into Network 1 is given by Equation 6.20.

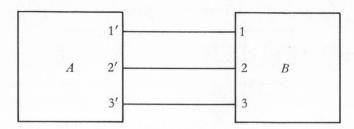

Figure 6.6 A three-terminal network connected to another three-terminal network.

Consider the three-terminal Network A in Figure 6.6. We can no longer say that terminals 1 and 2 constitute a port, for $i_{2'2}$ is not necessarily $-i_{1'1}$. All we can say is that by KCL, we have

$$i_{1'1} + i_{2'2} + i_{3'3} = 0, \tag{6.25}$$

and from KVL we have

$$v_{12} + v_{23} + v_{31} = 0. \tag{6.26}$$

Let us develop a formula for the energy into Network A. The Network A with the terminal voltages and currents labeled is again shown in Figure 6.7(a). It is further redrawn in Figure 6.7(b). As long as $i_{ac} + i_{bc} = i_2$, it is clear that the terminal characteristics of Network A are unchanged. In particular, if it is possible to make $i_{ac} = -i_1$ and $i_{bc} = -i_3$, then the situation is analogous to a 2-port network. But from the KCL equation in Equation 6.25, we have

$$i_2 = -i_1 - i_3. \tag{6.27}$$

Hence, if we make $i_{ac} = -i_1$ and $i_{bc} = -i_3$, i_2 will indeed turn out to be $-i_1 - i_3$ as desired. Now it is clear that the energy flow into Network A, which is the sum of the energy flows into the ports $1'a$ and $b3'$, is

$$\int_{t_1}^{t} \left[v_{1'a}i_1 + v_{b3'}i_{bc} \right] d\tau = \int_{t_1}^{t} \left[v_{12}i_1 + v_{23}(-i_3) \right] d\tau. \tag{6.28}$$

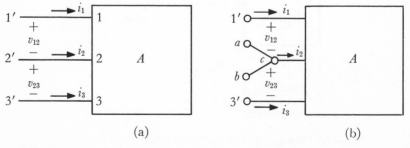

(a)   (b)

Figure 6.7 Terminal *v-i* characteristics of Network A in (a) are unchanged by splitting line 2 into two as shown in (b).

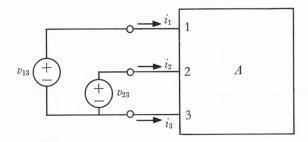

Figure 6.8 Interpretation of energy-flow calculation of Equation 6.30.

Since $v_{12} = v_{13} - v_{23}$ and $-i_3 = i_1 + i_2$, Equation 6.28 may be rewritten as

$$\text{Energy flow into } A = \int_{t_1}^{t} \left[(v_{13} - v_{23})i_1 + (i_1 + i_2)v_{23} \right] d\tau \quad (6.29)$$

or

$$W_A = \int_{t_1}^{t} (v_{13}i_1 + v_{23}i_2) \, d\tau. \quad (6.30)$$

Equation 6.30 has a particularly simple interpretation shown in Figure 6.8. Of course, the labeling of the terminals as 1, 2, and 3 is completely

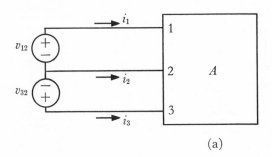

(a)

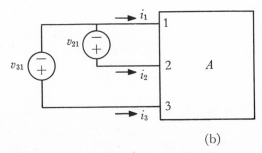

(b)

Figure 6.9 Total energy flow from sources in (a) is equal to total energy flow from sources in (b), and also equal to total energy flow from sources in Figure 6.8.

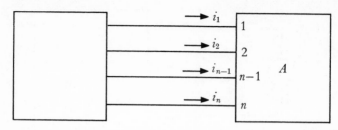

Figure 6.10   Total energy flow into Network *A* is equal to that in Figure 6.11.

arbitrary. Thus the energy flow into Network *A*, which is the energy flow from the sources in Figure 6.8, is equal to the energy flow from the sources in Figure 6.9(a) and also equal to the energy flow from the sources in Figure 6.9(b).

Similarly, it is a fairly straightforward proposition to show (see Problem 6-8) that the energy flow into the *n*-terminal Network *A* of Figure 6.10 is equal to the energy flow from the $n-1$ sources in Figure 6.11. The energy is

$$W_A = \int_{t_1}^{t} \sum_{k=1}^{n-1} v_{kn} i_k \, d\tau. \tag{6.31}$$

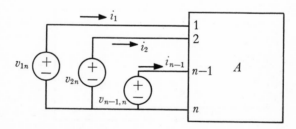

Figure 6.11   Total energy flow from the $n-1$ sources is equal to the total energy flow into Network *A* in Figure 6.10.

Again it should be emphasized that the terminal labeling is arbitrary and that terminals other than the *n*th may be used as the common return terminal.

● EXERCISES

6.4-1   In the network of Figure Exercise 6.4-1, suppose that the source v_{13} is a constant 10 volts, element *a* is $R_1 = 10$ ohms, and element *b* is $R_2 = 2$ ohms. Verify that the energy flow from the source for any time interval is equal to the sum of energy flows into the resistors.

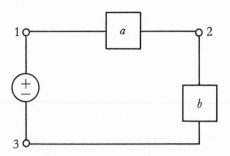

Figure Exercise 6.4-1

6.4-2 Repeat Exercise 6.4-1 for element b, a nonlinear resistor specified by $v_{23} = 2i_{23}^2$.

6.4-3 Repeat Exercise 6.4-1 for $R_2 = -2$ ohms.

6.4-4 In the network of Figure Exercise 6.4-1, suppose element a is a resistor $R = 10$ ohms and element b is an inductor $L = 2$ henrys. If $i_{12}(0) = 0$ and $i_{12}(t)$ is

$$i_{12}(t) = (1 - e^{-(R/L)t}) \qquad \text{for} \quad t \geq 0,$$

compute the energy delivered by the source from $t = 0$ to any arbitrary instant t and compare with the energy stored in L plus the energy dissipated in R.

6.4-5 For the network in Figure Exercise 6.4-1 and element values as given in Exercise 6.4-4, compute the average power from the source if $i_{12}(t) = \sin 5t$ and compare with the sum of average powers into R and into L.

6.4-6 In the network of Figure Exercise 6.4-6, the elements are resistors

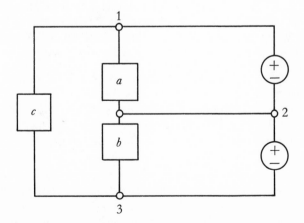

Figure Exercise 6.4-6

all equal to 2 ohms. For $v_{12} = 3$ and $v_{23} = 5$, verify that the total power from the sources is equal to the sum of the powers in each branch of the network.

6.5 Tellegen's theorem

The law of conservation of energy discussed in the previous section is not an additional postulate in network theory. It is implied by Kirchhoff's laws being satisfied. This is very reassuring. Specifically, it is an immediate consequence of Tellegen's theorem† which is next proved using Kirchhoff's laws.

Tellegen's theorem pertains to a network which is an arbitrary interconnection of n_k-port subnetworks where the number of ports n_k of the kth subnetwork as well as the number of subnetworks is arbitrary. The allowable interconnections among the subnetworks are restricted to those which involve the ports only. Let the sum of the number of ports of all the subnetworks be denoted by N. Assign subnetwork port voltage- and current-reference directions such that the current-reference arrow enters the port at the terminal with the + voltage reference. Let $i_1, i_2, \ldots, i_N$ be values of currents associated with the N ports such that KCL is satisfied. Let $v_1, v_2, \ldots, v_N$ be values of voltages associated with the N ports such that KVL is satisfied. In terms of the above notation, Tellegen's theorem states that

$$\sum_{k=1}^{N} v_k i_k = 0. \tag{6.32}$$

Notice that there is no mention of the nature of branch characteristics. Hence, v_k and i_k do not have to be related by the kth branch characteristic. The set $v_1, v_2, \ldots, v_N$ is any set of voltages which satisfies KVL for the given network. Likewise, $i_1, i_2, \ldots, i_N$ is any set of currents which satisfies KCL for the given network. Before we prove the theorem, let us consider a simple example, as shown on Figure 6.12.

EXAMPLE 6.5-1. The network in Figure 6.12 may be viewed as an interconnection of six 1-ports. The nature of the branches is immaterial and some of the branches may be sources or nonlinear elements. For some instant of time, let us pick values for $i_1, i_2, \ldots, i_6$ which conform with KCL. For instance let $i_1 = 3$, and $i_2 = 4$. Since KCL must be satisfied at node n, i_3 must be $-(3 + 4)$ so that $i_3 = -7$. Let $i_4 = 5$. KCL at node a yields $i_5 = -(i_1 + i_4) = -8$. KCL at node c yields $i_6 = i_3 - i_5 = 1$. KCL is satisfied at node b since $i_4 - i_2 - i_6 = 5 - 4 - 1 = 0$. Hence, the six current values satisfy

† B. D. H. Tellegen, "A General Network Theorem, with Applications," *Philips Research Reports*, **7** (1952), 259–269. Tellegen (1900–) is at Philips Research Laboratories, Eindhoven, The Netherlands.

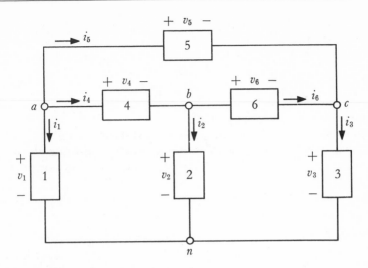

Figure 6.12 Network for illustrating Tellegen's theorem.

the conditions of the theorem. Similarly, we may assign any voltage values to $v_1, \ldots, v_6$ so long as KVL is satisfied. For example, $v_1 = 1$, $v_4 = 4$, and $v_2 = -3$ satisfy KVL around loop *abna*. Let $v_6 = 6$. Then for KVL to be satisfied in loop *bcnb*, v_3 must be -9. Finally, for KVL to be satisfied in loop *abca*, $v_4 + v_6 - v_5 = 0$ or $v_5 = 10$. Note that KVL is satisfied for any other loop of the network so that the voltage values chosen satisfy the theorem. Now we form $\Sigma v_k i_k$ and obtain

$$(1)(3) + (-3)(4) + (-9)(-7) + (4)(5) + (10)(-8) + (6)(1) = 0, \tag{6.33}$$

which is predicted by the theorem.   □

To prove the theorem, we label the terminals of the ports of the subnetworks by $a, b, c, \ldots$, and denote the voltages between the points $a, b, c, \ldots$, and a fixed reference or datum node by $v_a, v_b, v_c, \ldots$. Since the port voltages v_k for $k = 1, \ldots, N$ satisfy KVL, we may express v_k as the difference between two node voltages. For instance, if v_1 has a positive reference at a and a minus reference at b, $v_1 = v_a - v_b$ and

$$v_1 i_1 = v_a i_1 - v_b i_1. \tag{6.34}$$

Thus each $v_k i_k$ may be written as a difference similar to Equation 6.34. Form $\Sigma v_k i_k$ and collect terms as follows:

$$\sum_{k=1}^{N} v_k i_k = v_a \text{ [terms involving current entering or leaving node } a]$$
$$+ v_b \text{ [terms involving current entering or leaving node } b]$$
$$+ v_c \text{ [terms involving current entering or leaving node } c]$$
$$+ \cdots . \tag{6.35}$$

For any bracket above, say the factor multiplying v_a, the expression is simply the sum of currents leaving node a minus the sum of currents entering node a. But by KCL each such bracket is zero. Hence we have

$$\sum_{k=1}^{N} v_k i_k = 0,$$

which proves Tellegen's theorem.

Suppose that not only do the v_k and i_k satisfy KVL and KCL but also the branch characteristics so that the v_k and i_k constitute the network solution. Then $v_k i_k$ is the instantaneous power at the kth port and

$$\sum_{k=1}^{N} v_k i_k = \text{sum of instantaneous power at all ports of the network} = 0.$$
$$(6.36)$$

Since the network is the whole system, Equation 6.36 when integrated with respect to time gives one form of the law of conservation of energy. It states that the total instantaneous energy of the system does not change. Alternatively, we may say that the instantaneous power *out of* a portion of the network is equal to the instantaneous power *into* the rest of the network.

Even though this theorem might appear to be abstract and rather complex, it turns out to have many important applications in electrical engineering, one of which will be presented in Chapter 14.

● EXERCISES

6.5-1   (a) For the network in Figure Exercise 6.5-1, apply Tellegen's theorem.

(b) Suppose that v_1, v_2, i_1, and i_2 satisfy the branch equations. What is the significance of $v_1 i_1$? $v_2 i_2$? $v_s i_s$? Verify that Tellegen's theorem implies conservation of energy for this network.

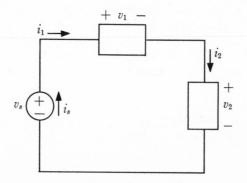

Figure Exercise 6.5-1

6.5-2   For the network of Figure Exercise 6.5-1 give an example of $v_1(t)$, $v_2(t)$, $v_s(t)$, $i_1(t)$, $i_2(t)$, and $i_s(t)$ which satisfy Tellegen's theorem.

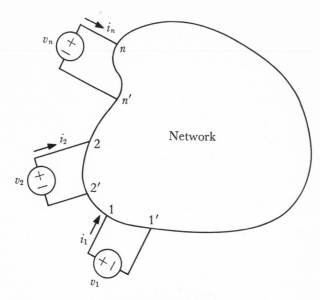

Figure Exercise 6.5-3

6.5-3   Show that for the network in Figure Exercise 6.5-3, the total power out of the n sources equals the total power into the n-port.

6.6   Energy considerations in a network with nonlinear elements

The key to the theory necessary to treat the general case is due to Chua† and involves converting a curve, such as in Figure 6.13, into two ordinary functions $i(x)$ and $v(x)$, where x is a parameter such as the length of the curve measured from some arbitrarily chosen point. For an introductory presentation, we shall restrict the discussion to the situations shown in Figure 6.2(a) or Figure 6.2(b) (current-controlled and voltage-controlled, respectively) which does not require Chua's approach.

The energy flow into a voltage-controlled or current-controlled non-linear resistor was derived in Section 6.1. Let us now examine the energy flow into a capacitor. Again, assuming the reference conventions in Figure 6.1(a), and the corresponding references for the v-q characteristic, the energy flow into the capacitor from t_0 to t_1 is

† L. O. Chua, *Nonlinear Network Theory* (New York: McGraw-Hill Book Company, Inc.), to be published.

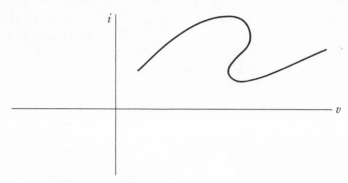

Figure 6.13 A resistor characteristic, which is neither current controlled nor voltage controlled.

$$W_c = \int_{t_0}^{t_1} v(t)i(t) \ dt. \tag{6.37}$$

For a charge-controlled capacitor, noting that $i(t) \ dt = dq(t)$ and in general that $v = v(q(t), t)$, a general function of q and t, we see that Equation 6.37 may be rewritten as

$$W_c = \int v(q(t), t) \ dq(t). \tag{6.38}$$

If the capacitor is time-invariant, then Equation 6.38 reduces to

$$W_c = \int_{q_0}^{q_1} v(q) \ dq, \tag{6.39}$$

which has a simple geometrical interpretation, as shown in Figure 6.14, as the area under the curve between $q = q_0$ and $q = q_1$. Furthermore, if the capacitor is linear and time-invariant, then we have

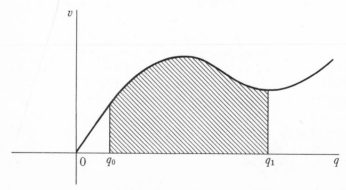

Figure 6.14 The lined area is the energy flow into a charge-controlled capacitor.

$$v = \frac{1}{C}q, \tag{6.40}$$

where C is a constant and

$$W_c = \int_{q_0}^{q_1} \frac{1}{C}q \, dq = \frac{1}{2C}(q_1^2 - q_0^2) \tag{6.41}$$

or

$$W_c = \tfrac{1}{2}C(v_1^2 - v_0^2), \tag{6.42}$$

where $q_1 = Cv_1$ and $q_0 = Cv_0$. Note that for the linear time-invariant case, W_c depends only on the initial q_0 (or v_0), the final q_1 (or v_1), and C. The manner in which q changes with time in going from $q(t_0)$ to $q(t_1)$ is immaterial. Likewise, for the nonlinear time-invariant capacitor, the manner in which q changes with time is immaterial. Only the initial and final values of q are of consequence. In addition, W_c depends on the particular nonlinear dependance of v on q as shown in Figure 6.14.

The calculation of energy flow into a voltage-controlled capacitor is slightly more involved. An example of a voltage-controlled capacitor characteristic is shown in Figure 6.15. We may still use the formulas as in Equations 6.37, 6.38, and 6.39. However, since v may not be a single-valued function of q, the integral symbolism has to be clarified further. Suppose that for the characteristic in Figure 6.15 we wish to determine the

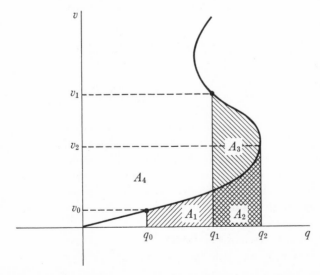

Figure 6.15 A voltage-controlled capacitor characteristic. The energy flow into the capacitor is $A_1 - A_3$.

energy flow into the capacitor from t_0 when $v = v(t_0)$ and $q = q(t_0)$ to t_1, when $v = v(t_1)$, $q = q(t_1)$. As v changes from v_0 to v_1, q changes from q_0 to q_2 and back to q_1 as indicated in the figure. We may compute the energy in steps, first corresponding to the energy when v changes from v_0 to v_2, and next corresponding to the energy when v changes from v_2 to v_1. For the first part, the energy is equal to the area under the lower part of the characteristic curve from q_0 to q_2. On the figure, using the indicated labels, this is $A_1 + A_2$. Next, as v changes from v_2 to v_1, q changes from q_2 to q_1. Since the increment dq is negative, the energy is $-(A_2 + A_3)$. Hence, the energy from v_0 to v_1 is

$$W_c = \int_{t_0}^{t_1} v(t) i(t)\ dt = \int_{q_0, v_0}^{q_1, v_1} v\ dq = A_1 + A_2 - (A_2 + A_3) = A_1 - A_3.$$
$$(6.43)$$

An alternative interpretation is provided by the integration-by-parts rule. Proceeding formally, we have

$$\int_{q_0, v_0}^{q_1, v_1} v\ dq = vq \Big|_{q_0, v_0}^{q_1, v_1} - \int_{q_0, v_0}^{q_1, v_1} q\ dv = v_1 q_1 - v_0 q_0 - \int_{v_0}^{v_1} q\ dv. \quad (6.44)$$

We note that since q is an ordinary function of v, the last integral in Equation 6.44 is an ordinary one. From the notation in Figure 6.15, we see that

$$\int_{v_0}^{v_1} q\ dv = A_4 + A_3. \tag{6.45}$$

We also note that the rectangular area $v_1 q_1$ minus the rectangular area $v_0 q_0$ is equal to

$$v_1 q_1 - v_0 q_0 = A_4 + A_1. \tag{6.46}$$

Therefore, we have

$$\int_{q_0, v_0}^{q_1, v_1} v\ dq = (A_4 + A_1) - (A_4 + A_3) = A_1 - A_3, \tag{6.47}$$

which is the same answer as in Equation 6.43. Equation 6.44 is taken as the definition for the integral of $v\ dq$ for a voltage-controlled capacitor. The right-hand side expression in Equation 6.44 defines what the integral means. If the capacitor is neither voltage-controlled nor charge-controlled, such as the curve in Figure 6.13 if the ordinate i is replaced by q, the procedure outlined above breaks down. This more general situation has been studied by Chua.

For an inductor model, the general energy formula of Equation 6.37 still holds. This time we note that $v\ dt$ is $d\psi$, so that we may write

$$W_L = \int_{t_0}^{t_1} v(t) i(t)\ dt = \int_{t_0}^{t_1} i[\psi(t),\ t]\ d\psi(t). \tag{6.48}$$

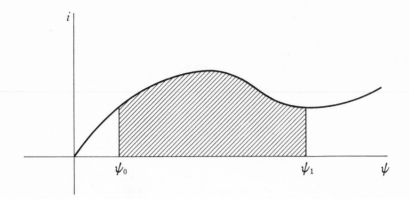

Figure 6.16   The lined area is the energy flow into a flux-controlled inductor.

Analogous to Equation 6.39, the time-invariant case reduces to

$$W_L = \int_{t_0}^{t_1} i[\psi(t)] \, d\psi(t) = \int_{(i_0, \psi_0)}^{(i_1, \psi_1)} i \, d\psi. \tag{6.49}$$

For a flux-controlled time-invariant inductor as shown in Figure 6.16, the energy flow into L from t_0 when $\psi = \psi(t_0) = \psi_0$ to t_1 when $\psi = \psi(t_1) = \psi_1$ is equal to the lined area.

The linear time-invariant L has a characteristic

$$i = \frac{1}{L}\psi, \tag{6.50}$$

where L is constant. Equation 6.49 reduces to

$$W_L = \int_{\psi_0}^{\psi_1} \frac{1}{L}\psi \, d\psi = \frac{1}{2L}(\psi_1^2 - \psi_0^2). \tag{6.51}$$

Since $Li_1 = \psi_1$ and $Li_0 = \psi_0$, Equation 6.51 may be written as

$$W_L = \tfrac{1}{2}L(i_1^2 - i_0^2). \tag{6.52}$$

The situation for the calculation of W_L into a current-controlled L is exactly analogous to the situation of calculating W_c into a voltage-controlled capacitor. The same integration-by-parts rule is used to define the integral of $i \, d\psi$ as

$$\int_{(i_0, \psi_0)}^{(i_1, \psi_1)} i \, d\psi = i_1\psi_1 - i_0\psi_0 - \int_{i_0}^{i_1} \psi \, di. \tag{6.53}$$

For a current-controlled inductor, the integral of $\psi \, di$ is well-defined, as shown in the example of Figure 6.17. The energy flow W_L into the inductor from $t = t_0$ corresponding to $i = i(t_0) = i_0$ and $\psi = \psi(t_0) = \psi_0$ to $t = t_1$

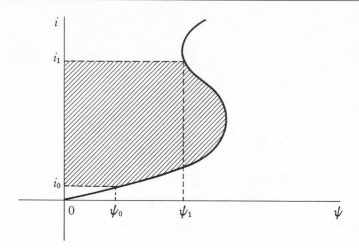

Figure 6.17 A current-controlled inductor characteristic.

corresponding to $i = i(t_1) = i_1$ and $\psi = \psi(t_1) = \psi_1$ is equal to the rectangular area $i_1\psi_1$ minus the rectangular area $i_0\psi_0$ minus the lined area.

From the foregoing discussion, we note that the energy W_L does not depend on how ψ (or i) varies with respect to time, provided only that L is time-invariant and either flux-controlled or current-controlled. The only pertinent data are the initial and final values of i and ψ and the particular nonlinear but time-invariant dependence between i and ψ (the inductor characteristic). For the linear time-invariant case, W_L depends on i_0, i_1, and L. In particular, if $i_0(t_0) = i_1(t_1)$, and $\psi(t_0) = \psi(t_1)$, then no matter how i varies in time between t_0 and t_1, $W_L = 0$ (see Equations 6.51 and 6.52). That is, no matter how much energy flows into L, the same amount of energy eventually flows out within the time interval $[t_0, t_1]$, provided the initial current and initial flux are equal to the final current and final flux, respectively. Similarly, for a time-invariant nonlinear inductor which is flux-controlled, Equation 6.49 shows that if $\psi_0 = \psi_1$, then $W_L = 0$. And if a time-invariant nonlinear inductor is current-controlled, then from Equation 6.53, we note that if $i_0 = i_1$, then the right-hand side integral is zero. Furthermore, since ψ is a single-valued function of i, $\psi_0 = \psi_1$ when $i_0 = i_1$. Hence, $W_L = 0$.

If the signals are periodic, then the currents (or fluxes) separated by one period in time are equal, so that the energy over one period is zero. This means that the average power is zero. We conclude that a time-invariant inductor which is either flux-controlled or current controlled is *lossless*. This result applies to arbitrary nonlinearities: The only restrictions are that the element must be time-invariant and either flux-controlled or current-controlled. That is, either i must be expressible as a function of

ψ, or ψ must be expressible as a function of i, and t must not appear explicitly. Because the time-invariant flux-controlled (or current-controlled) inductor model is lossless, it is said to be an *energy storage element* or a *conservative element*.

Likewise for a time-invariant capacitor which is either charge-controlled or voltage-controlled, Equations 6.39 and 6.44 show that if $q_0 = q_1$ or $v_0 = v_1$, then $W_C = 0$. Thus if q and v are periodic, the net energy flow into the capacitor over one period is zero so that the average power is zero. For this reason, a time-invariant charge-controlled (or voltage-controlled) capacitor is a *lossless* element. It is also an *energy storage element*. This result applies to arbitrary nonlinearities provided only that v can be expressed as a single-valued function of q or that q can be expressed as a single-valued function of v, and t does not appear explicitly.

However, the same cannot be said of the resistor model. For example, if R is a positive constant, then $p(t)$ is never negative and for $i \neq 0$, W_R is positive even if $i(t_0) = i(t_1)$ and $v(t_0) = v(t_1)$. Furthermore, the value of W_R depends on how v and i vary with respect to time during the interval. The most common type of resistor model is a positive constant R, and for this model W_R is positive whenever $i \neq 0$, that is, positive energy is always flowing into R. This is why a resistor is commonly called a *dissipative* or nonconservative element. For the general case, W_R is not always positive. For the same resistor W_R may be positive or negative depending on the time variation of i or v. For the negative constant R, W_R is always negative and thus behaves like a source of energy. We will call any resistor dissipative, keeping in mind that dissipation may be negative. The electric-energy dissipation is converted into heat energy.

For the time-varying capacitor and time-varying inductor, whether linear or nonlinear, there may be dissipation or energy generation. For instance, take the linear time-varying capacitor $C(t)$. Since

$$q(t) = C(t)v(t), \tag{6.54}$$

we have

$$W_C = \int_{t_0}^{t_1} \frac{1}{C(t)} q(t) \, dq(t), \quad C \neq 0. \tag{6.55}$$

The integration in Equation 6.55 cannot be carried out until the exact dependence of $q(t)$ on t is known. Moreover, even for the same $q(t_0)$ and $q(t_1)$, different variations of $q(t)$ with respect to t will result in different values of W_C. For example, for $C(t) = 1 - 2t$, $q(t) = t - t^2$, $t_0 = 0$, $t_1 = 1$, we have

$$W_C = \int_0^1 \frac{1}{(1-2t)} (t - t^2)(1 - 2t) \, dt = \left(\tfrac{1}{2} t^2 - \tfrac{1}{3} t^3 \right) \Big|_0^1 = \frac{1}{6}. \tag{6.56}$$

Note that $q(0) = q(1) = 0$, and $v(0) = v(1) = 0$ and yet $W_C \neq 0$. A similar situation obtains for the nonlinear time-varying capacitor. As an example, take

$$v(t) = \frac{1}{C(t)} q^2(t), \qquad (6.57)$$

where $C(t) = (1 - 2t)$, $q(t) = t - t^2$, $t_0 = 0$, $t_1 = 1$. Then we have

$$W_C = \int_0^1 \frac{1}{(1 - 2t)} (t - t^2)^2 (1 - 2t) \, dt$$

$$= \int_0^1 (t^2 - 2t^3 + t^4) \, dt = (\tfrac{1}{3} t^3 - \tfrac{2}{4} t^4 + \tfrac{1}{5} t^5) \Big|_0^1 \qquad (6.58)$$

$$= \tfrac{1}{3} - \tfrac{1}{2} + \tfrac{1}{5} - 0 = \tfrac{1}{30}.$$

Again $W_C \neq 0$, although $q(t_0) = q(t_1)$, $v(t_0) = v(t_1)$. The same situation is true for the time-varying inductor.

In summary, a resistor, whether time-invariant or not, and whether linear or nonlinear, dissipates (or generates) energy. A time-invariant capacitor, which is either charge-controlled or voltage-controlled, and a time-invariant inductor, which is either flux-controlled or current-controlled, whether linear or nonlinear, only store energy in their electric and magnetic fields, respectively. A time-varying capacitor and a time-varying inductor may dissipate or generate energy in addition to storing energy in the electric or magnetic field. An inductor which is neither flux-controlled nor current-controlled may dissipate energy. A capacitor which is neither charge-controlled nor voltage-controlled may dissipate energy also.

● EXERCISES

6.6-1   An initially uncharged capacitor $C = 1$ is connected to a current source whose waveform is shown in Figure Exercise 6.6-1(a). Compute the energy flow into the capacitor as a function of t. Repeat

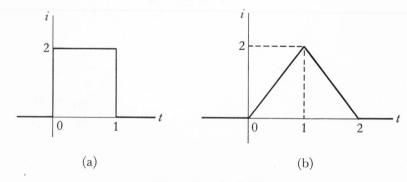

(a)   (b)

Figure Exercise 6.6-1

for the current waveform of Figure Exercise 6.6-1(b). For t greater than 2, compare the charges delivered by the two current sources. Compare the two energies for $t > 2$. What is the effect of reversing the terminals of the current sources?

6.6-2 A resistor $R = 2\Omega$ is connected across a current source whose waveform is shown in Figure Exercise 6.6-1(a). Plot W_R vs. t. Repeat for the source in Figure Exercise 6.6-1(b). What is the effect of reversing the terminals of the current sources?

6.6-3 The vi characteristic for a resistor is given by

$$v = \begin{cases} 2i, & \text{for} \quad i \geq 0, \\ 10i, & \text{for} \quad i < 0. \end{cases}$$

The resistor is then connected to a current source whose waveform is shown in Figure Exercise 6.6-1(a). Plot W_R vs. t. What is the effect of reversing the terminals of the current source?

6.6-4 Repeat Exercise 6.6-3 for the waveform shown in Figure Exercise 6.6-1(b).

6.6-5 An inductor $L = 3$ with zero initial flux is connected to a voltage source whose waveform is shown in Figure Exercise 6.6-1(a) where the ordinate i is replaced by v. Determine $W_L(t)$.

6.6-6 Repeat Exercise 6.6-5 for the waveform in Figure Exercise 6.6-1(a). What is the effect of reversing the terminals of the voltage source?

6.6-7 A nonlinear inductor is represented by the equation

$$i = \psi^2 - \psi.$$

The flux at $t = 0$ is 0, and, at $t = t_1$, the flux is equal to 1. Compute the energy flow W_L into the inductor from $t = 0$ to $t = t_1$.

6.6-8 Suppose that for the nonlinear inductor in Exercise 6.6-7 a voltage source as in Figure Exercise 6.6-1(b) is connected across L, where the ordinate i is replaced by v. Assuming that $\psi(0) = 0$, compute W_L into L from $t = 0$ to $t = 1$. What is the effect of reversing the terminals of the voltage source?

6.6-9 Suppose that a nonlinear inductor is represented by $\psi = i^2 - i$. The inductor is connected across a current source with a waveform as in Figure Exercise 6.6-1(b). Suppose that at $t = 0$ there is no initial flux in the inductor and $i(0) = 0$. Compute the energy flow into L from $t = 0$ to $t = 1$.

Problems

6-1 Determine whether the gyrator defined in Chapter 4 is passive. Also determine whether it is lossless.

6-2 Repeat Problem 6-1 for the negative convertor, voltage-inversion type, and current-inversion type.

6-3   Two linear time-invariant positive inductors are inductively coupled
       as in Figure 4.18 (p. 75) with $M \leq \sqrt{L_1 L_2}$. Determine whether the
       network is passive. Also determine whether the network is lossless.

6-4   In the network of Figure Exercise 6.4-6, suppose the elements are
       all resistors, $R_a = 1$, $R_b = 2$, $R_c = 3$, and $v_{12} = 2$ and $v_{23} = 4$. Com-
       pute the average power into each resistor. Now remove source v_{12}
       but add a source connected to terminals 1 and 3. What should the
       new source be so that the branch voltages and currents remain the
       same as before? Compute the power delivered from the new set of
       sources and compare to the power delivered from the former set
       of sources.

6-5   For the data in the first part of Problem 6-4, compute i_{21} and i_{23} in
       addition to the branch voltages, currents, and powers. Now replace
       v_{12} by a current source i_{21} with a value as computed previously.
       Likewise, replace v_{23} by a current source i_{23} with a value as com-
       puted before. Recompute the branch voltages, currents, and powers.
       Compute the powers from the current sources and compare with
       the powers into the R's.

6-6   Two networks are connected to each other by a cable containing
       three wires as in Figure 6.6. Certain measurements are made as
       follows: $I_{1'1} = 2$ amps (constant), $I_{22'} = 1$ amp, $v_{21} = 3$ volts, and
       $v_{13} = 4$ volts. Determine whether energy is flowing from B to A or
       A to B and how much.

6-7   For the network of Figure Exercise 6.4-6, suppose the data of the
       first part of Problem 6-4 are assumed. Now remove the sources and
       instead add three sources. Each new source is inserted in the lines,
       one to each line, and the three other terminals of the sources are
       connected together to form a new node. Determine the values with
       reference directions of each voltage source so that the branch volt-
       ages, currents, and powers remain the same.

6-8   Using a procedure analogous to the one used in Section 6.4, show
       that the energy flow into an n-terminal network such as the one in
       Figure 6.10 is given by the formula in Equation 6.31.

6-9   Suppose that in the network of Figure Exercise 6.4-1 element a is
       a resistor $R_a = -20$ ohms and element b is a resistor $R_b = 50$ ohms.
       Suppose that v_{13} is the input signal which is periodic and R_b is
       called the load or output resistor. Compute the average power
       delivered by the source and compute the average power delivered
       to the load. Is the output power less than, equal to, or greater than
       the input power? Explain the significance of your answer.

6-10   Repeat Problem 6-9 for $R_a = -20$ and $R_b = 10$.

6-11   Suppose that in the network of Figure Exercise 6.4-1 element b is
       a capacitor $C = 1$ μF and element a is a resistor $R = 10$ ohms. If

$v_{21} = 5 \sin(10^5 t + \theta)$, compute the average power from the source and the average power into R and C.

6-12   For a linear time-invariant capacitor C, show that the energy flow into C from t_1 to t_2 is

$$W_C = \int_{q(t_1)}^{q(t_2)} v \, dq = \int_{v(t_1)}^{v(t_2)} q \, dv.$$

6-13   Show that for a linear time-invariant inductor the energy flow into L from t_1 to t_2 is

$$W_L = \int_{\psi(t_1)}^{\psi(t_2)} i \, d\psi = \int_{i(t_1)}^{i(t_2)} \psi \, di.$$

6-14   (a) Give an example of a nonlinear time-invariant capacitor where the energy is not equal to

$$\int_{v(t_1)}^{v(t_2)} q \, dv.$$

(b) Give an example of a nonlinear time-invariant inductor where the energy is not equal to

$$\int_{i(t_1)}^{i(t_2)} \psi \, di.$$

6-15   In a mechanical system, momentum is a quantity which is associated with mass such that the time rate of momentum is the force accelerating the mass. Analogous to defining a capacitor by a q-v curve, a mass may be defined by a momentum-velocity curve. Similarly, a spring may be characterized by a force-displacement curve. Finally, a damper may be characterized by a force-velocity curve. Continuing the analogy, since force and velocity are analogous to voltage and current or current and voltage, the analogy of instantaneous electric power, voltage times current, is instantaneous mechanical power which is force times velocity, and mechanical energy is

$$W = \int_{t_1}^{t} f(\tau) v(\tau) \, d\tau,$$

where f is force and v is velocity.

(a) Show that the mechanical energy flow into a mass is

$$W_M = \int_{t_1}^{t_2} fv \, dt = \int v \, d\psi,$$

where ψ is momentum. Show that for a linear time-invariant mass

$$W_M = \tfrac{1}{2} M [v^2(t_2) - v^2(t_1)].$$

(b) Show that the mechanical energy flow into a spring is

$$W_K = \int_{t_1}^{t_2} fv \, dt = \int f \, dx,$$

where x is displacement. Show also that for a linear time-invariant spring,

$$W_K = \frac{1}{2K} [x^2(t_2) - x^2(t_1)],$$

where K is the compliance of the spring.

(c) Show that the instantaneous power into a linear damper is

$$P_D = Dv^2(t).$$

The time-invariant mass is said to store kinetic energy, the time-invariant spring is said to store potential energy, and the damper is said to dissipate energy. The above statement may be verified by a development analogous to that for R, L, and C.

6-16   Suppose that in the network of Figure Exercise 6.4-1 branch b is a positive constant capacitor C and branch a is a positive constant resistor R. The source v_{13} is a battery of voltage $v = E$ connected at $t = 0$. The capacitor is initially uncharged. The current is

$$i_{12}(t) = \frac{E}{R} e^{-t/RC}.$$

Compute the energy delivered to the capacitor after an infinitely long period of time. Compute the total energy flow from the source. Note that the ratio of the energy delivered to the capacitor and the total energy delivered by the source is independent of the values of E, R, and C.

6-17   Suppose that for the series RC network of Problem 6-16, C is a positive constant but R is a time-varying nonlinear resistor whose v–i characteristic is in the first and third quadrant. The capacitor is initially uncharged. The current is no longer an exponential but it is given that $i_{12} \to 0$ as $t \to \infty$. Compute the total energy delivered to C after an infinitely long period of time. Compute the total energy delivered by the battery after an infinitely long period of time. The ratio between the two energies is independent of the values of E and C and independent of the resistance characteristic: The efficiency of charging may not be improved upon by judicious choice of E, C, or R.

6-18   Suppose that the constant capacitor in Problem 6-17 is replaced by a nonlinear time-invariant passive charge-controlled and voltage-controlled capacitor described by $v = f(q)$. If $i(t) \to 0$ as $t \to \infty$, determine the total energy delivered to the capacitor after an infinitely long period of time. Determine the total energy delivered by the battery after an infinitely long period of time. Note that these two energies do not depend on the resistor characteristic.

6-19 A four-terminal network like that in Figure 6.10 with $n=4$ is such that $i_1(t) = 2 \sin (\omega_0 t + \alpha)$, $i_2(t) = 2 \sin (\omega_0 t - 120° + \alpha)$, $i_3(t) = 2 \sin (\omega_0 t - 240° + \alpha)$, $i_4(t) \equiv 0$, $v_{12}(t) = 100 \sin (\omega_0 t + 30°)$, $v_{23}(t) = 100 \sin (\omega_0 t - 90°)$, $v_{34}(t) = 100/\sqrt{3} \sin (\omega_0 t - 240°)$. Compute the average power into the network. What will happen if line 4 is disconnected?

6-20 Give an example of a voltage controlled time-invariant nonlinear active capacitor with a v-q characteristic in the first and third quadrant.

6-21 For the network in the figure, assign reference directions to the branch voltages and currents and verify Tellegen's theorem for any arbitrary distribution of voltages and currents which satisfy KVL and KCL.

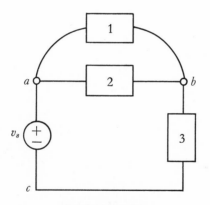

Figure Problem 6-21

6-22 (a) For the network in Figure Problem 6-21, show that the energy flow from the voltage source v_s is equal to the energy flow into branch 1 plus the energy flow into branch 2 plus the energy flow into branch 3, using Tellegen's theorem.
(b) Suppose that branch 3 of Figure Problem 6-21 is a current source with a reference direction from b to c, through branch 3. Does the result of part (a) still hold?
(c) For the condition of part (b), show that the energy flow from the voltage source v_s plus the energy flow from the current source i_3 is equal to the energy flow into branch 1 plus the energy flow into branch 2, using Tellegen's theorem.

Implications of Linearity in Networks   **7**

7.1 Characteristics of a linear system

Consider a system with one signal y labeled as output and another signal x labeled as input. We shall enumerate the characteristics that define this system as a linear system. The extension to systems with more inputs and more outputs will not be difficult.

A symbolic block diagram is given in Figure 7.1. In a network, the input signal x may be a current or a voltage in any part of the network, and the output y may be any current or voltage in any part of the network.

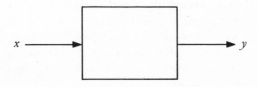

Figure 7.1   A symbolic block diagram of a single-input single-output system.

First we define the *zero-input response* of the system as the output y when the input is identically zero. Such a response is not necessarily zero since there may be initial charges on capacitors or initial fluxes in inductors. The set of initial conditions will be called the initial *state* of the system. Next we define the *zero-state response* as the output y due to an arbitrary input when all initial conditions are zero, i.e., when the initial state is zero. A system or network is said to be *zero-state linear* if the following two conditions are satisfied:

(1a) If y_1 is the zero-state response due to an arbitrary input x_1, then cy_1 is the zero-state response due to an input cx_1, where c is an arbitrary constant. This is called the *homogeneity* condition.

(2a) If y_1 is the zero-state response due to an arbitrary input x_1, y_2, the zero-state response due to another arbitrary input x_2 not equal to x_1 identically, then the zero-state response due to $x_1 + x_2$ is $y_1 + y_2$. This is known as the *additivity* condition or *superposition* condition.

EXAMPLE 7.1-1.   Suppose that the zero-state response of a system due to a unit step function $u(t)$ is $[1 - e^{-t}]u(t)$. If the system satisfies the homogeneity condition 1(a), then the zero-state response of the same system to a step function $10u(t)$ is $10[1 - e^{-t}]u(t)$. In fact, the zero-state response of the same system to a step function $Ku(t)$ is $K[1 - e^{-t}]u(t)$, where K is any real constant.   □

EXAMPLE 7.1-2.   As an example of the superposition or additivity condition suppose that the zero-state response due to a unit step is $[1 - e^{-t}]u(t)$, and suppose that the zero-state response due to a delayed negative step $-u(t-1)$ is $-[1 - e^{-(t-1)}]u(t-1)$. If the system obeys the superposition property 2(a), then the zero-state response due to an input $u(t) + [-u(t-1)]$ is $[1 - e^{-t}]u(t) - [1 - e^{-(t-1)}]u(t-1)$.   □

EXAMPLE 7.1-3.   Suppose that the systems in Examples 7.1-1 and 7.1-2 are identical. Then the system in Example 7.1-2 would also satisfy the homogeneity condition as in Example 7.1-1, in addition to the superposition condition. In this case, the system is said to be zero-state linear. From the given data in Examples 7.1-1 and 7.1-2, the zero-state response due to an input pulse $20[u(t) - u(t-1)]$ of height 20 and duration 1 time unit is $20[1 - e^{-t}]u(t) - 20[1 - e^{-(t-1)}]u(t-1)$.   □

If any of the above conditions is not satisfied the system is said to be *zero-state nonlinear*. Zero-state linearity is concerned with properties of a system when the initial state is zero. Another type of linearity with restrictions is *zero-input linearity*, to be defined below.

Let $(\alpha_1, \alpha_2, \alpha_3, \ldots, \alpha_n)$ denote a set of initial conditions or the initial state of a system. The quantity α_1 may be the initial current in inductor 1, α_2 may be the initial voltage in capacitor 2, and so forth. A system is said to be *zero-input linear* if it satisfies the following two conditions:

(1b) If the zero-input response for any arbitrary initial state $(\alpha_1, \alpha_2, \ldots, \alpha_n)$ is y_0, then the zero-input response due to an initial state $(C\alpha_1, C\alpha_2, \ldots, C\alpha_n)$ is Cy_0, where C is any arbitrary constant. This is the homogeneity condition.

(2b) If the zero-input response for an arbitrary initial state $(\alpha_1, \alpha_2, \ldots, \alpha_n)$ is y_α and the zero-input response for another arbitrary initial state $(\beta_1, \beta_2, \ldots, \beta_n)$ is y_β, then the zero-input response for an initial state $(\alpha_1 + \beta_1, \alpha_2 + \beta_2, \ldots, \alpha_n + \beta_n)$ is $y_\alpha + y_\beta$. This is the additivity condition.

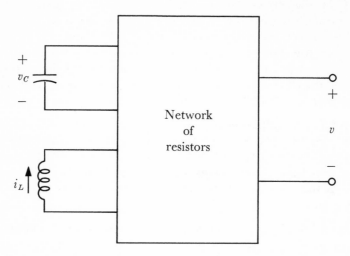

Figure 7.2 Network for illustrating zero-input linearity.

EXAMPLE 7.1-4.   Suppose that in the network of Figure 7.2, there are no inputs, but initial conditions of $v_c(0) = 10$ volts and $i_L(0) = -3$ amps are imposed. Let the zero-input response (due to initial conditions only) be given as $v(t) = [10e^{-t} \cos 2t]u(t)$. If the network satisfies the homogeneity condition 1(b), then if the initial conditions were changed to $v_c(0) = 40$ volts and $i_L(0) = -12$ amperes, the zero-input response would be $[40e^{-t} \cos 2t]u(t)$. This is because the new initial conditions are four times the old initial conditions, so that the new zero-input response is four times the old zero-input response.   □

EXAMPLE 7.1-5.   For the network of Figure 7.2, suppose that the zero-input response due to $v_C(0) = 8$ volts and $i_L(0) = 2$ amps is $e^{-t}[7 \cos 2t + 4 \sin 2t]u(t)$, and the zero-input response due to $v_C(0) = 2$ volts and $i_L(0) = -5$ amperes is $e^{-t}[3 \cos 2t - 4 \sin 2t]u(t)$. If the network satisfies the superposition property 2(b), then the response due to the sum of initial conditions, namely $v_C(0) = 8 + 2 = 10$ volts, and $i_L(0) = 2 - 5 = -3$ amperes is equal to the sum of the individual zero-input responses, namely $e^{-t}[7 \cos 2t + 4 \sin 2t]u(t) + e^{-t}[3 \cos 2t - 4 \sin 2t] = [10e^{-t} \cos 2t]u(t)$.   □

EXAMPLE 7.1-6.   Let us suppose that the network in Figure 7.2 is zero-input linear and the data in Exercise 7.1-4 and Exercise 7.1-5 apply. The problem is to determine the zero-input response due to the initial conditions $v_C(0) = 6$ volts and $i_L(0) = 4$ amperes. Since the network is zero-input linear, conditions 1(b) and 2(b) are satisfied. From condition 1(b), we know that if we multiply the initial conditions in Example 7.1-4 by a constant c_1, the zero-input response will be c_1 times the zero-input response given in Example 7.1-4. Similarly, if the initial conditions in Example 7.1-5 are multiplied by c_2, then the zero-input response will be c_2 times the zero-input response given in Example 7.1-5. Let us first determine c_1 and c_2 so that c_1 times the initial conditions in Example 7.1-4 added to c_2 times the initial conditions in Example 7.1-5 yields $v_C(0) = 6$ volts and $i_L(0) = 4$ amperes. Once c_1 and c_2 are found, then the required zero-input response may be computed by multiplying the zero-input response in Example 7.1-4 by c_1, that in Example 7.1-5 by c_2, and adding these two. Thus,

$$10c_1 + 8c_2 = 6 \tag{7.1}$$

and

$$-3c_1 + 2c_2 = 4. \tag{7.2}$$

Equation 7.1 is the condition for obtaining $v_C(0) = 6$ volts and Equation 7.2 is the condition for obtaining $i_L(0) = 4$ amperes. Solving for c_1 and c_2, we have

$$c_1 = \frac{\begin{vmatrix} 6 & 8 \\ 4 & 2 \end{vmatrix}}{\begin{vmatrix} 10 & 8 \\ -3 & 2 \end{vmatrix}} = \frac{12 - 32}{20 + 24} = -\frac{20}{44} = -\frac{5}{11} \tag{7.3}$$

and

$$c_2 = \frac{\begin{vmatrix} 10 & 6 \\ -3 & 4 \end{vmatrix}}{44} = \frac{40 + 18}{44} = \frac{58}{44} = \frac{29}{22}. \tag{7.4}$$

Thus the zero-input response due to $v_C(0) = -(5/11)(10)$ volts and $i_L(0) = -(5/11)(-3)$ amperes is $-(5/11)[10e^{-t} \cos 2t]u(t)$. The zero-input response due to $v_C(0) = (29/22)(8)$ volts and $i_L(0) = (29/22)(2)$ amperes is $(29/22)[e^{-t}(7 \cos 2t + 4 \sin 2t)]u(t)$. Hence, by the additivity property, the zero-input response due to $v_C(0) = -(5/11)(10) + (29/22)(8) = 6$ volts and $i_L(0) = -(5/11)(-3) + (29/22)(2) = 4$ amperes is

$$\text{Zero-input response} = -\frac{5}{11}[10e^{-t}\cos 2t]u(t)$$

$$+\frac{29}{22}[e^{-t}(7\cos 2t + 4\sin 2t)]u(t) \qquad (7.5)$$

$$= e^{-t}\left[\frac{103}{22}\cos 2t + \frac{58}{11}\sin 2t\right]u(t).$$

This is the zero-input response due to $v_C(0) = 6$ volts and $i_L(0) = 4$ amperes. $\square$

A third notion relating those of zero-state response and zero-input response is that of *decomposition*. A system is said to have the *decomposition property* if it satisfies the following condition:

(3) If y_0 is the zero-input response to an arbitrary initial state $(\alpha_1, \alpha_2, \ldots, \alpha_n)$ and y_1 is the zero-state response for an arbitrary input x, then the total response for the same initial state and the same input is $y_0 + y_1$. This condition must hold for any arbitrary initial state and any arbitrary input.

EXAMPLE 7.1-7.   Suppose that in the network of Figure 7.3 the zero-input response due to $v_C(0) = 10$ volts and $i_L(0) = -3$ amperes is $v(t) = [10e^{-t}\cos 2t]u(t)$, and the zero-state response due to $v_1(t) = u(t)$ is

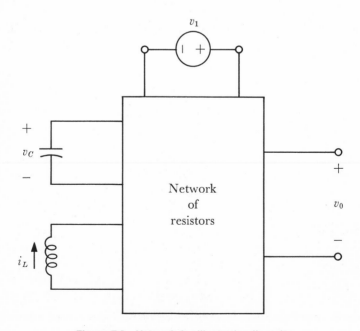

Figure 7.3 Network for illustrating linearity.

$v(t) = [1 - e^{-t} \cos 2t]u(t)$. If the network satisfies the decomposition property (3), then the response due to the input $v_1(t) = u(t)$ and the initial conditions $v_C(0) = 10$ volts and $i_L(0) = -3$ amperes acting simultaneously is

$$v(t) = [10e^{-t} \cos 2t]u(t) + [1 - e^{-t} \cos 2t]u(t). \quad \square \qquad (7.6)$$

Finally, we define a system to be *linear* if it is zero-state linear, zero-input linear, and it has the decomposition property. In other words, a system is linear (with no other qualifiers) if and only if it satisfies (1a), (2a), (1b), (2b), and (3) above. We may refer to a system as zero-state homogeneous, zero-state additive, zero-input homogeneous, zero-input additive, or decomposable, if it satisfies (1a), (2a), (1b), (2b), or (3), respectively.

For a system with more than one input to be linear, the conditions (1a), (2a), (1b), and (2b), must be satisfied for each input with all other inputs set equal to zero. In addition it must satisfy the following:

(3') If y_a is the zero-state response for an arbitrary input x_a with all other inputs set equal to zero, y_b is the zero-state response for an arbitrary input x_b with all other inputs set equal to zero, and so on up to the mth input if there are m inputs, and if y_0 is the zero-input response due to an arbitrary initial state, then the complete response due to the same initial state and all the same inputs acting simultaneously is $y_0 + y_a + y_b + \cdots + y_m$. This is the decomposition property. If there is more than one output port, then all the above conditions must hold for every output port for the system to be linear. Otherwise the system is nonlinear.

Note that in the definition of a linear system, the location of input and output signals must be identified. In a network, the signals are usually voltages and currents. A port is created by attaching wires to any pair of nodes or cutting a branch and exposing the pair of wires. For an n-port network, inputs must be restricted to port voltages and currents, and outputs must be restricted to port voltages and currents. Internal voltages and currents are not allowed as inputs and outputs. An n-port is said to be a linear n-port if for any choice of independent port voltages and port currents as inputs and for any choice of outputs from the remaining port currents and voltages, the resulting system is linear. A network is said to be linear if for any choice of ports, the resulting n-port is linear.

It is easy to verify that the network elements defined in Chapter 4 which have linear branch characteristics are linear networks. The two definitions of linearity for the network elements are consistent with each other. The definition in this section, however, applies to much more general networks, not only to single elements. For example, any arbitrary interconnection of linear elements can be shown to be a linear network.

The above defining properties of linear networks and systems make it possible to develop a general theory applicable to such systems. In particular, knowing the zero-state response due to a unit impulse allows us to obtain the zero-state response due to an arbitrary input as we shall see later in this chapter. Linear systems are simpler to study than nonlinear systems. In addition, the behavior of many nonlinear systems when the signals involved are "small" may be obtained by studying a linearized version of the nonlinear system. Finally, many systems, even with large signals, are approximately linear, and results obtained from a linear model are close enough to the actual case. For these reasons, the study of linear systems and networks is a major aspect of network or system theory.

● EXERCISES

7.1-1   Show that the resistor model with a linear branch characteristic is a linear 1-port.

7.1-2   Repeat Exercise 7.1-1 for an inductor model with a linear ψ–i characteristic. Take i as output and v as input. Repeat for v as output and i as input.

7.1-3   A linear time-invariant R and a linear time-invariant L and a voltage source v are connected in a series. Taking v as the input and i as the output, derive the differential equation relating i to v. Show that the system is zero-state linear.

7.1-4   Show that the system in Exercise 7.1-3 is zero-input linear.

7.1-5   Show that the system in Exercise 7.1-4 satisfies the decomposition property.

7.1-6   Show that a capacitor with a nonlinear q-v characteristic is a nonlinear 1-port network.

7.1-7   A system is described by the equation $(dy/dt)^2 + y^2 = x^2$, where x is the input and y is the output. Is the system linear? Is the system zero-state homogeneous?

7.1-8   Show that if a system is zero-state additive, then if y_1 is the zero-state response for an input x_1, the zero-state response due to an input Cx_1 is Cy_1, where C is a finite positive integer. (See Problem 7-3 for a more complicated version.)

7.1-9   Show that the zero-state response of a zero-state linear system to a zero input is zero.

7.1-10 For the network in Figure 7.2, suppose it is zero-input linear and the data in Example 7.1-5 apply. Determine the zero-input response due to $v_C(0) = 1$ volt and $i_L(0) = 0$.

7.1-11 Repeat Exercise 7.1-10 for $v_C(0) = 0$ and $i_L(0) = 1$ ampere.

7.1-12 Repeat Exercise 7.1-10 for $v_C(0) = 5$ volts and $i_L(0) = 8$ amperes.

7.1-13 For the network in Figure 7.3, assume that the data in Example 7.1-7 apply and assume that the network is linear. Determine the response due to an initial condition of $v_C(0) = -5$ volts and $i_L(0) = 1.5$ amperes, and an input of $3u(t)$.

7.2 The Thevenin and Norton theorems

Two theorems of importance in the analysis of networks were given independently by Helmholtz and later by Thevenin and by Norton. Because the theorems are widely known as Thevenin's theorem and Norton's theorem, we shall use these identifications in the discussion to follow. The Thevenin and Norton theorems provide a means for the simplification of network analysis by constructing equivalent networks. The original statements of these theorems were in terms of linear networks composed of linear, lumped, time-invariant elements. However, the theorems are valid for more general networks. In this section, we will state and prove the most general form of the theorems. In applications of the theorems in later chapters, various specializations will be made.

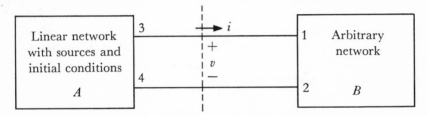

Figure 7.4 A linear 1-port network connected to an arbitrary (possibly nonlinear) network.

Let the 1-port network labeled A in Figure 7.4 be linear. It may contain sources as well as nonzero initial conditions (or initial state). Assume that the only connection between Network A and the arbitrary network is the pair of wires connected to terminals 1 and 2. There is no magnetic coupling between any coil in Network A and any coil in the arbitrary network. Furthermore, it is required that there be no controlled source in Network A which depends on any current or voltage in the arbitrary network except possibly the ones at the terminals, labeled v and i. Similarly, there is no controlled source in the arbitrary network which depends on any voltage or current in Network A except for v and i. The arbitrary network labeled Network B is not required to be linear.

To begin our discussion of the theorem, we construct the series network in Figure 7.5. The network is the same as Network A in Figure 7.4, except that all the independent sources are turned off, i.e., the independent voltage sources and the independent current sources are all set to zero. This means that a voltage source becomes a short circuit, while a current source becomes an open circuit. This may eliminate some elements from the network being considered, since they are either shorted or left dangling! All

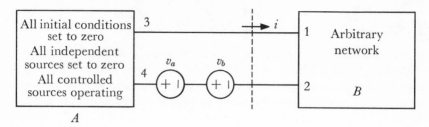

Figure 7.5 The linear Network A of Figure 7.4 is replaced by the same linear network with the independent sources turned off and the initial conditions set equal to zero. Then, v_a is made equal to v in Figure 7.4 when i is set to zero and all initial conditions are set to zero. Also, v_b is made equal to v in Figure 7.4 when i is set to zero and all independent sources are turned off.

the initial conditions are also set to zero. The voltage source $v_a(t)$ is made equal to the voltage $v(t)$ in Figure 7.4 when $i = 0$, and all the initial conditions in Figure 7.4 are equal to zero. The voltage source $v_b(t)$ is made equal to the voltage $v(t)$ in Figure 7.4 when i is zero, and all the independent sources in Network A of Figure 7.4 are set equal to zero. Thevenin's theorem states that for any arbitrary i, the voltage $v_{12}(t)$ in Figure 7.4 is identical to the voltage $v_{12}(t)$ in Figure 7.5, and the 1-port networks to the left of the dotted lines are said to be equivalent.

The proof follows as an immediate consequence of linearity. Since there are no connections between voltages and currents in Network A and those in the arbitrary network of Figure 7.4, the arbitrary current i may be treated as a source. We shall then determine the response v by adding the zero-input response and the zero-state response since Network A is linear. Since i is treated as a source, the zero-input response is the voltage v when all the independent sources are set equal to zero and when $i = 0$. Call this voltage v_b. Next determine the response v when the initial state is zero and $i = 0$. Call this voltage v_a. Finally, determine the response v when the initial state is zero and all the independent sources inside Network A are set equal to zero. Call this voltage v_c. Thus the zero-state response is $v_a + v_c$ and the complete response is

$$v_{12} = v_a + v_b + v_c. \qquad (7.7)$$

For the configuration of Figure 7.5, recall that the source v_a is made equal to the v_a above. Likewise, v_b is made equal to the v_b above. The voltage v_{34} in Figure 7.5 is equal to v_c by definition. Therefore, by KVL, the total response is

$$v_{12} = v_a + v_b + v_c, \qquad (7.8)$$

which is identical to the v_{12} of Figure 7.4 as given in Equation 7.7. This proves Thevenin's theorem!

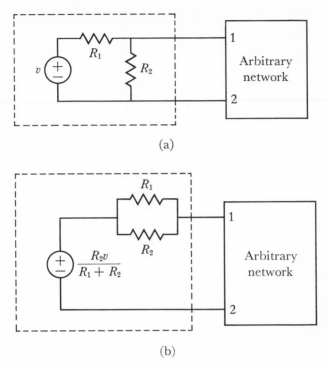

(a)

(b)

Figure 7.6 Example for using Thevenin's theorem when R_1 and R_2 are linear. The two 1-ports in the dotted boxes are equivalent.

EXAMPLE 7.2-1.   Consider the simple linear network in Figure 7.6(a) inside the dotted box. For $i = 0$ (arbitrary network is disconnected), v_{12} is

$$v_{12} = \frac{R_2}{R_1 + R_2} v. \tag{7.9}$$

This is the voltage v_a in the network of Figure 7.5. When $v = 0$, R_1 is simply in parallel with R_2, and we obtain the equivalent network in Figure 7.6(b). In this simple example there is no initial condition and $v_b = 0$. □

EXAMPLE 7.2-2.   Let us determine the Thevenin equivalent of the network in Figure 7.7(a). First we notice that there are no independent sources in the simple network so that $v_a = 0$. Next we determine the voltage v_b. This is the voltage that appears across terminals 1 and 2, when no external network is connected, due to initial conditions in the network. The capacitor is charged to Q coulombs so that the initial voltage across C is Q/C. Since there is no current flow under open-circuit conditions, the voltage v_b is equal to Q/C and it remains constant for all time. Finally, if we remove the charge Q, a simple uncharged capacitor remains. This is

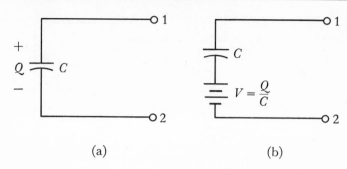

(a)   (b)

Figure 7.7 Thevenin equivalent of a charged constant capacitor. See Example 7.2-2.

the Network A in Figure 7.5. The Thevenin equivalent is shown in Figure 7.7(b). Since the voltage v_b is a constant, it is drawn as a battery in Figure 7.7(b). Thus we conclude that insofar as the terminal behavior of a charged linear time-invariant capacitor is concerned, the charged capacitor may be replaced by an uncharged capacitor in series with a constant voltage source equal to Q/C.   □

EXAMPLE 7.2-3.   Let us determine the Thevenin equivalent of the network to the left of terminals 1 and 2 in Figure 7.8. The first step is to disconnect the network to the right of terminals 1 and 2, that is, remove R_3. Next we determine v_a and v_b. Since there are no charged capacitors nor fluxed inductors, we expect a zero-input response of zero, that is, $v_b = 0$. The open-circuit voltage v_{12} due to V is the voltage v_a in the theorem and in Figure 7.5. Let us proceed with the determination of v_a. Note that the voltage across R_1 is V, and the current in R_1 from top to bottom is V/R_1.

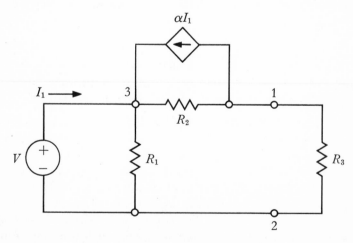

Figure 7.8   Network for Example 7.2-3.

Since R_3 is disconnected, there is no current in R_3, and the current in R_2 from left to right must be equal to αI_1 by KCL. By another application of KCL at node 3, we see that

$$I_1 + \alpha I_1 - \alpha I_1 - \frac{V}{R_1} = 0. \tag{7.10}$$

Hence

$$I_1 = \frac{V}{R_1}. \tag{7.11}$$

By KVL, the voltage v_{12} must be the sum of V and the voltage across R_2, which is v_{13}. Thus

$$v_{12}\big|_{\text{open-circuit}} = v_{13} + V = -(\alpha I_1)R_2 + V = \left(1 - \frac{\alpha R_2}{R_1}\right)V. \tag{7.12}$$

The required v_a is v_{12} in Equation 7.12. Finally we obtain the network with no initial conditions and *no independent sources*. Since the current-controlled current source αI_1 is not an independent source (it depends on I_1) it must not be turned off. To turn V off, we replace it by a short circuit. Since R_1 is across the short circuit, there will be no voltage across nor current in R_1, and R_1 may be disconnected without affecting the voltages and currents in the rest of the network. The complete Thevenin equivalent is shown in Figure 7.9. $\square$

The situation in Figure 7.4 may be represented by another equivalent configuration as shown in Figure 7.10. This is the configuration for Norton's theorem. We assume the same set of hypothesis that we did for Thevenin's theorem: Network A is linear and there is no internal coupling

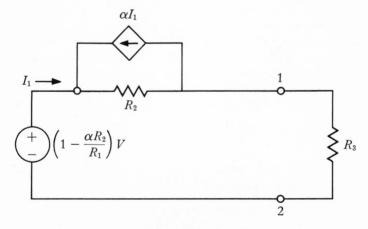

Figure 7.9 Thevenin equivalent for the network in Figure 7.8.

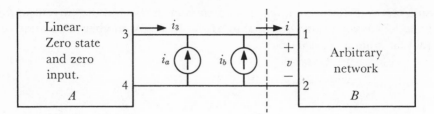

Figure 7.10 The linear network *A* of Figure 7.4 is replaced by the same network except that all the initial conditions and all internal independent sources are set equal to zero. The current source i_a is equal to *i* in Figure 7.4 if $v \equiv 0$ and the initial state is zero. The current source i_b is equal to the current *i* in Figure 7.4 if $v \equiv 0$ and all internal independent sources are set equal to zero.

between Network *A* and the arbitrary network, but Network *B* need not be linear.

To discuss Norton's theorem, we construct the network in Figure 7.10 as follows. Network *A* is the same as Network *A* of Figure 7.4, except that all the initial conditions are set equal to zero and all the inputs or independent sources are set equal to zero. By construction, the current source i_a is made equal to the current *i* that would flow in Figure 7.4 if all the initial conditions were set equal to zero and if *v* were set equal to zero. Likewise, i_b is made equal to the current *i* that would flow in Figure 7.4 if *v* were set equal to zero and if all the independent sources were set equal to zero. Norton's theorem states that for every arbitrary *v* the current in Figure 7.4 is identical to the current *i* in Figure 7.10, and the 1-ports to the left of the dotted lines are said to be equivalent.

The proof is similar to that for Thevenin's theorem. Since there are no internal couplings between the networks in Figure 7.4, we may treat the arbitrary voltage *v* as a voltage source. We shall then determine the response *i* by combining the effects of the inputs, the initial state, and *v*, since the network to the left of the dotted line is linear. Due to initial state above, with *v* = 0 and all inputs set to zero, the resulting response *i* is i_b. Due to the inputs above with initial state set to zero and *v* set to zero, the response *i* is i_a. Finally, denote the response *i*, when the initial state is set to zero and when the internal independent sources in *A* are set to zero, by i_c. Then, by linearity, the total response is

$$i = i_a + i_b + i_c. \tag{7.13}$$

Now for the network in Figure 7.10 we observe that the current i_3 is by definition the same as the current i_c. Hence, by KCL,

$$i = i_a + i_b + i_c, \tag{7.14}$$

which is identical to Equation 7.13, thus proving Norton's theorem.

EXAMPLE 7.2-4.   Consider the simple network in Figure 7.6 again. The zero-state zero-input network is the same as in Thevenin's theorem, R_1 in parallel with R_2. The current source is the current that flows through 1–2 when v_{12} is zero. Hence, the current is

$$i = \frac{v}{R_1}. \qquad (7.15)$$

This is i_a. The current i_b is zero since there is no initial condition. The complete Norton equivalent is shown in Figure 7.11.   □

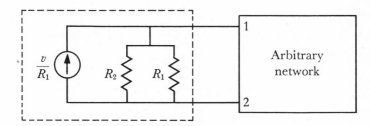

Figure 7.11   Norton's equivalent for the 1-port in Figure 7.6.

EXAMPLE 7.2-5.   Let us determine the Norton equivalent for the linear time-invariant fluxed inductor in Figure 7.12(a). Since there is no independent source to the left of terminals 1 and 2, $i_a = 0$. The current i_b is due to the initial current through the inductor. Following the procedure in the statement of Norton's theorem, we short terminals 1 and 2 and determine the resulting current. This is equal to I for all time since v_{12} is zero and $di/dt = 0$ so that i does not change. The zero-input zero-state network under consideration is simply an unfluxed inductor L. The Norton equivalent is shown in Figure 7.12(b).   □

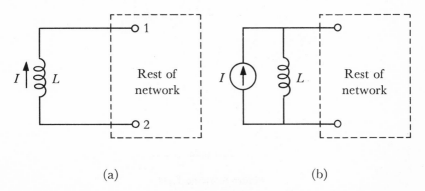

(a)   (b)

Figure 7.12   Norton equivalent of a fluxed constant inductor. See Example 7.2-5.

In summary, a linear two-terminal network is equivalent to a series combination of a voltage source and the same network except that the initial state (initial conditions) and the inputs are set equal to zero. This is Thevenin's theorem. Similarly, the original linear 1-port is equivalent to a parallel combination of a current source and the same network except that the initial state and the inputs are set equal to zero. This is Norton's theorem.

In setting the inputs to zero, the independent voltage sources are shorted, and the independent current sources are opened. The controlled, or dependent, sources are left alone.

● EXERCISES

7.2-1   Determine the Thevenin equivalent network for the linear network in Figure Exercise 7.2-1.

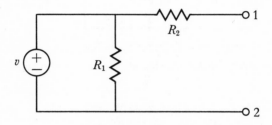

Figure Exercise 7.2-1

7.2-2   Determine the Norton equivalent network for the linear network in Figure Exercise 7.2-1.

7.2-3   Find the Thevenin equivalent for the network in Figure Exercise 7.2-3 containing a controlled source.

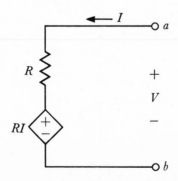

Figure Exercise 7.2-3

7.2-4   Find the Thevenin equivalent for the network in Figure Exercise 7.2-4 if $i(t)$ is a unit step $u(t)$ and C is initially uncharged and constant. Repeat for $i(t)$ equal to a unit impulse function and compare with the equivalent of a charged capacitor as given in Exercise 7.2-2.

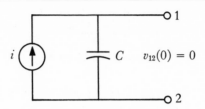

Figure Exercise 7.2-4

7.2-5   Find the Norton equivalent circuit for the network in Figure Exercise 7.2-5 where the voltage $v(t)$ is an arbitrary function of time.

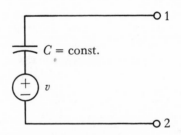

Figure Exercise 7.2-5

7.2-6   Find the Thevenin equivalent for the network in Figure Exercise 7.2-6 where $i(t)$ is an arbitrary current source.

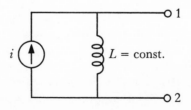

Figure Exercise 7.2-6

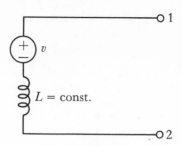

Figure Exercise 7.2-7

7.2-7   Find the Norton equivalent for the network in Figure Exercise 7.2-7 where $v(t)$ is an arbitrary voltage source. Assume that $i_L(0) = 0$.

7.3   Time-invariant systems

In Chapter 4, we defined time-invariant network elements. It is reasonable to define a time-invariant network as one which is composed of time-invariant network elements. Although we will be dealing with such networks most of the time, it is advantageous to employ a definition which is essentially as simple but not necessarily as restricted as the tentative one above. As a motivation for the definition we now give, we note that if we have a network of time-invariant elements, the response to any input waveform will not depend on the time of the day, assuming the same set of initial conditions. This is the basis for the following definition of a time-invariant system.

Suppose that a system with an arbitrary input $x(t)$ and an arbitrary initial state $(\alpha_1, \alpha_2, \ldots, \alpha_n)$ gives the response $y(t)$. The system is said to be time-invariant if an input $x(t - \Delta)$ and an initial state $(\alpha_1, \alpha_2, \ldots, \alpha_n)$ causes the response $y(t - \Delta)$ for any $\Delta > 0$. No matter what the initial state is, an arbitrary delay on the input function causes the same delay on the output function for all possible inputs. The initial state for the delayed input case is applied Δ time units later.

EXAMPLE 7.3-1.   Consider the network in Figure 7.3. Suppose that when $v_C(0) = 10$ volts, $i_L(0) = -3$ amperes, and $v_1(t) = u(t)$, the response $v(t)$ is as given in Equation 7.6. The initial state consists of the set of two quantities $v_C(0)$ and $i_L(0)$. Here, α_1 is 10 volts and α_2 is -3 amperes. Suppose that the network is time-invariant and instead of an input $v_1(t)$, which is a unit step, we have a delayed unit step $v_1(t) = u(t - 3)$ which is delayed by 3 time units. For an initial condition of $\alpha_1 = v_C(3) = 10$ volts and $\alpha_2 = i_L(3) = -3$ amperes, the response $v(t)$ for $t \geq 3$ is given by

$$v(t) = [10e^{-(t-3)} \cos 2(t-3)]u(t-3)$$
$$+ [1 - e^{-(t-3)} \cos 2(t-3)]u(t-3). \quad (7.16)$$

This is simply obtained from Equation 7.6 by replacing t by $t - 3$. The delay Δ is 3 time units. Notice that the initial condition for the delayed case is applied at $t = 3$, and not at $t = 0$. $\quad\square$

It is easy to verify that the elements defined in Chapter 4 which have time-invariant branch characteristics are time-invariant systems in the sense of the new definition. For example, for a current-controlled time-invariant resistor, we have $v = f(i)$. If $v_1(t)$ is the response due to $i(t)$, so that

$$v_1(t) = f[i(t)], \tag{7.17}$$

then the response to $i(t - \Delta)$ is

$$v_2(t) = f[i(t - \Delta)] = v_1(t - \Delta). \tag{7.18}$$

The situation is similar for a time-invariant capacitor and inductor.

The distinction between a time-invariant n-port and a time-invariant network is analogous to the distinction between linear n-ports and linear networks. That is, in the n-port case only port variables are allowed as inputs and outputs. A trivial example of a time-invariant 1-port network with time-varying elements is a series connection of R_1 and R_2, where R_1 and R_2 are time varying but such that $R_2 = K - R_1$, where K is a constant. However the network is time-varying. Any network of time-invariant elements will be time-invariant in the sense of the definition of this section meaning that provided the initial states are the same, delaying the inputs causes only a delay in the output, giving exactly the same waveform.

● **EXERCISES**

7.3-1   A system is described by $(dy(t)/dt) + 3y(t) = 2tx(t)$, where $y(t)$ is the output and $x(t)$ is the input. Is the system time-invariant?

7.3-2   Demonstrate that a capacitor with a characteristic $q = f(v)$ is a time-invariant system, where i is the output and v is the input.

7.3-3   Demonstrate that an inductor with a characteristic $\psi = g(i)$ is a time-invariant system, where v is the output and i is the input.

7.4   Linear time-invariant differential systems

A linear time-invariant differential system is a system which is linear in the sense of Section 7.1, time-invariant in the sense of Section 7.3, and describable by ordinary differential equations. If y is the output and x is the input, the linearity requirement restricts the ordinary differential equation to be of the form

$$a_n \frac{d^n y}{dt^n} + a_{n-1} \frac{d^{n-1} y}{dt^{n-1}} + \cdots + a_0 y = b_m \frac{d^m x}{dt} + \cdots + b_0 x, \tag{7.19}$$

where the a's and b's do not depend on x, y, or any of their derivatives of any order. The coefficients may be explicit functions of time. The time-invariance requirement restricts all the coefficients to be constants. If a system is described by Equation 7.19 where the coefficients are constants, then the system is said to be a linear time-invariant differential system. If any of the coefficients depends on time explicitly but not on x, y, or any of their derivatives of any order, the system is said to be a linear time-varying differential system.

If a network consists of linear time-invariant elements, then the branch constraints yield ordinary linear differential equations with constant coefficients relating branch voltages and branch currents. Furthermore, KCL and KVL are linear algebraic equations with constant coefficients involving branch voltages and branch currents. Hence we have a system of ordinary differential equations with constant coefficients, where some of the differential equations have order zero, i.e., are ordinary algebraic equations. From such a system, a single differential equation involving only one output may be obtained. Equation 7.19 shows the form when there is only one input. If there is more than one input, there may be additional terms on the right-hand side corresponding to the other inputs. For example, for two inputs, the differential equation is of the form

$$\sum_{k=0}^{n} a_k \frac{d^k y(t)}{dt^k} = \sum_{k=0}^{m} b_k \frac{d^k x_1(t)}{dt^k} + \sum_{k=0}^{r} c_k \frac{d^k x_2(t)}{dt^k}, \qquad (7.20)$$

where the a's, b's, and c's are constants and n, m, and r are integers which depend on the specific network.

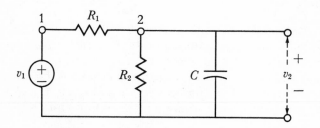

Figure 7.13 Three-element network with a first-order differential equation.

EXAMPLE 7.4-1. Consider the linear time-invariant network in Figure 7.13 where R_1, R_2, and C are constants. Here v_1 is the input and v_2 is the output. In order to obtain the differential equation relating v_2 to v_1, we apply KCL at node 1. First we note that the voltage v_{21} across R_1 is equal to $v_2 - v_1$. Writing summation of currents away from node 2 equal to zero, we have

$$\frac{v_2 - v_1}{R_1} + \frac{v_2}{R_2} + C \frac{dv_2}{dt} = 0 \qquad (7.21)$$

or

$$\frac{dv_2}{dt} + \frac{1}{RC} v_2 = \frac{1}{R_1 C} v_1, \qquad (7.22)$$

where $1/R_1 + 1/R_2 = 1/R$. This is a linear time-invariant differential system. $\square$

The *complementary solution* is the solution of a differential equation such as in Equation 7.20, with the right-hand side equal to zero. Such an equation is called a homogeneous differential equation:

$$\sum_{k=0}^{n} a_k \frac{d^k y(t)}{dt^k} = 0. \qquad (7.23)$$

In addition, if $y(t)$ satisfies the conditions at the initial instant, then $y(t)$ is said to be the *zero-input response*. The zero-state response on the other hand satisfies Equation 7.20 and zero conditions at the initial instant. The zero-state response will be considered further in the next chapter. In this section, we shall discuss the nature of the zero-input response for linear time-invariant differential systems.

It can be shown that the zero-input response and the zero-state response for a linear time-invariant differential system are unique. That is, if we obtain a time function which satisfies Equation 7.23 and the set of initial conditions, then regardless of how we arrive at the function, we are assured that the function we have is the correct zero-input response.

A trial solution of Equation 7.23 is attempted. We guess that the solution is $y = e^{st}$. If this is a solution, then it will satisfy Equation 7.23. We compute the left-hand side expression in Equation 7.23 for $y = e^{st}$ obtaining

$$\sum_{k=0}^{n} a_k \frac{d^k}{dt^k} (e^{st}) = \sum_{k=0}^{n} a_k s^k e^{st}$$

$$= e^{st}(a_n s^n + a_{n-1} s^{n-1} + \cdots + a_0). \qquad (7.24)$$

Since $e^{st} \neq 0$ for any finite s and t, the expression in Equation 7.24 can be zero only if

$$a_n s^n + \cdots + a_0 = 0. \qquad (7.25)$$

From the fundamental theorem of algebra, an nth degree algebraic equation as in Equation 7.25 has n roots, that is, n values of s which make the left-hand side in Equation 7.25 vanish. These n roots may or may not be distinct (or simple). For these values of s, e^{st} is a solution of Equation 7.23. Let s_1 be one of the roots. Then $e^{s_1 t}$ is a solution. Likewise $c_1 e^{s_1 t}$ is a solution, where c_1 is an arbitrary constant. This is easily verified by substituting in Equation 7.23.

Suppose first that all the roots of Equation 7.25 are distinct, i.e., different from each other. Then if s_1, s_2, . . . , s_n are the distinct roots of Equation 7.25, $e^{s_1 t}$, $e^{s_2 t}$, . . . , $e^{s_n t}$ will be solutions of Equation 7.23. Likewise, any linear combination of the solutions will be a solution of Equation 7.23. The most general complementary solution is (for distinct roots)

$$y = c_1 e^{s_1 t} + c_2 e^{s_2 t} + \cdots + c_n e^{s_n t}, \tag{7.26}$$

where c_1, c_2, . . . , c_n are arbitrary constants. This general solution satisfies Equation 7.23. However, in order to satisfy the conditions at the initial instant, the c_k must be chosen properly. If there are n linearly independent initial conditions, then the c_k are uniquely determined.

EXAMPLE 7.4-2.   Suppose that we have a series RLC circuit connected to a voltage source. Assuming that the elements are linear and time-invariant, we have

$$Ri + L\frac{di}{dt} + \frac{1}{C}\int_{t_1}^{t} i(\tau)\,d\tau + v_C(t_1) = v(t). \tag{7.27}$$

Differentiating once, we obtain

$$L\frac{d^2 i(t)}{dt^2} + R\frac{di(t)}{dt} + \frac{1}{C}i(t) = \frac{dv(t)}{dt}, \tag{7.28}$$

where i may be considered the output or response and $v(t)$ the input. The differential equation specifies the relationship between $i(t)$ and $v(t)$ for $t \geq t_1$, where t_1 is the instant at which the input is applied. The initial state or initial conditions are specified at $t = t_1$. These conditions may consist of $v_C(t_1)$ and $i(t_1)$, the current through the inductor. It is convenient to convert $v_C(t_1)$ in terms of functions of i. At $t = t_1$, we have the KVL equation as in Equation 7.27 except that $v = 0$. Since the integral from t_1 to t_1 is zero, we have

$$Ri(t_1) + L\frac{di}{dt}\bigg|_{t = t_1} + 0 + v_C(t_1) = 0. \tag{7.29}$$

Therefore we have

$$\frac{di}{dt}\bigg|_{t = t_1} = \frac{-v_C(t_1) - Ri(t_1)}{L}, \tag{7.30}$$

and the initial conditions are expressed as conditions on $i(t_1)$ and $di(t_1)/dt$ at the initial instant. The zero-input response is a solution of

$$L\frac{d^2 i}{dt^2} + R\frac{di}{dt} + \frac{1}{C}i = 0, \qquad t \geq t_1, \tag{7.31}$$

$$i(t_1) = \text{given number,} \tag{7.32}$$

$$i'(t_1) = \text{given number.} \tag{7.33}$$

That is, i is a zero-input response if it satisfies Equations 7.31, 7.32, and 7.33. As a numerical example, suppose $R/L = 3$ and $1/LC = 2$. Also, let $i(t_1) = 1$ and $di(t_1)/dt = 2$. Then Equation 7.31 becomes

$$\frac{d^2 i}{dt^2} + 3 \frac{di}{dt} + 2i = 0, \qquad t \geq t_1 \tag{7.34}$$

after dividing Equation 7.31 by L. Trying e^{st} as a solution, we have

$$\frac{d^2}{dt^2} e^{st} + 3 \frac{d}{dt} e^{st} + 2e^{st} = e^{st}(s^2 + 3s + 2). \tag{7.35}$$

The expression in Equation 7.35 is zero if

$$(s^2 + 3s + 2) = 0. \tag{7.36}$$

This is the case for $s = -1$ and $s = -2$. Hence, e^{-t} and e^{-2t} are solutions and

$$i = C_1 e^{-t} + C_2 e^{-2t} \tag{7.37}$$

is a solution of Equation 7.34, where C_1 and C_2 are arbitrary constants. This is easily verified by direct substitution in Equation 7.34. Next we solve for C_1 and C_2 so that the i in Equation 7.37 satisfies Equations 7.32 and 7.33. For simplicity, suppose $t_1 = 0$. Then, from Equation 7.37 we have

$$C_1 + C_2 = i(0) = 1. \tag{7.38}$$

Differentiating Equation 7.37, we have

$$\frac{di(t)}{dt} = -C_1 e^{-t} - 2C_2 e^{-2t}. \tag{7.39}$$

At $t = 0$, Equation 7.39 becomes

$$\frac{di(0)}{dt} = -C_1 - 2C_2 = 2. \tag{7.40}$$

From Equations 7.38 and 7.40 we may solve for C_1 and C_2 which turn out to be $C_1 = 4$ and $C_2 = -3$. So

$$i(t) = 4e^{-t} - 3e^{-2t} \tag{7.41}$$

satisfies Equation 7.34 for $t \geq 0$, and $i(0) = 1$ and $di(0)/dt = 2$ as specified. The $i(t)$ in Equation 7.41 is, then, the unique zero-input response. $\square$

Next consider the case in which the roots in Equation 7.25 are not all distinct. For example, suppose that a root s_1 is a double root so that $(s - s_1)^2$ is a factor of the nth degree polynomial in Equation 7.25. Then not only is $e^{s_1 t}$ a solution as discussed earlier, but so is $t e^{s_1 t}$. This can be seen from the following discussion when we use the operator notation $D = d/dt$. Write Equation 7.23 as

$$\sum_{k=0}^{n} a_k D^k y = 0, \tag{7.42}$$

where

$$D^k y = \frac{d^k y}{dt^k}.$$

We may rewrite Equation 7.42 as

$$(a_n D^n + a_{n-1} D^{n-1} + \cdots + a_0) y = 0 \tag{7.43}$$

with the understanding that the expression on the left-hand side is defined as the left-hand side of Equation 7.42. From the n factors of the expression in the left-hand side of Equation 7.25, we may factor Equation 7.43 into

$$a_n (D - s_n)(D - s_{n-1}) \cdots (D - s_1) y = 0. \tag{7.44}$$

Suppose now that s_2 and s_1 are equal so that s_1 is a double root of Equation 7.25. Then we want to check whether $t e^{s_1 t}$ is a solution of the differential equation in Equation 7.44. We have

$$a_n (D - s_n)(D - s_{n-1}) \cdots (D - s_1)(D - s_1)[t e^{s_1 t}] =$$

$$[a_n (D - s_n)(D - s_{n-1}) \cdots (D - s_3)](D - s_1)[e^{s_1 t} + s_1 t e^{s_1 t} - s_1 t e^{s_1 t}]$$

$$= [a_n (D - s_n)(D - s_{n-1}) \cdots (D - s_3)](D - s_1) e^{s_1 t} \tag{7.45}$$

$$= a_n (D - s_n)(D - s_{n-1}) \cdots (D - s_3)[s_1 e^{s_1 t} - s_1 e^{s_1 t}]$$

$$= a_n (D - s_n)(D - s_{n-1}) \cdots (D - s_3) 0 = 0.$$

Therefore $t e^{s_1 t}$ is a solution if s_1 is a double root. By a similar procedure, it can be shown that if s_1 is a triple root of Equation 7.25, then not only are $e^{s_1 t}$ and $t e^{s_1 t}$ solutions but also $t^2 e^{s_1 t}$. In general, if s_1 is a root of multiplicity r_1, then $e^{s_1 t}, t e^{s_1 t}, t^2 e^{s_1 t}, \ldots, t^{r_1 - 1} e^{s_1 t}$ are all solutions, so that

$$y = C_1 e^{s_1 t} + C_2 t e^{s_1 t} + C_3 t^2 e^{s_1 t} + \cdots + C_{r_1} t^{r_1 - 1} e^{s_1 t} \tag{7.46}$$

is a solution also. This means that for the nth-order homogeneous differential equation of Equation 7.23, we may always write a general solution containing n linearly independent constants.

EXAMPLE 7.4-3.   Suppose we have the differential equation

$$(D + 1)^3 (D + 2)(D + 3)^2 y = 0. \tag{7.47}$$

Then the solutions are e^{-3t}, $t e^{-3t}$, e^{-2t}, e^{-t}, $t e^{-t}$, and $t^2 e^{-t}$, and the most general complementary solution is

$$Y = C_1 e^{-3t} + C_2 t e^{-3t} + C_3 e^{-2t} + C_4 e^{-t} + C_5 t e^{-t} + C_6 t^2 e^{-t}, \quad (7.48)$$

which contains six arbitrary constants. The differential equation is, of course, sixth order, and six independent initial conditions are required. □

● EXERCISES

7.4-1 For the linear time-invariant network in Figure Exercise 7.4-1, derive the differential equation relating the output v_L to the input v.

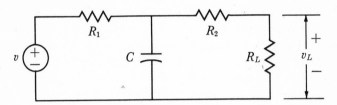

Figure Exercise 7.4-1

7.4-2 For the linear time-invariant network in Figure Exercise 7.4-2, derive the differential equation relating the output v_{ab} to the input v.

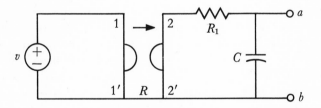

Figure Exercise 7.4-2

7.4-3 Find the general complementary solution for the differential equation

$$\frac{d^2 y}{dt^2} + y = 0.$$

7.4-4 Find the general complementary solution for the differential equation

$$\frac{d^3 y}{dt^3} + \frac{d^2 y}{dt^2} + \frac{dy}{dt} + y = 0.$$

7.4-5   Find the general complementary solution for the differential equation

$$(D + 2)^4 (D + 3)y = 0.$$

7.4-6   Find the zero-input response for the system described by the differential equation in Exercise 7.4-3 if $y(0) = 1$, $y'(0) = 1$.

Problems

7-1   Show that the ideal transformer model of Chapter 4 (p. 78) is a linear 2-port network.

7-2   Show that two linear, time-invariant, magnetically coupled coils as shown in Figure 4.18 (p. 75) form a linear network.

7-3   Show that if a system is zero-state additive, then, if y_1 is the zero-state response due to an input x_1, the output due to Cx_1 is Cy_1, where C is any finite integer (including negative integers).

7-4   Repeat Problem 7-3 for C equal to a finite rational number (finite ratio of two integers). [*Hint:* Do Problem 7-3 first, so that the result in Problem 7-3 may be assumed.] So if $x_1 \to y_1$, $nx_1 \to ny_1$. Let $x_2 = (n/m)x_1 \to y_2$. Then $(m/n)x_2 = x_1 \to y_1$ and $mx_2 \to ny_1 = my_2$ $\therefore x_2 = (n/m)x_1 \to (n/m)y_1$. The symbol $x \to y$ means that y is the zero-state response for an input x. Since any irrational number may be approximated arbitrarily closely by a rational number, this problem shows that a zero-state additive system is "practically" zero-state linear. This is why in practical cases, additivity or superposition is used as a definition of linearity. Similarly, using exactly the same proof, it can be shown that a zero-input additive system implies that for an arbitrary initial state $(\alpha_1, \alpha_2, \ldots, \alpha_n)$ yielding a zero-input response y, the arbitrary initial state $(C\alpha_1, C\alpha_2, \ldots, C\alpha_n)$ yields Cy, provided that C is any arbitrary finite *rational* number. Hence a system which is zero-input additive, zero-state additive, and decomposable, is "practically" linear.

7-5   Determine the Thevenin equivalent of a linear time-varying charged capacitor with a charge $q(t_1)$ at t_1.

7-6   Determine the Norton equivalent of a linear time-varying inductor with an initial current $i(t_1)$ at t_1.

7-7   A sinusoidal signal generator has a Thevenin equivalent resistance of 300 ohms and a Thevenin equivalent source voltage V volts rms. The signal generator is to be connected to a 100-ohm load. For some reason, it is desired that the equivalent resistance to the left of the load be 100 ohms. This may be done by connecting a resistance R across the generator as shown in the figure. Determine the value for R that will do this.

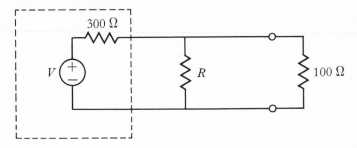

Figure Problem 7-7

7-8   Find the Thevenin equivalent for the network in the figure. Would your answer be affected if R were replaced by an arbitrary network?

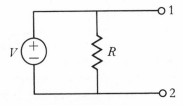

Figure Problem 7-8

7-9   Find the Norton equivalent for the network in the figure. Would your answer be affected if R were replaced by an arbitrary network?

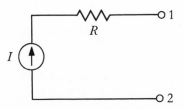

Figure Problem 7-9

7-10 The approximate terminal behavior of a practical battery is displayed as a straight line in the figure. Find its Thevenin equivalent.

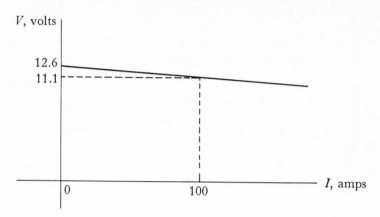

Figure Problem 7-10

7-11 The voltage v in the network of Figure Problem 7-11(a) is identically zero. What will be the current i as in Figure Problem 7-11(b) if the terminals in (a) are short circuited? How about the current in Figure Problem 7-11(c)? Given any physical n-port network with sources as in (a), there is a *unique* set of values for currents and voltages throughout the network for any given set of port currents and voltages. In other words, the current through a branch cannot have two values at the same time. Likewise for voltages. From this fact, what can you say about the distribution of currents and voltages in (b) and (c) as compared to that of (a) of the figure?

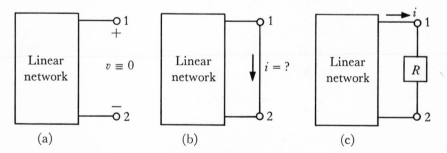

Figure Problem 7-11

7-12 The voltage v in the network of Figure Problem 7-12(a) is equal to $v(t)$. Suppose a voltage source whose variation is identical to $v(t)$

is connected to the terminals as in (b). What will be the current $i(t)$? How about the current in (c)? See Problem 7-11 and answer the last question there for the networks in Figure Problem 7-12.

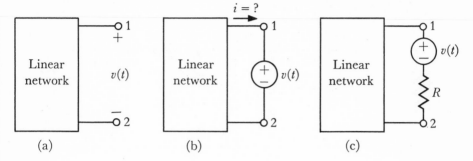

Figure Problem 7-12

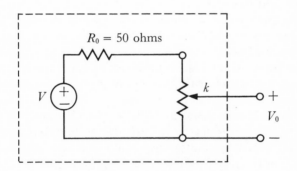

Figure Problem 7-13

7-13 A potentiometer, a resistance with an adjustable position tap, is commonly used to obtain an adjustable source of voltage from a fixed source of voltage, as shown in the figure. We have a sinusoidal signal generator of 10 volts rms and an internal resistance of 50 ohms. The tap on the potentiometer may be adjusted from lowest position (coincident with bottom terminal) to highest position (coincident with top terminal). Specify a value of potentiometer resistance so that the dissipation in the potentiometer is no more than 0.05 watt. If k denotes the fraction of potentiometer resistance included between the bottom terminal and the top, plot the magnitude of output voltage V_0 vs. k. If k is linearly proportional to the angular position of the potentiometer knob, is the variation of V_0 linear with respect to angular position of knob setting? Plot the Thevenin resistance as a function of k.

7-14 Calculate the voltage v_{ab} in the figure. [*Hint:* Use Thevenin's theorem repeatedly.]

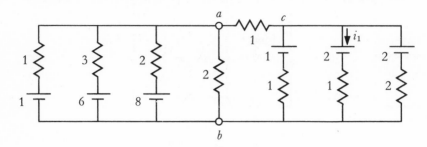

Figure Problem 7-14

7-15 For the network of Figure Problem 7-14, calculate i_{ac}. It is desired to make the current i_{ac} equal to zero by inserting a battery in series with the resistor. What value of battery voltage must be used. Indicate polarity.

7-16 For the network of Figure Problem 7-14, calculate i_1, the current through the branch with a battery of 2 volts in series with a 1-ohm resistor.

7-17 Suppose in Figure Problem 7-14 we add a battery of 3 volts of zero internal resistance across ab with the positive terminal connected to a and similarly a battery of 1 volt across cb with the positive terminal connected to b. What is the new value for i_{ac}?

7-18 In the network of Figure Problem 7-18(a), R and C are positive constants. Taking v_c as the output, show that the zero-input response is as shown in Figure Problem 7-18(b) for $t \geqslant t_1$, the initial instant. Note the effect of longer or shorter time constant on the shape of the waveform.

7-19 In the network shown, the switch K is in position a for a long period of time (say 24 hours) and then at $t = 0$ is switched from a to b. Find the current $i(t)$ that results after the switching occurs. Use numerical values wherever possible. The original voltage on the 1 F capacitor is zero.

7-20 In the network of the figure, the switch K is closed at $t = 0$. Find the current $i(t)$ in the circuit. Evaluate any arbitrary constants and substitute numerical values wherever possible. The initial voltage on the right-hand side capacitor is zero.

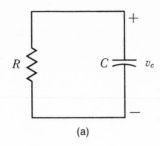

(a)

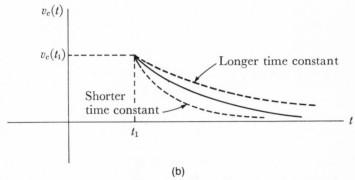

(b)

Figure Problem 7-18

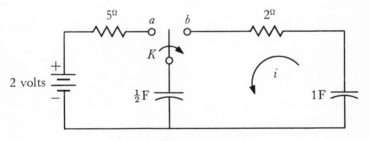

Figure Problem 7-19

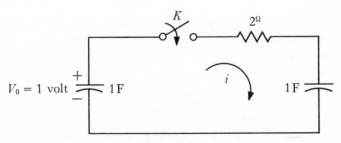

Figure Problem 7-20

7-21   In the linear time-invariant network shown, K is closed at $t = 0$. The capacitors have initial values of voltage on them marked V_a and V_b. (a) Find $v_{C_1}(t)$ and $v_{C_2}(t)$ for $t \geq 0$. (b) Check this result by verifying that $v_{C_1}(\infty) = v_{C_2}(\infty)$.

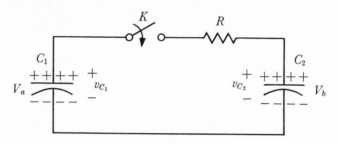

Figure Problem 7-21

7-22   The series network shown consists of two charged capacitors in series with a resistor. Before the switch is closed, the voltmeter marked VM 1 reads +10 volts and VM 2, +4 volts. At $t=0$ the switch is closed. You are to find the two voltmeter readings when the system has again reached a steady state (i.e., at least 10 time constants after the closing of the switch).

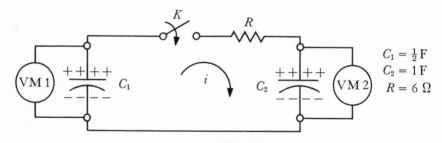

Figure Problem 7-22

7-23   Consider the network given for Problem 7-21. For that network, $R = 2$ ohms, $C_1 = 1$ farad, and $C_2 = \frac{1}{2}$ farad. At the time switch K is closed, each capacitor carries a charge of 1 coulomb. Find the voltage $v_{C_2}(t)$ for $t \geq 0$.

7-24   Show that the system represented by Equation 7.20 is zero-state linear.

7-25   Assuming that initial conditions are given by $y(0)$, $y'(0)$, . . . , $y^{(n-1)}(0)$, show that the system represented by Equation 7.20 is zero-input linear. The results in Problems 7-24 and 7-25 show that the system represented by Equation 7.20 is linear.

7-26 Find the Thevenin equivalent network with respect to port *ab* for the linear time-invariant network of the figure. Note that I_1 is the current in R_1 and that this current controls the current source of the network. The network of this problem is a linear incremental equivalent network for a transistor. If possible, combine the resistors and controlled source into a single resistor.

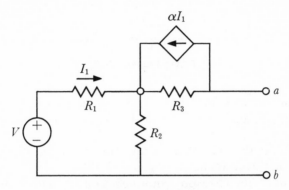

Figure Problem 7-26

7-27 Repeat Problem 7-26 for the network given in the figure. Observe that the voltage v_k is the voltage across R_k with respect to ground. This network is a linear incremental model for an electronic circuit known as a *cathode follower*.

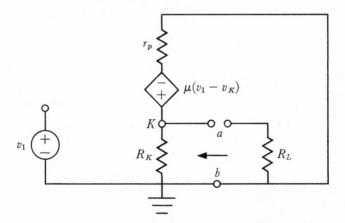

Figure Problem 7-27

7-28   For the linear time-invariant network in Figure Problem 7-28 with v_{12} as output and v_1 as input, determine the differential equation relating v_1 to v_{12}.

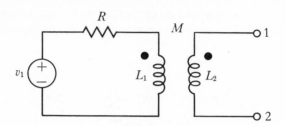

Figure Problem 7-28

7-29   For the network of Figure 7.13, suppose $R_1 = R_2 = 100$ ohms, $C = .01 \ \mu F$, and $v_2(0) = 1$ volt. Determine the zero-input response for $t \geqslant 0$.

7-30   Determine the Thevenin equivalent for a linear time-invariant fluxed inductor as shown in Figure 7.12(a).

7-31   Determine the Norton equivalent for a linear time-invariant charged capacitor as shown in Figure 7.7(a).

7-32   Show that if $y(t)$ is the zero-state response for an input $x(t)$ of a linear time-invariant differential system, then $dy(t)/dt$ is the zero-state response for an input $dx(t)/dt$.

7-33   Repeat Problem 7-32 for a linear time-invariant system which is not necessarily a differential system.

7-34   Show that if $y(t)$ is the zero-state response for an input $x(t)$ of a linear time-invariant system, the zero-state response for

$$\int_{t_1}^{t} x(\tau) \ d\tau \quad \text{is} \quad \int_{t_1}^{t} y(\tau) \ d\tau,$$

where t_1 is the initial instant.

Further Implications of Linearity:

Convolution and Impulse Response **8**

8.1 Simple application of linearity and time-invariance

Suppose that the zero-state response of a linear time-invariant network to an input $i(t)$ that starts from $t = 0$ is $v(t)$. Then from the time-invariance principle introduced in the last chapter the response to $i(t - \Delta)$ is $v(t - \Delta)$ for any $\Delta > 0$. If an input $i(t)$ is delayed by Δ, the output is simply delayed by an amount Δ. From linearity, an input $i(t) - i(t - \Delta)$ will result in a zero-state response of $v(t) - v(t - \Delta)$. Furthermore, by linearity again, an input $[i(t) - i(t - \Delta)]/\Delta$ results in a zero-state response of $[v(t) - v(t - \Delta)]/\Delta$, because $1/\Delta$ is just a simple scale factor. In the limit, as Δ is taken to be arbitrarily small, $[i(t) - i(t - \Delta)]/\Delta$ approaches the time derivative of $i(t)$, and $[v(t) - v(t - \Delta)]/\Delta$ approaches the time derivative of $v(t)$. If these derivatives exist, we have the useful conclusion that if the zero-state response of a linear time-invariant network to an input $i(t)$ is $v(t)$, then the zero-state response of the same network to $di(t)/dt$ is $dv(t)/dt$. Actually, if we use a more general notion of derivative, the above conclusion still holds even when i and v do not possess ordinary derivatives. For instance, $i(t)$ may have a jump discontinuity at $t = t_1$. In this case $di(t)/dt$

contains an impulse function at $t = t_1$. Similarly, $i(t)$ may contain an impulse at $t = t_2$ and $di(t)/dt$ will have a doublet at $t = t_2$. One must be especially careful in noting whether $i(t)$ has singularities at $t = 0$ in order to obtain the correct $di(t)/dt$.

EXAMPLE 8.1-1.   Suppose that the zero-state response of a linear time-invariant network to a unit step function $u(t)$ is $v(t) = e^{-t}$, $t \geq 0$. Then the zero-state response to $\delta(t) = du(t)/dt$ for $t > 0$ is $dv(t)/dt = -e^{-t}$. However, we note that since the zero-state response to $u(t)$ for $t < 0$ is zero, then $v(t)$ has a jump discontinuity at $t = 0$. Now $v(t)$ may be written as

$$v(t) = e^{-t}u(t) = u(t) - (1 - e^{-t})u(t) \qquad (8.1)$$

and

$$\frac{dv(t)}{dt} = \delta(t) - e^{-t}u(t). \qquad (8.2)$$

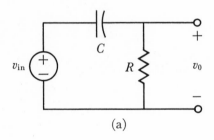

(a)

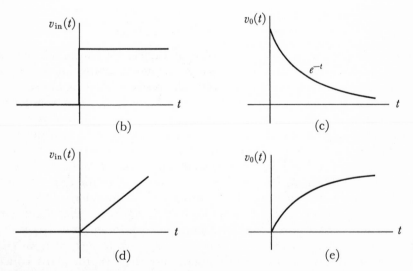

Figure 8.1 If the zero-input response for v_{in} as in (b) is v_0 in (c), then the zero-input response for v_{in} as in (d) is v_0 in (e).

If a function $i(t)$ has a discontinuity of a at t_1, that is, $i(t_1+) - i(t_1-) = a$, then $di(t)/dt$ will contain an impulse at $t = t_1$ of area a as was shown in Chapter 2.

By similar arguments as above, we see that if the zero-state response of a linear time-invariant network due to $i(t)$ is $v(t)$, where $i(t)$ starts at 0, then the zero-state response of the same network due to an input

$$\text{Input} = \int_0^t i(\tau)\, d\tau \qquad (8.3)$$

is

$$\text{Response} = \int_0^t v(\tau)\, d\tau. \qquad \square \quad (8.4)$$

EXAMPLE 8.1-2.   In the linear time-invariant network of Figure 8.1, it is given that the output voltage $v_0(t)$, when C is initially uncharged and $v_{\text{in}}(t)$ is a unit step, is e^{-t} for $t \geq 0$ and zero for $t < 0$. If instead of v_{in} being a unit step, we have a unit ramp, which is the integral of a unit step, then the output will be the integral of e^{-t} or

$$v_{\text{out}} = \int_0^t e^{-t}\, dt = 1 - e^{-t}, \qquad t \geq 0. \qquad \square \quad (8.5)$$

From the above results, we see that it is possible to obtain the zero-state response of a linear time-invariant network due to an input whose waveform is piecewise linear in time from our knowledge of the unit-step response. The first step in the analysis is to express the input function as a linear combination of steps and ramps with appropriate delays. Since ramps are integrals of steps, we have the input expressed as a linear combination of steps and integrals of steps with various delays. The output is obtained by an application of superposition, in terms of the known response to a unit step.

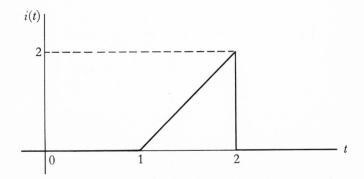

Figure 8.2 Pulse input for Example 8.1-3.

EXAMPLE 8.1-3.   Consider the triangular pulse of Figure 8.2. Suppose that for the network in Figure 8.1(a) the zero-state output due to a unit-step input $u(t)$ is $e^{-t}u(t)$. The problem is to determine the output due to the pulse input shown in Figure 8.2. The first step is to express the pulse $i(t)$ in terms of the step function. In this case, $i(t)$ is expressible as the linear combination of two delayed ramps and one delayed step:

$$i(t) = 2r(t-1) - 2r(t-2) - 2u(t-2). \qquad (8.6)$$

From linear time-invariance, we obtain the output as

$$v(t) = 2\int_0^t e^{-(\tau-1)}u(\tau-1)\ d\tau - 2\int_0^t e^{-(\tau-2)}u(\tau-2)\ d\tau - 2e^{-(t-2)}u(t-2). \ \square$$
$$(8.7)$$

● EXERCISES

8.1-1   Sketch the ramps and step of Equation 8.6 and graphically verify that the sum is the pulse of Figure 8.2. Sketch the components of the total response due to the individual terms in Equation 8.6 of Example 8.1-3.

8.1-2   Express the pulse of Figure Exercise 8.1-2 in terms of steps and ramps. Let $v(t)u(t)$ be the zero-state response of a linear time-invariant network due to a unit-step function input $u(t)$. Express the zero-state response of the same network due to the pulse input of Figure Exercise 8.1-2.

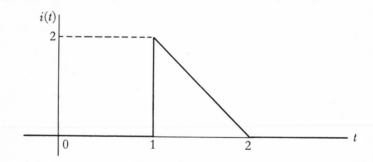

Figure Exercise 8.1-2

8.1-3   Repeat Exercise 8.1-2 if $v(t)u(t)$ is the zero-state response due to a unit impulse $\delta(t)$.

8.1-4   Determine the derivative of the pulse in Figure 8.2. You may have to use singularity functions.

8.1-5   Repeat Exercise 8.1-4 for the pulse in Figure Exercise 8.1-2.

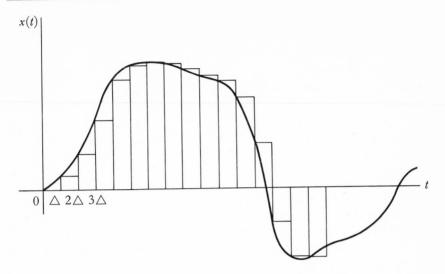

Figure 8.3 Staircase approximation of a continuous function.

8.2 The convolution integral

Consider a continuous function $x(t)$, which is 0 for $t < 0$, as the input to a linear time-invariant network. Let $s(t)$ denote the zero-state response due to a unit step $u(t)$ and let $h(t)$ denote the zero-state response due to a unit impulse $\delta(t)$. Suppose that we approximate $x(t)$ by a staircase function which is a sum of rectangular pulses as in Figure 8.3. The approximate $x(t)$ is designated by an asterisk superscript as

$$x^*(t) = \sum_{k=0}^{[t/\Delta]} x(k\Delta) \left[\frac{u(t - k\Delta) - u(t - k\Delta - \Delta)}{\Delta} \right] \Delta, \qquad (8.8)$$

where $[t/\Delta]$ denotes the largest integer closest in value to t/Δ. From the principle of linear time-invariance, the zero-state response to $x^*(t)$ is

$$y^*(t) = \sum_{k=0}^{[t/\Delta]} x(k\Delta) \left[\frac{s(t - k\Delta) - s(t - k\Delta - \Delta)}{\Delta} \right] \Delta. \qquad (8.9)$$

As Δ becomes arbitrarily small, it is convenient to change notation and denote $k\Delta$ by τ. As we pass to the limit, $\Delta \rightarrow d\tau$, we see that

$$\frac{u(t - k\Delta) - u(t - k\Delta - \Delta)}{\Delta} \Delta \rightarrow \delta(t - \tau) \, d\tau, \qquad (8.10)$$

$$\frac{s(t - k\Delta) - s(t - k\Delta - \Delta)}{\Delta} \rightarrow h(t - \tau), \qquad (8.11)$$

$$x*(t) \to \int_0^t x(\tau)\delta(t - \tau) \; d\tau = x(t), \tag{8.12}$$

and

$$y*(t) \to \int_0^t x(\tau)h(t - \tau) \; d\tau = y(t). \tag{8.13}$$

That is, the zero-state response of a linear time-invariant network due to an input $x(t)$ which starts at $t = 0$ and which is continuous is

$$y(t) = \int_0^t x(\tau)h(t - \tau) \; d\tau. \tag{8.14}$$

Equation 8.14 is known as the *convolution integral*. Few equations are of more importance in electrical engineering! If $x(t)$ is not continuous but if it is expressible as the sum of a continuous function $x_1(t)$ and a finite number of step functions, impulse functions, and possibly higher-order singularity functions, then we may write

$$x(t) = x_1(t) + \sum_{k=1}^{N_a} a_k u(t - \alpha_k) + \sum_{k=1}^{N_b} b_k \delta(t - \beta_k)$$

$$+ \sum_{k=1}^{N_c} c_k \delta'(t - \gamma_k) + \text{finite number of higher}$$
$$\text{order singularity functions.} \tag{8.15}$$

The singularity functions mentioned in the equation are the higher ordered derivatives of the step, impulse, etc. The zero-state response may be obtained by considering the terms in Equation 8.15 one at a time, if the network is linear.

We note that the impulse response function $h(t)$ is zero for $t < 0$ because it is the response of a physical network and there can be no zero-state response before the input is applied. To ensure that this fact is not overlooked, it may be helpful to write $h(t)$ as $h(t)u(t)$.

The response due to $x_1(t)$ is obtained by means of the convolution integral of Equation 8.14. The response due to the step functions may be obtained by integrating the impulse response with corresponding delay as in Section 8.1. Thus, the response due to $a_k u(t - \alpha_k) = x_2(t)$ is

$$a_k \int_0^t h(\tau - \alpha_k) \; d\tau = \begin{cases} \int_0^t a_k u(\tau - \alpha_k)h(\tau - \alpha_k) \; d\tau, \\ \\ 0, \quad \text{for} \quad t < \alpha_k, \\ \\ \int_{\alpha_k}^t a_k h(\tau - \alpha_k) \; d\tau, \quad \text{for} \quad t \geq \alpha_k. \end{cases} \tag{8.16}$$

By a substitution of variables, replace $\tau - \alpha_k$ by $t - \xi$, $d\tau = -d\xi$. Then we have

$$\int_{\alpha_k}^{t} a_k h(\tau - \alpha_k) \, d\tau = \int_{\alpha_k}^{t} a_k h(t - \xi) \, d\xi = \int_{0}^{t} a_k u(\xi - \alpha_k) h(t - \xi) \, d\xi$$

$$= \int_{0}^{t} a_k u(\tau - \alpha_k) h(t - \tau) \, d\tau. \tag{8.17}$$

Since $a_k u(t - \alpha_k)$ is $x_2(t)$, Equation 8.17 is really a convolution integral as in Equation 8.14, where $a_k u(\tau - \alpha_k) = x_2(\tau)$. Similarly, for a typical impulse component $b_k \delta(t - \beta_k) = x_3(t)$, the zero-state response is

$$b_k h(t - \beta_k) u(t - \beta_k) = \int_{0}^{t} b_k \delta(\tau - \beta_k) h(t - \tau) \, d\tau. \tag{8.18}$$

Again, since $x_3(t) = b_k \delta(t - \beta_k)$, Equation 8.18 is really a convolution integral as in Equation 8.14. In conclusion, if the input to a linear time-invariant network is a continuous function plus a finite number of higher ordered singularity functions, the zero-state response may be obtained by a convolution integral as in Equation 8.14. In Equation 8.14, the lower limit 0 is replaced by t_1 if the signal input starts at t_1 instead of 0. The upper limit t may be replaced by ∞ without changing the value of the integral if $h(t)$ corresponds to a physical network, because $h(t - \tau) = 0$, for $\tau > t$, so that the integral from t to ∞ is zero and no contribution is made to the integral.

The convolution integral of Equation 8.14 may be written in a different form by a change of variables. Let $\tau = t - \xi$ so that $d\tau = -d\xi$, and when $\tau = 0$, $\xi = t$, and when $\tau = t$, $\xi = 0$. Then we have

$$\int_{0}^{t} x(\tau) h(t - \tau) \, d\tau = -\int_{t}^{0} x(t - \xi) h(\xi) \, d\xi = \int_{0}^{t} x(t - \xi) h(\xi) \, d\xi. \tag{8.19}$$

Since ξ is a dummy variable in Equation 8.19, we may use τ, and so we obtain

$$\int_{0}^{t} x(\tau) h(t - \tau) \, d\tau = \int_{0}^{t} x(t - \tau) h(\tau) \, d\tau. \tag{8.20}$$

By the convolution of $x(t)$ and $h(t)$, where $x(t) = 0$ for $t < 0$ and $h(t) = 0$ for $t < 0$, we mean the integrations of Equation 8.20. Both forms yield the same answer, of course.

The convolution integral may be used to show that for a linear time-invariant system the zero-state response to an arbitrary input $x(t)$ may be obtained from a knowledge of the zero-state response due to a unit impulse $\delta(t)$ which is denoted by $h(t)$. By the time-invariance principle, the zero-state response to $\delta(t - \tau)$, where τ is a parameter, is $h(t - \tau)$. By linearity, we may scale the input by $x(\tau) \, d\tau$ and expect the response to be scaled by the same factor. Thus, an input $x(\tau)\delta(t-\tau)\,d\tau$ function of t will produce a zero-state response $x(\tau)h(t-\tau)\,d\tau$ which is a function of t. But the input function $x(t)$ may be resolved into a sum (or integral) of impulse functions as in Equation 8.12 or approximately as a sum of pulse functions as in Equation 8.8. Applying linearity once more, we then obtain the zero-state response by adding (integrating) the individual contributions $x(\tau)h(t-\tau)\,d\tau$ for various values of τ as in Equation 8.13. This is the essence of convolution.

EXAMPLE 8.2-1.   The unit impulse response of a linear time-invariant network is $h(t) = 1$ for $t \geq 0$ and $h(t) = 0$ for $t < 0$, that is, $h(t) = u(t)$. Let us compute the zero-state response of the network to an input pulse $x(t) = u(t) - u(t-1)$ which is a pulse of unit height and unit duration. From the convolution integral in Equation 8.14, we have for $t \geq 0$

$$y(t) = \int_0^t x(\tau)h(t-\tau)\,d\tau = \int_0^t [u(\tau) - u(\tau-1)]u(t-\tau)\,d\tau. \quad (8.21)$$

For t less than 1, the integrand is simply equal to 1 so that the integral is equal to t. For t greater than or equal to 1 the integrand is zero from $\tau = 1$ to $\tau = t$ and equal to 1 for $\tau < 1$. Hence, for $t \geq 1$,

$$y(t) = \left[\int_0^1 1 \cdot d\tau + \int_1^t 0 \cdot d\tau\right] = 1, \quad (8.22)$$

and the zero state response due to the pulse is

$$y(t) = \begin{array}{ll} t & \text{for} \quad 0 \leq t < 1, \\ 1 & \text{for} \quad t \geq 1, \\ 0 & \text{for} \quad t < 0. \end{array} \qquad \square \quad (8.23)$$

EXAMPLE 8.2-2.   The unit impulse response of a linear time-invariant network is $e^{-t}u(t)$. To be determined is the zero-state response to an input

$$x(t) = \delta(t) + \delta(t-1) + e^{-2t}u(t). \quad (8.24)$$

The zero-state response due to the individual terms in $x(t)$ may be determined first and then, by the principle of superposition, we may obtain the required zero-state response. The zero-state response due to an input $\delta(t)$ is $e^{-t}u(t)$ from the given data. By time-invariance, the zero-state response due to an input $\delta(t-1)$ is $e^{-(t-1)}u(t-1)$. The main problem that remains is the determination of the zero-state response due to $e^{-2t}u(t)$. From the convolution integral in Equation 8.14, we have

$$y(t) = \int_0^t e^{-2\tau}u(\tau)e^{-(t-\tau)}u(t-\tau)\,d\tau \quad (8.25)$$

for $t \geq 0$. Since $u(\tau)u(t-\tau) = 1$ for τ between 0 and t, we have

$$y(t) = \int_0^t e^{-t}e^{-\tau}d\tau = e^{-t}\left[-e^{-\tau}\Big|_0^t\right] \tag{8.26}$$

$$= e^{-t}(1 - e^{-t}) \qquad \text{for} \quad t \geq 0.$$

The zero-state response for $t < 0$ is, of course, zero so that we may multiply the response in Equation 8.26 by $u(t)$. The complete zero-state response due to the input $x(t)$ in Equation 8.24 is

$$y(t) = [e^{-t}u(t) + e^{-(t-1)}u(t-1) + e^{-t}(1 - e^{-t})u(t)]. \quad \square \tag{8.27}$$

● **EXERCISES**

8.2-1   The unit impulse response of a linear time-invariant network is $h(t) = e^{-t}$, $t \geq 0$, $h(t) = 0$, $t < 0$. Compute the zero-state response due to a unit-step input $x(t) = u(t)$ by the convolution of $h(t)$ and $x(t)$. Verify that the two forms of the convolution of $h(t)$ and $x(t)$ as given in Equation 8.20 yield the same answer.

8.2-2   Compute the convolution of $h(t)$ of Exercise 8.2-1 and $x(t) = u(t) - u(t-1)$.

8.2-3   Repeat Exercise 8.2-2 for $x(t)$ equal to the pulse $i(t)$ in Figure 8.2.

8.2-4   From the convolution integral in Equation 8.14, verify that a linear network is zero-state homogeneous and zero-state additive. (Review definitions of Section 7-1.)

8.2-5   For the unit impulse response of Exercise 8.2-1, compute the zero-state response for a sinusoidal input that is turned on at $t = 0$,

$$x(t) = [\sin t]u(t).$$

8.3   Graphical interpretation of convolution

The discussion of this section is centered on the convolution integral of Equation 8.14. From the given functions $x(t)$ and $h(t)$, which are assumed to be zero for $t < 0$, we form $x(\tau)$ and $h(t-\tau)$ as functions of τ for a specific value of t. Then we form the product $x(\tau)h(t - \tau)$. The area under the curve $x(\tau)h(t - \tau)$ plotted vs. τ from $\tau = 0$ to $\tau = t$ is the value of $y(t)$ for the chosen value of t. This may be carried out for every chosen value of t. Each of the steps we have mentioned above should be familiar to the reader. The only possible difficulty may be in the interpretation of $h(t-\tau)$ plotted vs. τ. From the conventional meaning of function notation, $h(t-\tau)$ is interpreted as the expression for $h(t)$, with t replaced by $t - \tau$. Let us investigate the graphical significance of this simple substitution of variables.

First recall that the plot of $h(\tau)$ vs. τ is exactly the same as the plot of $h(t)$ vs. t. For example, if $h(t)$ vs. t is as shown on Figure 8.4(a), then $h(\tau)$ vs. τ is as shown in Figure 8.4(b). Next form a function $g(\tau)$ which is ob-

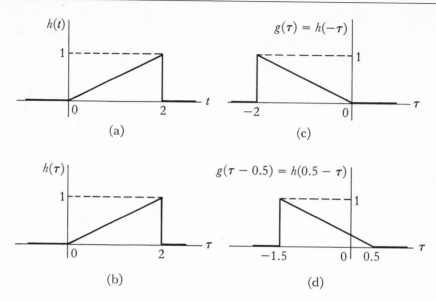

Figure 8.4 Illustration for forming $h(t-\tau)$ versus τ for $t = 0.5$ from $h(t)$ versus t.

tained from $h(\tau)$ by replacing τ by $-\tau$ so that $g(\tau) = h(-\tau)$. The plot of $g(\tau)$ vs. τ would be the mirror image about the vertical axis of the plot of $h(\tau)$ vs. τ. This is illustrated by Figure 8.4(c). Finally consider $g(\tau - t)$, where t is a positive constant. From Chapter 2 we recall that $g(\tau - t)$ vs. τ is a delayed version of $g(\tau)$ vs. τ, since t is a positive constant. This means that $g(\tau - t)$ is shifted to the right compared to $g(\tau)$. This is illustrated in Figure 8.4(d) for $t = 0.5$. Since $g(\tau) = h(-\tau)$, then $g(\tau - t) = h[-(\tau - t)] = h(t - \tau)$. Hence, given a plot of $h(t)$ vs. t, the plot of $h(t - \tau)$ vs. τ for a positive constant t is obtained by folding or reflecting the plot of $h(t)$ about the vertical axis, relabeling the abscissa by τ, and shifting to the right by an amount t, if t is positive.

From the given functions $x(t)$ and $h(t)$, convolution may be carried out graphically (or at least the mathematical operations may be visualized this way) for a specific value of t. Note that $x(\tau)h(t - \tau)$ vs. τ is the point-by-point product of $x(\tau)$ and $h(t - \tau)$ for various values of τ and a fixed value of t. Thus, if either $x(\tau)$ or $h(t - \tau)$ is zero for a value of τ, the product is zero for the same value of τ.

EXAMPLE 8.3-1. The convolution of $x(t)$ shown in Figure 8.5(a) and $h(t)$ shown in Figure 8.4(a) will be obtained. First note that for t negative, the product $x(\tau)h(t - \tau)$ is zero for all τ, so that the area under the curve is zero as expected. Next consider t to be some value between 0 and 1. Then, typically, $h(t - \tau)$ will be as shown in Figure 8.5(b). The product $x(\tau)h(t - \tau)$ is shown in Figure 8.5(c). The area under the curve between 0 and t is the value of the convolution integral for a specific value of t.

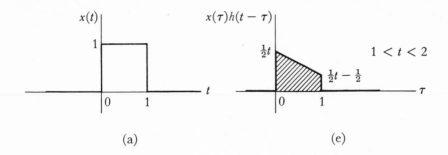

(a)   (e)

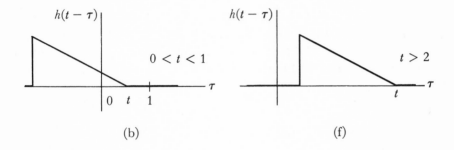

(b)   (f)

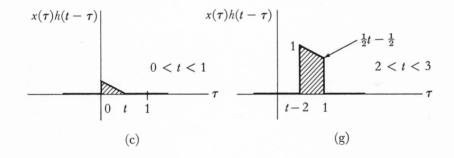

(c)   (g)

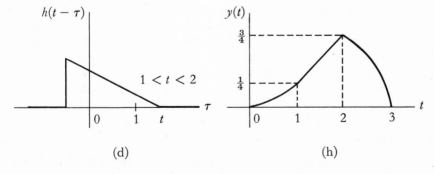

(d)   (h)

Figure 8.5 Illustration for graphical convolution.

This area is the hatched portion of Figure 8.5(c). Since the slope of the triangle is $-\frac{1}{2}$, the ordinate of $x(\tau)h(t-\tau)$ for $\tau = 0$ is $(\frac{1}{2})t$. Hence the area is $(\frac{1}{2})(\frac{1}{2})(t)t = \frac{1}{4}t^2$. This means that for t between 0 and 1, as the value of t increases, the value of the convolution integral increases as the square of t. Thus we have

$$y(t) = \int_0^t x(\tau)h(t-\tau)\,d\tau = \frac{1}{4}t^2, \qquad \text{for} \quad 0 \le t \le 1. \qquad (8.28)$$

For t between 1 and 2, a typical plot of $h(t-\tau)$ is shown in Figure 8.5(d) and the product $x(\tau)h(t-\tau)$ is shown in Figure 8.5(e). The value of the integral is the area under the curve

$$y(t) = \tfrac{1}{2}[\tfrac{1}{2}t + (\tfrac{1}{2}t - \tfrac{1}{2})] \times 1 = \tfrac{1}{2}t - \tfrac{1}{4}, \qquad \text{for} \quad 1 \le t \le 2. \quad (8.29)$$

Thus for t between 1 and 2, $y(t)$ increases linearly with t. For $t > 2$, $h(t-\tau)$ is shown in Figure 8.5(f). The product $x(\tau)h(t-\tau)$ for $2 < t < 3$ is shown in Figure 8.5(g). The area under the curve is

$$y(t) = \tfrac{1}{2}[1 + (\tfrac{1}{2}t - \tfrac{1}{2})] \times [1 - (t-2)] = \tfrac{1}{4}(t+1)(3-t), \qquad \text{for} \quad 2 \le t \le 3, \tag{8.30}$$

which decreases parabolically with t until it reaches zero for $t = 3$. For $t > 3$, the product $x(\tau)h(t-\tau)$ is zero, so that the area under the curve is zero. The convolution $y(t)$ is plotted vs. t in Figure 8.5(g). $\qquad \square$

● EXERCISES

8.3-1   For $h(t)$ and $x(t)$ of Exercise 8.2-1, prepare a sequence of plots for the graphical determination of $y(1)$. Verify that the same value $y(1)$ is obtained regardless of whether $h(t)$ or $x(t)$ is folded and shifted.

8.3-2   Obtain the convolution of the pulse in Figure Exercise 8.1-2 and the rectangular pulse in Figure 8.5(a) with the aid of a sequence of appropriate plots.

8.3-3   Obtain the convolution of the pulse in Figure 8.5(a) with itself, and plot $y(t)$ vs. t.

8.3-4   Verify that for $t > 0$, $h(t-\tau)$ may be obtained from $h(t)$ by relabeling abscissa, shifting to the left by an amount t, and then folding with respect to the vertical axis. Give a series of equations to support your answer.

8.3-5   Repeat Exercise 8.3-3 for the pulse in Figure 8.2.

8.3-6   Prepare a sequence of sketches for the graphical determination of the convolution in Example 8.2-1.

8.4 Impulse response from differential equations

Suppose that in analyzing a linear time-invariant network the following differential equation is obtained:

$$a_n \frac{d^n y}{dt^n} + a_{n-1} \frac{d^{n-1} y}{dt^{n-1}} + \cdots + a_0 y = b_m \frac{d^m x}{dt^m} + b_{m-1} \frac{d^{m-1} x}{dt^{m-1}} + \cdots + b_0 x, \qquad (8.31)$$

where y is the output or response-time function which may be voltage or current and $x(t)$ is the input or excitation-time function which is again either voltage or current. The zero-input response was treated in the previous chapter. In the previous section, it was demonstrated that the zero-state response can be obtained by convolution which involves the unit-impulse response $h(t)$. Then, by the decomposition property of linear systems, we can add the zero-state response to the zero-input response to obtain the complete response. The remaining question is how one obtains the unit-impulse response. This will be obtained by first considering the zero-state response for the modified equation

$$a_n \frac{d^n y}{dt^n} + a_{n-1} \frac{d^{n-1} y}{dt^{n-1}} + \cdots + a_0 y = x = u(t). \qquad (8.32)$$

If the solution to Equation 8.32 is available, then by applying the results of Section 8.1, the solution to Equation 8.31 for $x(t) = \delta(t)$ is obtained immediately. Thus, if $y_0(t)$ is the solution of Equation 8.32, then $y_1(t) = dy_0(t)/dt$ is the solution of Equation 8.32 with $u(t)$ replaced by $\delta(t)$. The solution of Equation 8.31 for $x = \delta(t)$, in terms of $y_1(t)$, is

$$h(t) = b_m \frac{d^m}{dt^m} y_1(t) + b_{m-1} \frac{d^{m-1}}{dt^{m-1}} y_1(t) + \cdots + b_0 y_1(t) \qquad (8.33)$$

from linear time-invariance, as developed in Section 8.1. The crux of the problem then is the solution of Equation 8.32.

Since we are dealing with physical networks, the zero-state response to $u(t)$ for $t < 0$ is zero. For $t \geq 0$, we may replace $u(t)$ by 1. Also, since the zero-state response is sought, we set all initial conditions to zero. So we wish to solve

$$a_n \frac{d^n y}{dt^n} + \cdots + a_0 y = 1, \qquad \text{for} \quad t \geq 0, \qquad (8.34)$$

and

$$y(0) = 0, \qquad y'(0) = 0, \ldots, y^{(n-1)}(0) = 0, \qquad y(t) = 0, \qquad t < 0.$$

From the previous chapter, we recall that $y_c(t)$, the complementary solution, is the solution of the homogeneous part of a differential equation containing n arbitrary constants. Let $y_c(t)$ denote the complementary solution of Equation 8.34. Suppose $a_0 \neq 0$. Then $y = 1/a_0 = $ constant satisfies Equation 8.34. Furthermore, $y = 1/a_0 + y_c$ also satisfies Equation 8.34. Although $y = 1/a_0$ may not satisfy all the initial conditions, $y = 1/a_0 + y_c$ contains n arbitrary constants. This makes it possible to choose the n constants so that the n initial conditions are satisfied. From the uniqueness property of the solution, the function thus obtained is the unique solution satisfying Equation 8.34 and zero initial conditions.

EXAMPLE 8.4-1.   Consider the equation

$$\frac{d^2y}{dt^2} + 3\frac{dy}{dt} + 2y = 1. \tag{8.35}$$

Then $y = \frac{1}{2}$ satisfies Equation 8.35 and so does

$$y = \frac{1}{2} + c_1 e^{-2t} + c_2 e^{-t}. \tag{8.36}$$

We choose c_1 and c_2 so that $y(0) = 0$ and $y'(0) = 0$. Then we have

$$\left. \begin{array}{l} y(0) = \frac{1}{2} + c_1 + c_2 = 0 \\ y'(0) = -2c_1 - c_2 = 0 \end{array} \right\}, \text{ so that } c_1 = \frac{1}{2} \text{ and } c_2 = -1. \tag{8.37}$$

Hence

$$y(t) = \frac{1}{2} + \frac{1}{2} e^{-2t} - e^{-t} \tag{8.38}$$

satisfies Equation 8.36 and $y(0) = 0$, and $y'(0) = 0$.   □

Suppose that in Equation 8.34, $a_0 = 0$ but $a_1 \neq 0$. Then it is readily verified that $y = (1/a_1)t$ satisfies Equation 8.34 and so does $y = (1/a_1)t + y_c$. The constants in the y_c component are evaluated to satisfy the initial conditions as before.

EXAMPLE 8.4-2.   For the equation

$$\frac{d^2y}{dt^2} + 3\frac{dy}{dt} = 1, \tag{8.39}$$

$y = (\frac{1}{3})t$ is a solution. So is

$$y = \frac{1}{3}t + c_1 + c_2 e^{-3t}. \tag{8.40}$$

Then c_1 and c_2 are chosen so that $y(0) = 0$, $y'(0) = 0$:

$$\left. \begin{array}{l} y(0) = c_1 + c_2 = 0 \\ y'(0) = \frac{1}{3} - 3c^2 = 0 \end{array} \right\}. \text{ Thus, } c_1 = -\frac{1}{9} \text{ and } c_2 = \frac{1}{9};$$

and

$$y = \frac{1}{3}t - \frac{1}{9} + \frac{1}{9}e^{-3t} \tag{8.41}$$

satisfies Equation 8.39 as well as $y(0) = 0$ and $y'(0) = 0$.   □

In general, if the lowest-order derivative that is present in Equation 8.34 is the kth, then the solution is of the form

$$y = \frac{t^k}{k! \, a_k} + y_c, \tag{8.42}$$

and the constants in the complementary function y_c are evaluated so that the initial conditions $y(0), y'(0), \ldots, y^{(n-1)}(0)$ are all zero (see Exercise 8.4-5). Once the solution of Equation 8.34 (which satisfies the initial conditions) is obtained, then its derivative is the solution of

$$a_n \frac{d^n y}{dt^n} + \cdots + a_0 y = \delta(t), \qquad t \geq 0, \tag{8.43}$$

where $y(0) = 0, y'(0), \ldots, y^{(n-1)}(0) = 0$. By the technique discussed in Section 8.1, the impulse response $h(t)$ for the network described by Equation 8.31 is obtained by means of Equation 8.33.

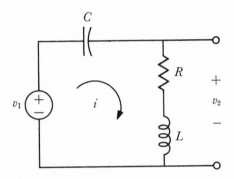

Figure 8.6   Network for Example 8.4-3.

EXAMPLE 8.4-3. For the network in Figure 8.6 where R, L, and C are constants, and initial conditions are assumed to be zero, we see that KVL around the loop yields

$$\frac{1}{C} \int_0^t i(\tau) \, d\tau + Ri(t) + L \frac{di}{dt}(t) = v_1(t) \tag{8.44}$$

or

$$\frac{1}{C} i(t) + R \frac{di}{dt}(t) + L \frac{d^2 i}{dt^2}(t) = \frac{dv_1}{dt}(t). \tag{8.45}$$

Suppose that the output is $v_2(t)$, where

$$v_2(t) = Ri(t) + L \frac{di}{dt}(t). \tag{8.46}$$

We may eliminate i from Equations 8.45 and 8.46 to obtain a differential equation in v_2. Differentiate Equation 8.45 and multiply by L/R to obtain

$$\frac{L}{RC} \frac{di}{dt} + L \frac{d^2 i}{dt^2} + \frac{L^2}{R} \frac{d^3 i}{dt^3} = \frac{L}{R} \frac{d^2 v_1}{dt^2}. \tag{8.47}$$

Now add Equations 8.45 and 8.47. Thus we obtain

$$\frac{1}{RC}\left(Ri + L\frac{di}{dt}\right) + \frac{d}{dt}\left(Ri + L\frac{di}{dt}\right) + \frac{L}{R}\frac{d^2}{dt^2}\left(Ri + L\frac{di}{dt}\right)$$

$$= \frac{L}{R}\frac{d^2v_1}{dt^2} + \frac{dv_1}{dt} \quad (8.48)$$

or

$$\frac{L}{R}\frac{d^2v_2}{dt^2} + \frac{dv_2}{dt} + \frac{1}{RC}v_2 = \frac{L}{R}\frac{d^2v_1}{dt^2} + \frac{dv_1}{dt}. \quad (8.49)$$

Since initial conditions are zero, $v_2(0)$ and $v_2'(0)$ are zero.

Now let us compute the impulse response for a given set of values for L/R and $1/RC$. Suppose $L/R = 1$ and $1/RC = 1$. Then the characteristic equation corresponding to the homogeneous differential equation is $m^2 + m + 1 = 0$, with roots $m_1 = -\frac{1}{2} + j(\sqrt{3}/2)$ and $m_2 = -\frac{1}{2} - j(\sqrt{3}/2)$. Then the solution of

$$\frac{d^2v_2}{dt^2} + \frac{dv_2}{dt} + v_2 = u(t), \quad (8.50)$$

$v_2(0) = 0$, and $v_2'(0) = 0$, is

$$v_2 = 1 + c_1e^{[-(1/2) + j(\sqrt{3}/2)]t} + c_2e^{[-(1/2) - j(\sqrt{3}/2)]t}, \quad t \geq 0,$$
$$v_2 = 0, \quad \text{for} \quad t < 0. \quad (8.51)$$

Matching initial conditions, we have

$$\left. \begin{array}{l} v_2(0) = 0 = 1 + c_1 + c_2 \\[2ex] v_2'(0) = 0 = \left(-\frac{1}{2} + j\frac{\sqrt{3}}{2}\right)c_1 + \left(-\frac{1}{2} - j\frac{\sqrt{3}}{2}\right)c_2 \end{array} \right\} . \text{ So} \quad \begin{array}{l} c_1 = -\frac{1}{2} + j\frac{1}{2\sqrt{3}}, \\[2ex] c_2 = -\frac{1}{2} - j\frac{1}{2\sqrt{3}}. \end{array} \quad (8.52)$$

Hence, after some simplification the solution for Equation 8.50 may be written as

$$v_2(t) = \left[1 + \frac{2e^{-(1/2)t}}{\sqrt{3}} \cos\left(\frac{\sqrt{3}}{2}t + \frac{5\pi}{6}\right)\right]u(t). \quad (8.53)$$

Note that $v_2(0+) = 0$. So the derivative of $v_2(t)$ in Equation 8.53 is

$$\frac{dv_2}{dt} = \left[\frac{2}{\sqrt{3}}e^{-(1/2)t}\cos\left(\frac{\sqrt{3}}{2}t + \frac{5\pi}{6}\right) - e^{-(1/2)t}\sin\left(\frac{\sqrt{3}}{2}t + \frac{5\pi}{6}\right)\right]u(t)$$

$$\quad (8.54)$$

$$= \left[-\frac{2}{\sqrt{3}}\sin\left(\frac{\sqrt{3}}{2}t\right)\right]u(t).$$

Again, note that $dv_2/dt(0+) = 0$. The impulse response for the original network with $L/R = 1$, $1/RC = 1$ is obtained by applying the procedure of Equation 8.33. Thus we have

$$h(t) = \frac{d^2 y_1}{dt^2} + \frac{dy_1}{dt},$$ (8.55)

where

$$y_1(t) = \left[\frac{2}{\sqrt{3}} e^{-(1/2)t} \sin \frac{\sqrt{3}}{2} t \right] u(t).$$ (8.56)

Since $y_1(0+) = 0$, we have

$$\frac{dy_1}{dt} = \left[-\frac{1}{\sqrt{3}} e^{-(1/2)t} \sin \frac{\sqrt{3}}{2} t + e^{-(1/2)t} \cos \frac{\sqrt{3}}{2} t \right] u(t).$$ (8.57)

Since $y_1'(0+) = 1$ but $y_1'(0-) = 0$, $y_1(t)$ has a jump discontinuity at $t = 0$ which is of height equal to one, and

$$\frac{d^2 y_1}{dt^2} = \delta(t) + \left[\frac{1}{2\sqrt{3}} e^{-(1/2)t} \sin \frac{\sqrt{3}}{2} t \right.$$

$$-\frac{1}{2} e^{-(1/2)t} \cos \frac{\sqrt{3}}{2} t$$

$$-\frac{1}{2} e^{-(1/2)t} \cos \frac{\sqrt{3}}{2} t$$

$$\left. -\frac{\sqrt{3}}{2} e^{-(1/2)t} \sin \frac{\sqrt{3}}{2} t \right] u(t)$$

$$= \left[-e^{-(1/2)t} \cos \frac{\sqrt{3}}{2} t \right.$$

$$\left. -\frac{1}{\sqrt{3}} e^{-(1/2)t} \sin \frac{\sqrt{3}}{2} t \right] u(t).$$ (8.58)

Hence we obtain

$$h(t) = \delta(t) - \left[\frac{2}{\sqrt{3}} e^{-(1/2)t} \sin \frac{\sqrt{3}}{2} t \right] u(t).$$ (8.59)

The $\delta(t)$ component is due to a jump discontinuity of 1 at $t = 0$ for $dy_1(t)/dt$. □

In problems where initial conditions are given at an initial instant t_1 (such as $t_1 = 0$) and inputs applied at t_1, it is sometimes convenient to compute the response and the derivatives of the response at an instant just after $t = t_1$ (that is $t = t_1+$). The quantities $y(t_1+)$, $y'(t_1+)$, ..., $y^{(n-1)}(t_1+)$ are computed. These numbers are then considered to be the initial conditions at $t = t_1+$. The impulse response that is necessary for the computation of the zero-state response is then obtained for $t > t_1$ (excluding $t = t_1$).

Thus, in the above example, the impulse response $h(t)$ will not contain an impulse for $t > 0$. However, in this case, it is necessary to compute the new initial conditions at $t = 0+$.

In this section, we have discussed one procedure for obtaining the impulse response for a linear time-invariant system. The convolution of the impulse response with a given input (starting at t_1) yields the zero-state response for $t \geqslant t_1$. In Chapter 7 we discussed how one may obtain the zero-input response for $t \geqslant t_1$ for initial conditions specified at t_1. For a linear system, the complete response is given by the sum of the zero-input response and the zero-state response.

● EXERCISES

8.4-1   For the linear time-invariant network in Figure Exercise 8.4-1 where v is the input, obtain the impulse response if v_{23} is the output.

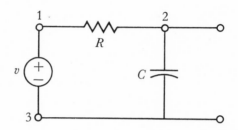

Figure Exercise 8.4-1

8.4-2   Repeat Exercise 8.4-1 for v_{12} as the output.
8.4-3   A linear time-invariant system is represented by the differential equation

$$\frac{d^2y(t)}{dt^2} + 2\frac{dy(t)}{dt} + y(t) = \frac{dx(t)}{dt} + 3x(t),$$

where $y(t)$ is the output and $x(t)$ is the input. Determine the impulse response of the system.

8.4-4   Repeat Exercise 8.4-3 if the differential equation is

$$\frac{d^3y(t)}{dt^3} + 4\frac{d^2y(t)}{dt^2} = \frac{dx(t)}{dt} + 2x(t).$$

8.4-5   Verify that the function y in Equation 8.42 satisfies the differential equation in Equation 8.34 if $a_k \neq 0$ and $a_{k-1} = a_{k-2} = \cdots = a_0 = 0$.
8.4-6   For the problem in Example 8.4-3, verify that if the values of c_1 and c_2 as obtained in Equation 8.52 are substituted in the expression for v in Equation 8.51, then the resulting expression for v may be simplified into that given in Equation 8.53.

8.5　Exponential resolution of signals

In this section, we discuss another implication of linearity which also serves as a bridge to the topics of Chapter 9. In past chapters, we have frequently encountered signals having the form e^{st} where s was real, imaginary, or complex. Now it turns out that many signals of importance may be expressed as sums of signals of this form. The most familiar one is the cosine function which may be expressed as one half of the sum of $e^{j\omega t}$ and $e^{-j\omega t}$. We call the procedure of writing signals in this form the exponential resolution of signals.

Once the signal is resolved into the sum of exponentials, the total response may be found by summing the responses due to the individual exponentials using the principle of superposition. An input, $x(t)$, containing terms like e^{-t}, e^{j2t}, etc. may be written in the general form

$$x(t) = \sum_{k=1}^{n} C_k e^{s_k t}. \tag{8.60}$$

The response due to each term in this equation is $y(t, s)$. The sum of all such zero-state responses due to $x(t)$ is

$$y(t) = \sum_{k=1}^{n} C_k y(t, s_k). \tag{8.61}$$

While these two equations appear to be formidable and complicated, the actual process turns out to be very simple indeed, as we shall show.

Consider a linear network described by a differential equation of the form of Equation 8.31. In Equation 8.31, suppose that $x(t) = e^{st}$, where s is an arbitrary number which may be complex. Of course, if s is complex, so is e^{st}, and $x(t)$ is not a physically realizable input for the network. Nevertheless, it is mathematically expedient to consider e^{st} as the excitation in the differential equation. In the actual network, we may easily obtain the response due to the real part of e^{st} as the real part of the response due to the complex input e^{st} by virtue of the superposition principle. From the right-hand side of Equation 8.31, the substitution of $x(t) = e^{st}$ yields

$$\sum_{i=0}^{m} b_i \frac{d^i}{dt^i} x(t) = \sum_{i=0}^{m} b_i s^i e^{st}, \tag{8.62}$$

which is just e^{st} times a scale factor that does not depend on t. Noting this fact, we decide that $y = A e^{st}$, where A does not depend on t, is a likely candidate for a solution. Substituting $y = A e^{st}$ for the left-hand side, we have

$$\sum_{i=1}^{n} a_i \frac{d^i}{dt^i} y(t) = \sum_{i=1}^{n} a_i s^i A e^{st}. \tag{8.63}$$

Provided that

$$\sum_{i=1}^{n} a_i s^i \neq 0, \tag{8.64}$$

that is, provided that s is not equal to a characteristic root, then

$$y = \frac{\sum_{i=1}^{m} b_i s^i}{\sum_{i=1}^{n} a_i s^i} e^{st} \tag{8.65}$$

will satisfy Equation 8.31 for $x = e^{st}$, and it is called a *particular integral.*

EXAMPLE 8.5-1.   Suppose that in Example 8.4-3, $L/R = 1$ and $1/RC = 1$. Let $v_1 = e^{-2t}$. Then

$$v_2(t) = \frac{(-2)^2 + (-2)}{(-2)^2 + (-2) + 1} e^{-2t} = \frac{2}{3} e^{-2t} \tag{8.66}$$

satisfies Equation 8.49.   □

If the complementary solution y_c is added to the particular integral $y = Ae^{st}$, the sum will still satisfy Equation 8.31. The constants in y_c may be chosen so as to satisfy the zero initial conditions, thus obtaining the zero-state response.

EXAMPLE 8.5-2.   For the above example, a particular solution for $x = e^{st}$ is

$$v_2(t) = \frac{s^2 + s}{s^2 + s + 1} e^{st}. \tag{8.67}$$

From this, we may obtain the particular solution for $x = \cos \omega t$, since

$$\cos \omega t = \frac{e^{j\omega t} + e^{-j\omega t}}{2}. \tag{8.68}$$

By superposition, the corresponding particular solution for $x = \cos \omega t$ is

$$y(t) = \frac{1}{2}\left[\frac{(j\omega)^2 + (j\omega)}{(j\omega)^2 + (j\omega) + 1} e^{j\omega t} + \frac{(-j\omega)^2 + (-j\omega)}{(-j\omega)^2 + (-j\omega) + 1} e^{-j\omega t} \right]. \tag{8.69}$$

We note that the second term is simply the complex conjugate of the first, so that the sum is just twice the real part of the first. Hence we have

$$y(t) = Re\left[\frac{(j\omega)^2 + (j\omega)}{(j\omega)^2 + (j\omega) + 1} e^{j\omega t} \right]. \tag{8.70}$$

It is convenient to express the complex coefficient of $e^{j\omega t}$ in Equation 8.70

in exponential form:

$$\frac{(j\omega)^2 + (j\omega)}{(j\omega)^2 + (j\omega) + 1} = Ae^{j\theta}, \tag{8.71}$$

where A is the magnitude and θ is the phase angle. The details for computing A and θ are developed in Chapter 9. Both A and θ depend on the parameter ω. In terms of A and θ, Equation 8.70 may be written as

$$y(t) = Re[Ae^{j(\omega t + \theta)}] = A\cos(\omega t + \theta). \tag{8.72}$$

For this example, we see that the particular solution for $\cos \omega t = Re\{e^{j\omega t}\}$ is equal to the real part of the solution for $e^{j\omega t}$.   □

● EXERCISES

8.5-1   For the network of Example 8.5-1, obtain $v_2(t)$ when $v_1 = e^{-2t}u(t)$, $v_2(0+) = 1$, $v_2'(0+) = -2$.

8.5-2   For the network in Figure 8.6, let v_3 be the voltage across the capacitor. Assign a plus reference on the left-hand side terminal of C, and write the differential equation for v_3 in terms of v_1. For $v_1 = e^{st}$, obtain v_3 which satisfies the differential equation. Assume that s does not equal any of the characteristic roots.

8.5-3   Suppose that in Figure 8.6, $v_c(0-) = 0$ and $i(0-) = 0$. In Equation 8.44, the lower limit in the integral is understood to be 0−. By taking $t = 0+$, verify that $v_2(0+) = v_1(0+)$. Differentiate Equation 8.44 once and verify that $v_2'(0+) = v_1'(0+)$. Verify that for the $v_2(0+)$ and $v_2'(0+)$ given in Exercise 8.5-1, C and L have zero initial voltage and current, respectively.

8.5-4   Consider the differential equation in Equation 8.31. Denote the polynomial $b_m s^m + b_{m-1} s^{m-1} + \cdots + b_0$ by $P(s)$ and the polynomial $a_n s^n + a_{n-1} s^{n-1} + \cdots + a_0$ by $Q(s)$. Assume that none of the characteristic roots is pure imaginary. Suppose that $x(t)$ is periodic and it has a series representation

$$x(t) = \sum_{n=-\infty}^{\infty} C_n e^{jn\omega_0 t},$$

where C_n's are complex numbers and ω_0 is the fundamental angular frequency. Determine a $y(t)$ which satisfies Equation 8.31 for $x(t)$ given as above. Since $x(t)$ is real, the numbers C_n and C_{-n} are complex conjugates.

Problems

8-1   The signal $v_{\text{in}}(t)$ is applied to the RC network of Figure 8.1(a). The time constant of the network is 1 millisecond. Using superposition,

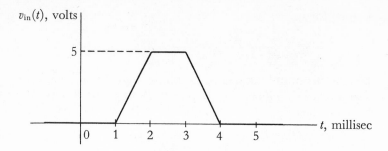

Figure Problem 8-1

determine the output $v_0(t)$. [*Hint:* Express $v_{in}(t)$ as a combination of step and ramp functions.] The capacitor is initially uncharged.

8-2   For the network in Figure Problem 8-2, if $R_1 = 100$ ohms, $R_2 = 300$ ohms, and $C = 10\mu F$, determine $i_2(t)$ for $v_1(t) = v_2(t) = u(t)$, a unit step voltage. Assume that $v_c(0) = 0$.

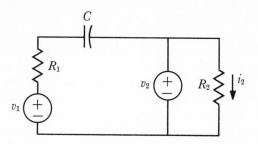

Figure Problem 8-2

8-3   Repeat Problem 8-2 for $v_1(t)$ and $v_2(t)$ as shown in the figure.

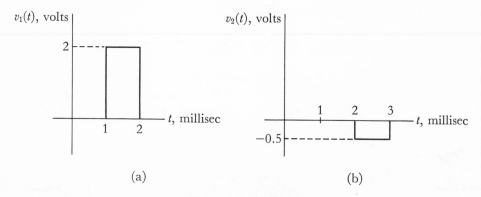

Figure Problem 8-3

8-4 What is the power delivered by each of the batteries? How does this compare with the sum of the powers delivered by each battery when the other one is turned off? Explain.

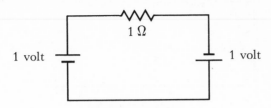

Figure Problem 8-4

8-5 Suppose that in the network of Figure Problem 8-2, v_2 is a controlled source $v_2 = R i_2$, where R is a constant. Assuming $v_1(t) = e^{st}$, determine the current through R_1. Assume that s is not a characteristic root.

8-6 In Figure Problem 8-6, suppose v_1 is a controlled source $v_1 = A v_2$, where A is a constant. Assuming $i_2(t) = e^{st}$, find the voltage across the current source that satisfies the differential equations of the network.

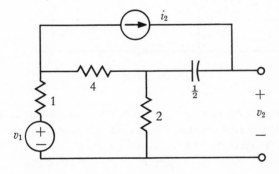

Figure Problem 8-6

8-7 In the network of Figure Problem 8-2, suppose $v_1(t) = \sin t$ and $i_2(t) = 2 \sin t$. Determine $v_2(t)$ with numerical values for A and θ in $v_2(t) = A \sin (t + \theta)$, which satisfies the network differential equations.

8-8 Using superposition, find the voltage v_2 across the 1-ohm resistor in the network given in the figure.

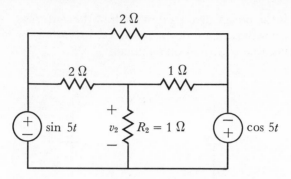

Figure Problem 8-8

8-9   In the network of the figure, it is given that $v_1(t) = 10 \sin t$ and
$i_2(t) = \sin (t + \pi/2)$. We wish to connect a sinusoidal current source
across *ab* such that the voltage there is zero. If this is possible, find
the equation of the current source and indicate the reference direction you assumed. If it is not possible, explain why not.

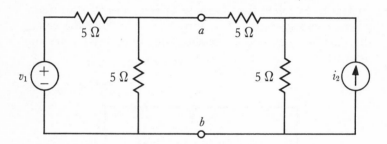

Figure Problem 8-9

8-10   In Figure Problem 8-9, suppose that v_1 and i_2 are related by $v_1 = Ri_2$,
where R is a real constant. For what constant R is $v_{ab} \equiv 0$? The voltage v_1, is arbitrary but not equal to zero.

8-11   In the network of the figure $R_1 = R_2 = 1000$ ohms, $C = 100 \; \mu\text{F}$, $v(t)$
is a step function $100 \, u(t)$, and the initial voltage V_0 on the capacitor
is 50 volts. Determine the voltage across the capacitor as a function
of time.

8-12   Repeat Problem 8-11 with $v(t)$ equal to a pulse as shown in the
figure.

8-13   For a unit-step input of current to the network of the figure, the
response voltage is $v(t) = (1 - e^{-t})u(t)$. Find the response voltage
for the same network but with the triangular pulse input shown
in (b) of the figure.

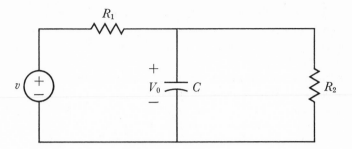

Figure Problem 8-11

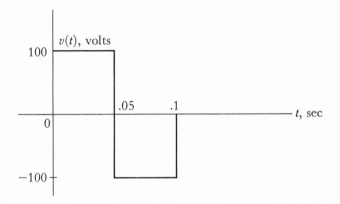

Figure Problem 8-12

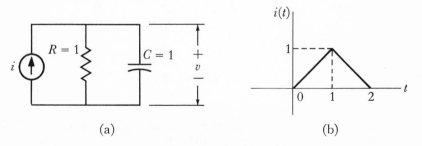

Figure Problem 8-13

8-14   The network shown is excited by a voltage source having a waveform described by the equation $v_s(t) = V_1 \sin(\omega t + \phi)u(t)$. The
current in the network, $i(t)$, contains a term of the general form
$i_t(t) = K_1 e^{-\alpha t}$ which will be identified as the transient current term.
Assume that C is initially uncharged and that there is no initial current in L. (a) With the switch in position a, determine the value of ϕ
that will cause the transient current term to vanish. (b) Repeat part
(a) but with the switch in position b.

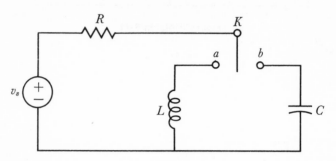

Figure Problem 8-14

8-15   The network in Figure Problem 8-15 contains a switch K which is
moved from a to b instantaneously at $t = 0$. Find $v_2(t)$ that results
using numerical values where possible. Assume that the switch was
in position a for a long time and that the initial current in the 2H
inductor is zero.

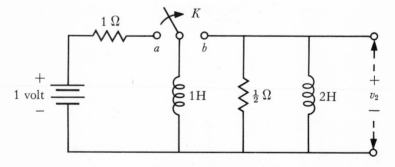

Figure Problem 8-15

8-16   The voltage source in the network of Figure Problem 8-16 is
$v_s(t) = e^{-\alpha t}u(t)$. Find $v_2(t)$ if $v_2(0) = 0$.

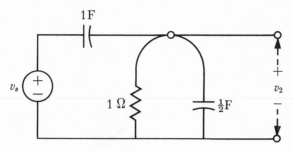

1F

v_s $+$ $-$

$1\ \Omega$

$\frac{1}{2}$F

v_2

Figure Problem 8-16

8-17 Repeat Problem 8-16 if $v_s(t)$ is as given, but $v_2(0) = 1$ volt.

8-18 For the network of Figure Problem 8-6, (a) determine the impulse response v_2 due to v_1 (b) determine the impulse response v_2 due to i_2.

8-19 (a) Determine the impulse response of the network in Figure Problem 8-13. (b) Determine the zero-state response due to the triangular pulse, by convolution.

8-20 Determine and sketch the convolution of the two pulses in Figure Problem 8-3.

8-21 Determine the impulse response of the network in Figure Problem 8-16.

8-22 (a) Determine the impulse response of the network in Figure Problem 8-13. (b) From (a), determine the zero-state response due to $i(t) = e^{-2t}u(t)$, by convolution. (c) Verify the answer in (b) by finding a function $v = Ae^{-2t}$ which satisfies the network differential equation for $i = e^{-2t}$ and then adding the complementary function. The constants must be determined to satisfy initial conditions.

8-23 In Equation 8.31, suppose $x = e^{s_1 t}$, where s_1 is a simple (not multiple) characteristic root. Let

$$Q(s) = \sum_{i=1}^{n} a_i s^i \qquad \text{and} \qquad P(s) = \sum_{i=1}^{m} b_i s^i.$$

Show that

$$y = \frac{P(s_1)}{Q'(s_1)} te^{s_1 t}$$

satisfies Equation 8.31 where $Q'(s)$ is the derivative of $Q(s)$, for $n = 2$, $m = 2$.

8-24 Repeat Problem 8-23 for a general n and a general m.

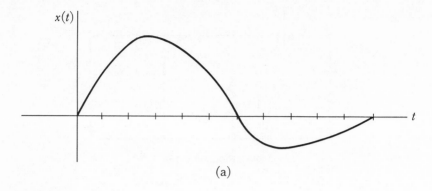

(a)

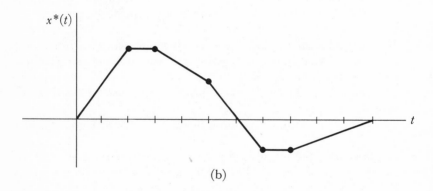

(b)

8-25   The following approximation for convolution was suggested by
E. A. Guillemin:† To find the convolution of $x(t)$ and $h(t)$, approximate $x(t)$ by $x^*(t)$ which consists of straight line segments joined together (piecewise linear approximation). The derivative of $x^*(t)$
consists of a staircase curve and the second derivative of $x^*(t)$ is a
train of impulses of various delays and various areas. The response
to $x''^*(t)$ is simply obtained. Then by linear time-invariance, the
response due to $x^*(t)$ is obtained by a double integration of the
response to $x''^*(t)$. Suppose we choose n points on the curve of
$x(t)$, t_1, t_2, . . . , t_n and suppose $x^*(t)$ is obtained by joining the
points $x(t_1)$, $x(t_2)$, . . . , $x(t_n)$ by straight lines. Find a formula for
the response to $x^*(t)$ if the impulse response is denoted by $h(t)$.

† E. A. Guillemin, *Theory of Linear Physical Systems* (New York: John Wiley and Sons, Inc.,
1963), 390.

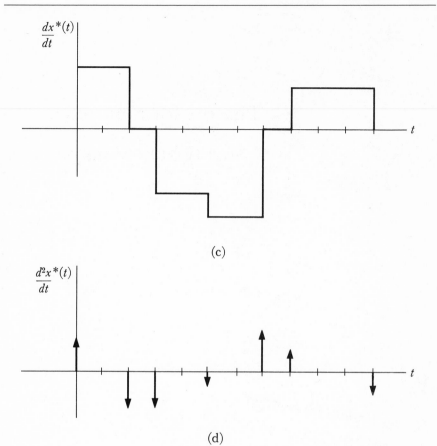

(c)

(d)

Figure Problem 8-25

Phasors for Sinusoidal

Steady-State Analysis   **9**

For the simple networks we studied in the previous chapter, the assumption of linear time-invariant models for the network elements leads to ordinary linear differential equations with constant coefficients. This type of equation will also be obtained for more complicated networks if the elements are assumed to be linear and time-invariant. The choice of linear time-invariant models is a simplifying one. The resulting mathematical problem is a few orders of magnitude simpler than that for time-varying or nonlinear models in most cases. Fortunately, for many purposes, the simple models yield sufficiently accurate results. Most of the methods of analysis in this book are slanted towards solving linear network problems.

We have already encountered the sinusoidal signal to some extent in Chapter 2. We now study useful methods of analyzing the behavior of linear time-invariant networks with sinusoidal excitations or input signals. In particular, only the *steady-state* behavior will be considered. By sinusoidal steady-state, we shall mean that we are considering network behavior *after* the sinusoidal excitations have been applied for arbitrarily large durations in the past. We consider only the class of networks for which the complementary solution y_c eventually approaches zero. We shall also restrict the frequencies of the sinusoidal sources to be identical for simplicity. At this point, we reiterate the reasons, of which there are several, for devoting considerable time to the study of very special input signals under very special conditions. First, many signal sources are sinusoidal and, in most cases, a steady-state analysis is sufficient. Giant generators that supply electricity to industry are almost all sinusoidal; many electronic oscillators have sinusoidal waveforms. Second and more significant, as we mentioned in the previous chapter, most nonsinusoidal signals may be represented by a sum (or integral) of sinusoids of various frequencies. Linearity, then, allows us to express the response as a sum of responses to the various sinusoids. Linearity also makes it possible to break up the analysis into two simpler problems: analysis of the network excited by an elementary signal; and superposition (addition or integration) of responses due to elementary signals.

9.1   Addition of sinusoids of the same frequency

We shall demonstrate the important fact that the sum of any number of sinusoids of the same frequency but each with arbitrary amplitude and phase is itself a sinusoid with the same frequency. Let us start by considering

$$v(t) = V_1 \sin \omega t + V_2 \cos \omega t. \tag{9.1}$$

It is claimed that this is of the form

$$v(t) = V \sin (\omega t + \theta). \tag{9.2}$$

Expanding the right-hand side of Equation 9.2, we have

$$v(t) = V \cos \theta \sin \omega t + V \sin \theta \cos \omega t. \tag{9.3}$$

If the $v(t)$'s in Equations 9.1 and 9.2 are to be equal, then we must have

$$V_1 = V \cos \theta, \qquad V_2 = V \sin \theta \tag{9.4}$$

or

$$V = \sqrt{V_1^2 + V_2^2} \qquad \text{and} \qquad \theta = \tan^{-1}\frac{V_2}{V_1}. \tag{9.5}$$

Thus if V and θ are chosen as specified in Equation 9.5, the two terms in Equation 9.1 may be combined into a single term as in Equation 9.2.

Suppose that we now add an arbitrary number of sinusoids of the same frequency but with arbitrary amplitudes and phase, that is,

$$v(t) = \sum_{n=1}^{N} V_n \sin (\omega t + \theta_n). \tag{9.6}$$

Expanding each term, we obtain

$$v(t) = \sum_{n=1}^{N} \left[V_n \cos \theta_n \sin \omega t + V_n \sin \theta_n \cos \omega t \right]$$

$$= \left[\sum_{n=1}^{N} V_n \cos \theta_n \right] \sin \omega t + \left[\sum_{n=1}^{N} V_n \sin \theta_n \right] \cos \omega t. \tag{9.7}$$

We see that this is of the same form as Equation 9.1. The following conclusion follows immediately. The amplitude of the resulting sinusoid is equal to the square root of the sum of the squares of the coefficient of $\sin \omega t$ and the coefficient of $\cos \omega t$ in Equation 9.7. The phase angle θ is the arctangent of the ratio of the coefficient of $\cos \omega t$ to the coefficient of $\sin \omega t$. In equation form, the result is expressed by Equation 9.5.

EXAMPLE 9.1-1.   Let it be required to express the signal

$$v(t) = \sin 2\pi(60)t + 3\sqrt{2} \sin \left[2\pi(60)t + \pi/4 \right]$$
$$= \sin 377t + 3\sqrt{2} \sin (377t + \pi/4)$$

as a single sinusoid. Expanding the second term and collecting, we have

$$v(t) = 4 \sin 377t + 3 \cos 377t = 5 \sin (377t + \tan^{-1}\tfrac{3}{4}). \quad \square$$

● EXERCISES

9.1-1   Express the following summations of sinusoids in the general form $K \sin (\omega t + \theta)$:

(a) $i_1(t) = 3 \sin t + 4 \cos t$,

(b) $v_2(t) = 15 \sin 3t + 7 \cos 3t$,

(c) $i_3(t) = 3 \sin t + 4 \cos (t + \pi/4)$,

(d) $q_1(t) = 13 \sin (t - \pi/4) - 5 \cos (t + \pi/4)$,

(e) $v_1(t) = 2 \sin (t - \pi/2) + 5 \cos t$.

9.1-2   Repeat Exercise 9.1-1 but expressing the summations of sinusoids in the general form $K' \cos (\omega t + \phi)$.

9.2 Complex-number arithmetic

In Chapter 2, we noted that the sinusoidal function is related to the exponential function $e^{j\omega t}$. It turns out that analysis using $e^{j\omega t}$ is much simpler and that sinusoidal steady-state response is readily obtainable from the response due to $e^{j\omega t}$. Notice, however, that $e^{j\omega t}$ is a complex function. In this section we summarize the basic complex-number arithmetical operations that we shall often use.

First we consider the representation of complex numbers. A complex number C is said to be in rectangular or Cartesian form if it is written as

$$C = a + jb, \tag{9.8}$$

where a and b are real numbers and $j = \sqrt{-1}$. A convenient geometrical interpretation of a complex number is that of a point in a plane called the *complex plane*. In Equation 9.8, a is called the *real part* of C and b is called the *imaginary part* of C. In symbols, we have

$$a = \operatorname{Re} C \quad \text{and} \quad b = \operatorname{Im} C. \tag{9.9}$$

Notice that both the real part and imaginary part are real numbers. In the complex plane, the real and imaginary parts are considered as perpendicular components. As a convention, the real part is taken as the horizontal component and the imaginary part as the vertical component. For example, the number $-3 - j2$ is plotted as point P in Figure 9.1. The location of a point in the complex plane may alternatively be specified by giving its radial distance from the origin and the angle made between the radial line passing through the point and the positive real axis. Angle is measured positively in the counterclockwise direction. In symbolic form, we may write $C = |C|\underline{/\theta}$, where the complex number C is specified by the *magnitude* or radial distance $|C|$ and the *phase angle* θ. This representation is called the *polar form*. The real quantities $|C|$ and θ are illustrated in Figure 9.1. Since the two representations refer to the same complex number, a, b, $|C|$, and θ must be interrelated. Referring to Figure 9.1, we see that

$$a = |C| \cos \theta \tag{9.10}$$

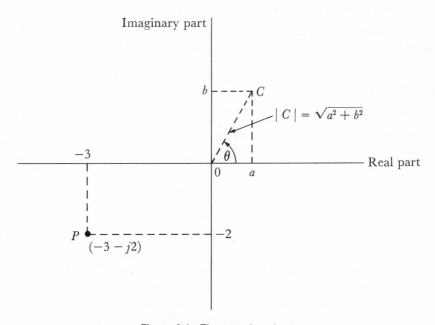

Figure 9.1 The complex plane.

and

$$b = |C| \sin \theta, \tag{9.11}$$

or

$$|C| = \sqrt{a^2 + b^2} \tag{9.12}$$

and

$$\theta = \tan^{-1} \frac{b}{a}. \tag{9.13}$$

Equations 9.10 and 9.11 may be used for converting from polar to rectangular form and Equations 9.12 and 9.13 for converting from rectangular to polar form. In actual numerical problems, Equations 9.12 and 9.13 may not be the most efficient to use. For instance, in using a slide rule it may be more convenient to use

$$|C| = a \sec \theta \quad \text{or} \quad |C| = b \operatorname{cosec} \theta, \tag{9.14}$$

where θ is calculated from Equation 9.13 or

$$\theta = \cot^{-1} \frac{a}{b}. \tag{9.15}$$

The student should familiarize himself with the solution of these equations with his own slide rule. *In using Equation 9.13 or Equation 9.15, care should be taken in determining the correct quadrant.*

EXAMPLE 9.2-1.   Suppose we wish to convert $2 - j2$ to polar form. The angle θ is

$$\theta = \tan^{-1} \frac{-2}{2} = \frac{-\pi}{4}, \tag{9.16}$$

so that the number is $2\sqrt{2} \; \underline{/-\pi/4}.$ □

EXAMPLE 9.2-2.   The angle θ for $-2 + j2$ is

$$\theta = \tan^{-1} \frac{2}{-2} = \frac{3\pi}{4}, \tag{9.17}$$

so that

$$-2 + j2 = 2\sqrt{2} \; \underline{/3\pi/4}. \qquad\qquad \square \tag{9.18}$$

Referring to Figure 9.1 again, we see that

$$C = a + jb = |C| \cos \theta + j|C| \sin \theta = |C| \, (\cos \theta + j \sin \theta). \tag{9.19}$$

But from Euler's formula we have

$$\cos \theta + j \sin \theta = e^{j\theta}, \tag{9.20}$$

so that we may write

$$C = |C|e^{j\theta}. \tag{9.21}$$

Equation 9.21 is known as the *exponential form*. It contains the same information as the polar form.

The *conjugate* of a complex number C is defined as one whose real part is equal to that of C and whose imaginary part is equal to the negative of that of C. It is denoted by C^*. Thus if $C = a + jb$, we have

$$C^* = a - jb. \tag{9.22}$$

The *sum* of two complex numbers C_1 and C_2 is defined as

$$C = C_1 + C_2 = C_2 + C_1 = (a_1 + a_2) + j(b_1 + b_2), \tag{9.23}$$

where a_1 and a_2 are the real parts and b_1 and b_2 the imaginary parts of C_1 and C_2, respectively. Graphically, the complex numbers may be added by the parallelogram law as shown in Figure 9.2. Likewise, for the *difference* $C_1 - C_2$, we have

$$C = C_1 - C_2 = (a_1 - a_2) + j(b_1 - b_2). \tag{9.24}$$

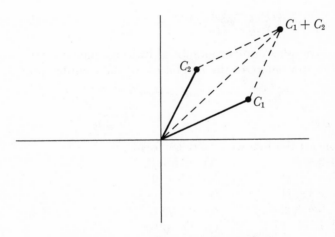

Figure 9.2   Sum of two complex numbers.

The *product* $C = C_1C_2$ is defined as

$$C_1C_2 = (a_1 + jb_1)(a_2 + jb_2) = a_1a_2 + j(b_1a_2 + a_1b_2) + j^2b_1b_2. \tag{9.25}$$

Since $j^2 = -1$, we have

$$C_1C_2 = (a_1a_2 - b_1b_2) + j(a_1b_2 + a_2b_1). \tag{9.26}$$

If C_1 and C_2 are in exponential or polar form, the answer is very easily obtained as

$$C_1C_2 = (|C_1|e^{j\theta_1})(|C_2|e^{j\theta_2}) = |C_1||C_2|e^{j(\theta_1 + \theta_2)}. \qquad (9.27)$$

Thus the magnitude of the product of two complex numbers is equal to the product of the magnitudes of the individual complex numbers, and the phase angle of the product is equal to the sum of the individual phase angles. For the *quotient* or ratio of two complex numbers, we have

$$\frac{C_1}{C_2} = \frac{|C_1|e^{j\theta_1}}{|C_2|e^{j\theta_2}} = |C_1|e^{j\theta_1}\left(\frac{1}{|C_2|}e^{-j\theta_2}\right) = \frac{|C_1|}{|C_2|}e^{j(\theta_1 - \theta_2)}. \qquad (9.28)$$

The magnitude of the ratio of two complex numbers is equal to the ratio of the magnitudes of the individual complex numbers. If the numbers are in rectangular form, they may be converted to exponential form and then Equation 9.28 can be applied. Alternatively, we may proceed to make the calculation in rectangular form. If

$$\frac{C_1}{C_2} = \frac{a_1 + jb_1}{a_2 + jb_2} \qquad (9.29)$$

is multiplied by C_2^*/C_2^*, we have

$$\frac{(a_1 + jb_1)(a_2 - jb_2)}{(a_2 + jb_2)(a_2 - jb_2)} = \frac{(a_1a_2 + b_1b_2) + j(b_1a_2 - a_1b_2)}{a_2^2 + b_2^2}. \qquad (9.30)$$

Note that a complex number multiplied by its conjugate yields a real number equal to the square of the magnitude of the complex number, that is

$$CC^* = a^2 + b^2 = |C|^2. \qquad (9.31)$$

● **EXERCISES**

9.2-1   Convert the following to polar form:
   (a) $3 - j4$ (f) $-12 + j5$
   (b) $-3 - j4$ (g) $-5 + j0$
   (c) $-3 + j4$ (h) $0 + j8$
   (d) $6.5 + j2.0$ (i) $0 - j8$
   (e) $1.5 + j13$ (j) $15 - j0.5$

9.2-2   Convert the following to rectangular form:
   (a) $5e^{j\pi/2}$ (f) $6 \,\underline{/30°}$
   (b) $2e^{j\pi/4}$ (g) $6 \,\underline{/-30°}$
   (c) $10e^{-j\pi/2}$ (h) $12 \,\underline{/105°}$
   (d) $8e^{j5\pi/6}$ (i) $2 \,\underline{/135°}$
   (e) $3e^{j\pi}$ (j) $4.5 \,\underline{/360°}$

9.2-3   Evaluate the following sums:
   (a) $(6.5 + j2.0) + (8 + j13)$
   (b) $12 \,\underline{/105°} + 6 \,\underline{/30°}$
   (c) $8e^{j5\pi/6} + 6 \,\underline{/-30°}$

9.2-4   Evaluate the following products:
   (a) $(3 - j4)(-3 - j4)$
   (b) $(-12 + j5)(1.5 + j13)$
   (c) $3e^{j\pi}(15 - j0.5)$
   Answers should be in exponential form.
9.2-5   Verify that the conjugate of $e^{j\theta}$ is $e^{-j\theta}$.
9.2-6   Verify that the conjugate of the product of two complex numbers is equal to the product of the conjugates of the two complex numbers.

9.3   Phasors and rotating phasors

   In the preceding section, we introduced the complex number as a point in a plane called the complex plane. Geometrically, the addition of two complex numbers may be carried out by drawing a parallelogram where the rays passing through the origin and the two points form adjacent sides. The diagonal between the two sides then represents the sum. Alternatively, we may use the triangle as shown in Figure 9.3(a) and (b). Note that we have attached arrows to the lines. These directed lines will be called *phasors*. Insofar as addition is concerned, these phasors behave exactly like two-dimensional vectors. However, in situations where both complex numbers and space vectors are involved (representation of time-varying electromagnetic fields for example), some confusion may arise if the same name is used for two different concepts. The use of the word phasor to represent the complex number is widely accepted and is now conventional in electrical engineering.

   To add phasors, we simply arrange them in head-to-tail fashion as shown in Figure 9.3(b). The sum is obtained as a phasor whose head is at the unconnected head of one of the component phasors and whose tail is at the unconnected tail of another component phasor. Thus, in Figure 9.3(b), the head of B is unconnected and the tail of A is unconnected. The order in which the component phasors are joined end to end is immaterial. Note that the resultant phasor in Figure 9.3(c) is the same as that of Figure 9.3(b).

   We might wonder what the difference is between an ordinary complex number and a phasor. Recall that a complex number is considered a point in the complex plane whose location or coordinate is specified in several ways, one of which is by its distance from the origin and the angle θ the ray makes with the positive real axis. Another is by its Cartesian or rectangular coordinates. To visualize the geometrical addition of complex numbers, however, it is convenient to detach the rays from the origin and move them around. When this is done, it is important to keep track of which end of the ray was formerly connected to the origin. For the phasor, it is the tail end that corresponds to the origin. The length of the phasor corresponds to the magnitude of the complex number, and the angle θ of

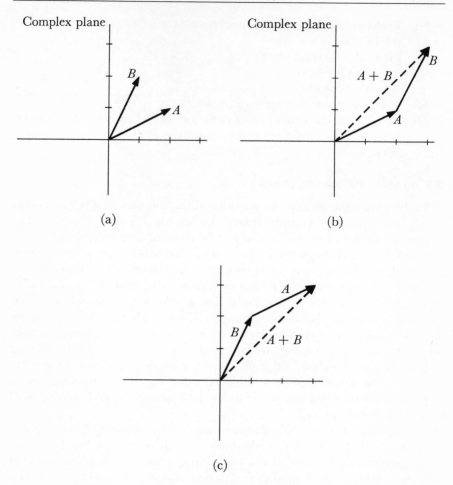

Figure 9.3 Addition of complex numbers by use of directed quantities called phasors.

the complex number corresponds to the angle the phasor makes with the positive real axis as shown in Figure 9.4. Note that the angle is measured positively in the counterclockwise direction from the positive real axis. The plane in which the phasor is drawn is really not the same complex plane where numbers are represented as points whose distances from the origin are important. Here distance from the origin is not important. We must know just the direction of the positive real axis. Conventionally, this is horizontal and to the right. We shall call this plane the *phasor plane*. Thus the difference between the complex number and the phasor is geometrical. Algebraically, they are the same.

Phasors may be used to actually add several complex quantities graphically. However, its more important use is as an aid in visualizing the

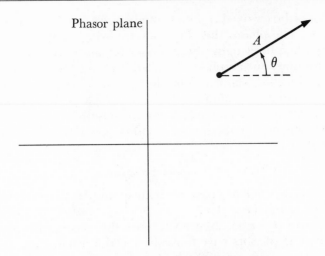

Figure 9.4 Phasor is specified by length and direction. Its actual location in the plane carries no information.

various steps in an analysis. Usually, a simple sketch of the phasors together with the additions and other required operations roughly carried out serves as a rough guide in detecting arithmetical mistakes in the calculations made later on.

EXAMPLE 9.3-1. Suppose we wish to add 3 $\underline{/0}$, 4 $\underline{/30°}$, and 6 $\underline{/-45°}$. A graphical addition is shown in Figure 9.5. The phasor in dotted lines is the resultant. □

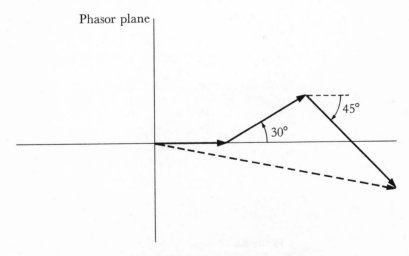

Figure 9.5 Example of phasor addition.

Instead of ordinary fixed complex numbers, we may have complex functions of time. The phasor then becomes a moving phasor. An important case occurs when the length of the phasor remains constant but its angle changes with time. Such a phasor is called a *rotating phasor*. It corresponds to a complex function whose magnitude is constant. An important example is $e^{j\omega t}$. The magnitude is always one and the angle at time t is ωt radians. The phasor $e^{j\omega t}$ rotates counterclockwise for positive ω and positive t and, if ω is constant, the frequency of rotation is constant and equal to ω radians/sec. Since

$$e^{j\omega t} = \cos \omega t + j \sin \omega t,$$

the real part and imaginary part are both sinusoidal. Another example of a rotating phasor is $(1 + j1)e^{jt} = \sqrt{2}e^{j\pi/4}e^{jt} = \sqrt{2}e^{j(t + \pi/4)}$. The real part of this is $\sqrt{2} \cos (t + \pi/4)$. Figure 9.6 shows the rotating phasor $Ae^{j(\omega t + \theta)}$.

If two rotating phasors have the same speed of rotation, their sum is a rotating phasor of the same speed of rotation. For example, if we have

$$V_1(t) = (1 + j2)e^{j10t}, \tag{9.32}$$

$$V_2(t) = (3 + j1)e^{j10t}, \tag{9.33}$$

then

$$V_1(t) + V_2(t) = (4 + j3)e^{j10t} = 5e^{j[10t + \tan^{-1} (3/4)]}. \tag{9.34}$$

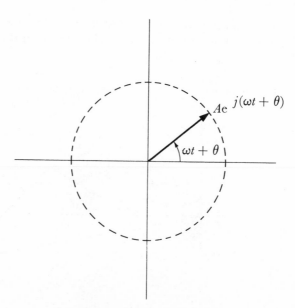

Figure 9.6 A rotating phasor.

The frequency ω is the rate of change or time derivative of the total phase angle of the various rotating phasors. In each case, ω is 10 radians/sec if t is in seconds.

If the real part of $V_1(t)$ above is added to the real part of $V_2(t)$, the result is equal to the real part of $[V_1(t) + V_2(t)]$. Likewise, the sum of the imaginary parts of two complex numbers or functions is equal to the imaginary part of the sum of the complex numbers or functions. This commutative property of the real-part operation (or the imaginary-part operation) and addition is a key to the use of rotating phasors for sinusoidal steady-state analysis. Thus, to add several sinusoidal functions of the same frequency, we write the individual functions as real parts (or imaginary parts) of appropriate rotating phasors. Then we perform the addition on the rotating phasors and take the real part (imaginary part) of the sum. For example, if we have

$$v_1(t) = 2\sqrt{2}\sin(10t + \pi/4), \tag{9.35}$$

$$v_2(t) = 2\sin 10t + \cos 10t, \tag{9.36}$$

then if we write $v_1(t)$ and $v_2(t)$ as imaginary parts of $V_1(t)$ and $V_2(t)$, we have

$$V_1(t) = 2\sqrt{2}e^{j(10t + \pi/4)} = 2e^{j10t} + j2e^{j10t}, \tag{9.37}$$

$$V_2(t) = 2e^{j10t} + je^{j10t}, \tag{9.38}$$

$$V_1(t) + V_2(t) = (4 + j3)e^{j10t} = 5e^{j[10t + \tan^{-1}(3/4)]}, \tag{9.39}$$

and

$$v_1(t) + v_2(t) = \text{Im}[V_1(t) + V_2(t)] = 5\sin\left[10t + \tan^{-1}\tfrac{3}{4}\right]$$
$$= 5\sin(10t + 36.9°). \tag{9.40}$$

We may alternatively represent $v_1(t)$ and $v_2(t)$ as real parts of a new set of $V_1(t)$ and $V_2(t)$, so that we have

$$V_1(t) = 2\sqrt{2}e^{j(10t - \pi/4)} = -j2e^{j10t} + 2e^{j10t}, \tag{9.41}$$

$$V_2(t) = -2je^{j10t} + e^{j10t}, \tag{9.42}$$

$$V_1(t) + V_2(t) = (3 - j4)e^{j10t}, \tag{9.43}$$

$$v_1(t) + v_2(t) = \text{Re}[V_1(t) + V_2(t)] = \text{Re}[5e^{j[10t - \tan^{-1}(4/3)]}]$$
$$= 5\cos(10t - 53.1°) = 5\sin(10t + 36.9°), \tag{9.44}$$

which is, of course, the same answer as before.

The procedure is summarized in Figure 9.7. Here we have used $V_k \cos(\omega t + \theta_k) = \text{Re}V_k e^{j(\omega t + \theta_k)}$. Alternatively, we may use $V_k \sin(\omega t + \alpha_k) = \text{Im}V_k e^{j(\omega t + \alpha_k)}$.

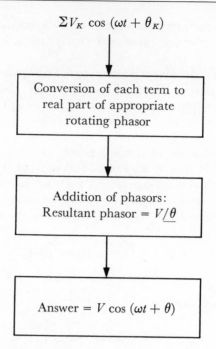

$$\Sigma V_K \cos (\omega t + \theta_K)$$

Conversion of each term to
real part of appropriate
rotating phasor

Addition of phasors:
Resultant phasor = $V\underline{/\theta}$

Answer = $V \cos (\omega t + \theta)$

Figure 9.7 Steps in the use of phasors for adding sinusoidal functions. In equation form, we have

$$\Sigma V_k \cos (\omega t + \theta_k) = \Sigma Re[V_k e^{j(\omega t + \theta_k)}] = Re\Sigma[V_k e^{j(\omega t + \theta_k)}]$$
$$= Re\{e^{j\omega t}[\Sigma V_k e^{j\theta_k}]\} = Re\{e^{j\omega t}Ve^{j\theta}\} = V \cos (\omega t + \theta).$$

● EXERCISES

9.3-1   With the aid of a protractor and scale, graphically determine the sum

$$A = 5 \underline{/20°} + 3 \underline{/60°} + 8 \underline{/180°} + 2 \underline{/-240°}.$$

9.3-2   If *A* is an arbitrary phasor, draw
(a) *jA* relative to *A*,
(b) −2*jA* relative to *A*,
(c) (1 − 2*j*)*A* relative to *A*,
(d) *A** relative to *A*.

9.3-3   Add $10 \sin (377t + 30°)$ and $5 \cos (377t + 45°)$ using phasors.

9.3-4   Suppose in Exercise 9.3-3, we add 10° to the angles of both terms, what will the new sum be? Suppose, instead, we subtract 30° from the angles of both terms, what will the new sum be? In view of the above consideration, is it possible to factor out a complex number so as to make one term in the phasor additions always a real number?

9.3-5   The current through a series RL circuit is a sinusoid

$$i(t) = I_0 \sin(\omega t + \theta_0).$$

Determine the magnitude and phase angle of the voltage across the series connection in terms of R, L, I_0, ω, and θ_0. Specify reference directions in your circuit diagram.

9.4   Steady-state response to $e^{j\omega t}$

We have already seen that the sum of rotating phasors of the same frequency ω results in a rotating phasor of the same frequency. We shall now demonstrate that if we apply a hypothetical rotating-phasor input signal to a linear time-invariant network or system, the steady-state output is also a rotating phasor of the same frequency.

EXAMPLE 9.4-1.   Let us first consider as an example a network or system described by

$$2\frac{dy(t)}{dt} + 8y(t) = x(t), \tag{9.45}$$

where $y(t)$ is the output signal and $x(t)$ is the input signal. This equation may describe, for example, a series RL circuit excited by a voltage source, where $R = 8$ ohms, $L = 2$ henrys, and current is the output variable. Let us apply a hypothetical input $x(t) = e^{j\omega t}$ in Equation 9.45. The fact that no such physical signal exists does not preclude its usefulness in analysis. We shall show how it relates to a physical sinusoidal response. We shall verify that the steady-state output is of the form

$$y(t) = He^{j\omega t}, \tag{9.46}$$

where H may be complex and may depend on ω. More specifically, we shall investigate if the *particular solution* of Equation 9.45 is of the form as given in Equation 9.46. That is, we shall substitute Equation 9.46 and $x(t) = e^{j\omega t}$ in Equation 9.45 and see if the equality holds. Thus we have

$$2(j\omega He^{j\omega t}) + 8He^{j\omega t} \overset{?}{=} e^{j\omega t}$$

$$H(8 + j2\omega)e^{j\omega t} \overset{?}{=} e^{j\omega t}. \tag{9.47}$$

Clearly, if H is chosen as

$$H = \frac{1}{8 + j2\omega}, \tag{9.48}$$

then Equation 9.47 holds. So the particular solution for an input $e^{j\omega t}$ is

$$y(t) = \frac{1}{8 + j2\omega}e^{j\omega t}. \tag{9.49}$$

Note that this is a complex time function, i.e., it has real and imaginary parts. This is not surprising since our hypothetical input is also complex. However, for our physical system, real input signals necessarily produce only real output signals. Thus, if the input is cos ωt, the output is a real signal $y_r(t)$, and, if the input signal is sin ωt, the output signal is a real signal $y_i(t)$. Furthermore since our system is linear, if we scale (multiply) the input by a constant A, the output will also be scaled by the same constant. The constant could be anything including a complex number. Thus, if the input is j sin ωt, the output is $jy_i(t)$, where $y_i(t)$ is the output due to sin ωt. Since $e^{j\omega t}$ is equal to cos $\omega t + j$ sin ωt and since our system is linear, superposition tells us that the output due to $e^{j\omega t}$ is

$$y(t) = y_r(t) + jy_i(t). \tag{9.50}$$

But we have calculated the output due to $e^{j\omega t}$ previously, and it is given in Equation 9.49. That is, we have

$$y(t) = \text{Re}\left[\frac{1}{8 + j2\omega} e^{j\omega t}\right] + j\text{Im}\left[\frac{1}{8 + j2\omega} e^{j\omega t}\right]. \tag{9.51}$$

We conclude that in this case an input $x(t) = \cos \omega t$ will produce

$$y_r(t) = \text{Re}\left[\frac{1}{8 + 2j\omega} e^{j\omega t}\right] = \frac{1}{\sqrt{64 + 4\omega^2}} \cos\left(\omega t - \tan^{-1}\frac{2\omega}{8}\right). \tag{9.52}$$

Likewise, for an input $x(t) = \sin \omega t$, the output will be

$$y_i(t) = \text{Im}\left[\frac{1}{8 + 2j\omega} e^{j\omega t}\right] = \frac{1}{\sqrt{64 + 4\omega^2}} \sin\left(\omega t - \tan^{-1}\frac{2\omega}{8}\right). \tag{9.53}$$

If instead of $e^{j\omega t}$, we have $Ae^{j\theta}e^{j\omega t}$ as input, then because of linearity, the rotating-phasor output is

$$y(t) = \frac{Ae^{j\theta}}{8 + j2\omega} e^{j\omega t}, \tag{9.54}$$

and for the real input A cos $(\omega t + \theta)$, the output would be

$$y_r(t) = \frac{A}{\sqrt{64 + 4\omega^2}} \cos\left(\omega t + \theta - \tan^{-1}\frac{2\omega}{8}\right). \tag{9.55}$$

Thus we see that sinusoidal inputs produce sinusoidal responses as particular solutions. □

For more general situations, our linear time-invariant network or system will be described by a differential equation:

$$a_n\frac{d^n y(t)}{dt^n} + a_{n-1}\frac{d^{n-1}y(t)}{dt^{n-1}} + \cdots + a_0 y(t) =$$

$$b_m\frac{d^m x(t)}{dt^m} + b_{m-1}\frac{d^{m-1}x(t)}{dt^{m-1}} + \cdots + b_0 x(t). \tag{9.56}$$

Just as before, a hypothetical rotating-phasor input $e^{j\omega t}$ will produce a rotating-phasor output. We again assume the form in Equation 9.46 and substitute in Equation 9.56. We obtain

$$[a_n(j\omega)^n + a_{n-1}(j\omega)^{n-1} + \cdots + a_0]He^{j\omega t} =$$
$$[b_m(j\omega)^m + b_{m-1}(j\omega)^{m-1} + \cdots + b_0]e^{j\omega t}. \quad (9.57)$$

So that for

$$H = \frac{b_m(j\omega)^m + b_{m-1}(j\omega)^{m-1} + \cdots + b_0}{a_n(j\omega)^n + a_{n-1}(j\omega)^{n-1} + \cdots + a_0} = |H| \underline{/\theta}, \quad (9.58)$$

Equation 9.57 becomes an identity provided that $j\omega$ is not a characteristic root. Again, the response due to $\cos \omega t$ is

$$\text{Re}[|H|e^{j\theta}e^{j\omega t}] = |H| \cos(\omega t + \theta). \quad (9.59)$$

Also, if the input is $A \cos(\omega t + \alpha)$, the response will be

$$\text{Re}[Ae^{j\alpha}|H|e^{j\theta}e^{j\omega t}] = A|H| \cos(\omega t + \theta + \alpha). \quad (9.60)$$

The use of phasors has something to do with the determination of $|H|$ and θ in Equation 9.58. The phasor method of this section is a special case of the analysis of the previous chapter using exponential signals e^{st}, where $s = j\omega$.

●   **EXERCISES**

9.4-1   For the network of Figure Exercise 9.4-1, obtain the differential equation relating the input $i(t)$ to the output $v_{12}(t)$, where R, L, and C are constants. For $C = .05\mu\text{F}$, $R = 10$ ohms, and $L = 100$ millihenry, and $i(t) = 10^{-3} \sin(10^4 t + \pi/6)$, determine the steady-state component of v_{12}.

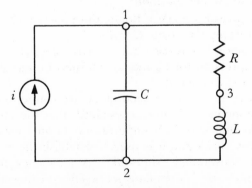

Figure Exercise 9.4-1

9.4-2 Using the circuit parameters of Exercise 9.4-1 for the network in Figure Exercise 9.4-1, determine the input that will cause the steady-state output $v_{12}(t)$ to be sin $10^4 t$.

9.4-3 For simplicity, assume that all the elements in the network of Figure Exercise 9.4-3 have value 1. Determine the differential equation relating $v_{13}(t)$ to $v(t)$ and express $v_{13}(t)$ in the form $v_{13}(t) = V \cos (t + \alpha)$ if $v(t) = \sin t + 2 \cos t$.

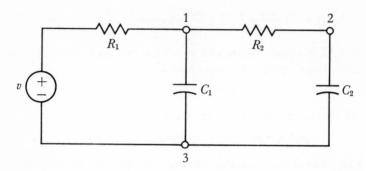

Figure Exercise 9.4-3

9.4-4 Repeat Exercise 9.4-3 for $v_{23}(t)$ as output instead of $v_{13}(t)$.

Problems

9-1 The signal voltage for a given element is known to be given by the equation $v_a(t) = 10 \sin 3t - 20 \sin (3t + \pi/4)$ volts. When an rms reading voltmeter is connected across this element, what value will it read? Show the method.

9-2 Given the phasor in rectangular coordinates $V_1 = 5 \sqrt{3} + j5$. Rotate this phasor $-75°$. What is the rectangular representation of the phasor in its rotated position?

9-3 Given the phasor $5 + j5\sqrt{3}$. Rotate this phasor $-15°$ and express the result in rectangular form, $C = A + jB$.

9-4 In the equation $V_0 \cos (\omega t + \phi_0) = V_1 \cos (\omega t + \phi_1) + V_2 \cos (\omega t + \phi_2)$, find an expression for V_0 and ϕ_0 in terms of the real, positive quantities, V_1, V_2, ϕ_1, and ϕ_2.

9-5 Three wires in a circuits laboratory are connected to a common point. Ammeters are used to establish that the effective (or rms) current in one wire is 5 amperes and in another 10 amperes. A cathode ray oscillograph is used to establish the fact that the currents are substantially sinusoidal. A frequency meter reads 60 Hertz (which is 377 radians/sec). The oscillograph shows that the current read as 5 amperes reaches its maximum 1/200 sec before the 10-ampere current. Write equations for the three currents, determining numerical values whenever possible. Positive reference directions are towards the junction.

9-6 Two components connected in series are labeled A and B. An rms-reading voltmeter records 10 volts across A, 25 volts across B, and 15 volts across the combination of A and B. All of these voltages are sinusoidal. Assuming that the voltage across A is the reference (it has the form $V \sin \omega t$), write expressions for the three voltages, determining numerical values for constants whenever possible.

9-7 Using Euler's relationship, show that

$$\sin \omega t = \frac{1}{2j} \left[e^{j\omega t} - e^{-j\omega t} \right]$$

and

$$\cos \omega t = \tfrac{1}{2} \left[e^{j\omega t} + e^{-j\omega t} \right].$$

9-8 The results given in the last problem show that $\sin \omega t$, which is a real function, is expressed in terms of complex rotating phasors. Draw a phasor diagram to show that this particular combination of rotating phasors is indeed real (having values only on the real axis of the complex plane) for all values of ωt.

9-9 Repeat Problem 9-8 for the cosine function of Problem 9-7.

9-10 In the equation

$$V_0 \sin (\omega t + \phi_0) = \sum_{k=1}^{N} V_k \cos (\omega t + \phi_k),$$

find expressions for V_0 and ϕ_0 in terms of the real, positive quantities $V_1, V_2, V_3, \ldots, V_n$ and $\phi_1, \phi_2, \ldots, \phi_n$.

9-11 In Figure Problem 9-11, the voltage source v_b is sinusoidal and has the same frequency as v_a which is $v_a(t) = 2 \sin \omega_0 t$. The voltage $v_a + v_b$ has the value $v_a + v_b = 10 \sin (\omega_0 t + \theta_t)$.
(a) Find v_b if $\theta_t = 0°$; if $\theta_t = 90°$; if $\theta_t = 180°$; $\theta_t = -90°$.

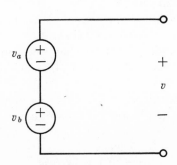

Figure Problem 9-11

(b) Draw the appropriate phasors for V_a, V_b and $V_a + V_b$ for the values of θ_t in (a).

9-12   Verify that the conjugate of the ratio of two complex numbers is equal to the ratio of their conjugates.

9-13   Determine the polar form of A:

$$A = \frac{(8 + j6)(3.6 - j5)}{10 \, \underline{/120°} - (-8.5 - j2)}.$$

9-14   Is the product of the real parts of two complex numbers equal to the real part of the product of the complex numbers? Answer the same question for the ratio.

9-15   Show that the real part of the derivative of a rotating phasor is equal to the derivative of the real part of the rotating phasor. Likewise for the imaginary part.

9-16   Given a linear system described by a linear ordinary differential equation with real constant coefficients, show that the response due to $e^{-j\omega t}$ is equal to the conjugate of the response due to $e^{j\omega t}$. Thus, since

$$\cos \omega t = \frac{e^{j\omega t} + e^{-j\omega t}}{2},$$

demonstrate that if $e^{j\omega t}$ produces $He^{j\omega t}$, $\cos \omega t$ produces $\mathrm{Re}[He^{j\omega t}]$.

9-17   The waveforms of the currents in six of seven wires connected at a junction are sinusoidal and have the same frequency. What can you say about the waveform of the current in the seventh wire? Explain.

9-18   If the steady-state voltage across a certain portion of a linear time-invariant network is $v(t) = 45 \sin(377t + 20°) + 10 \cos(377t - 10°)$ due to a source $i(t) = \cos 377t$ somewhere in the network, what would the voltage response be at the same terminal-pair if the current were $3 \sin(377t - 30°)$?

9-19   The sum of three phasors, A, B, and C is equal to zero. Phasor A has length 5 and zero angle. Phasors B and C have angles $-105°$ and $150°$, respectively. Compute the magnitudes of B and C both graphically and analytically.

9-20   Expand the functions e^{jx}, $\cos x$, and $\sin x$ in Maclaurin's series and demonstrate that $e^{jx} = \cos x + j \sin x$.

9-21   If $A(t)$ is a rotating phasor, what can you say of the product $A(t)A^*(t)$? How about the ratio $A(t)/A^*(t)$? The sum $A(t) + A^*(t)$? The difference $A(t) - A^*(t)$?

9-22   (a) If we use the phasor $1 \, \underline{/0°}$ corresponding to $\cos \omega t = \mathrm{Re}[e^{j\omega t}]$, what should be the phasors corresponding to

    (1) $v_1(t) = \sin \omega t$,

    (2) $v_2(t) = 5 \sin(\omega t + 30°)$,

    (3) $v_3(t) = 8 \cos(\omega t - 30°) + 6 \cos \omega t$.

(b) Repeat (a) if we use the phasor $1 \underline{/0°}$ to correspond to sin $(\omega t + 30°) = \text{Im}[e^{j(\omega t + 30°)}]$.

(c) Add the sinusoidal functions $v_1(t)$, $v_2(t)$, and $v_3(t)$ in (a) by using the phasors in (a). Repeat, using the phasors in (b).

9-23 The signal $v(t)$ is equal to the sum

$$v(t) = 8.5 \sin (1000t - 30°) + 5 \sin (1000t - 90°)$$
$$+ 4 \cos (1000t - 45°) + 10 \sin (1000t + \theta).$$

For what value of θ is the peak value of $v(t)$ the largest?

9-24 Repeat Problem 9-23 for the value of θ that makes the peak value $v(t)$ the smallest.

9-25 The input and output voltages, $x(t)$ and $y(t)$, respectively, in a linear time-invariant network are related by

$$\frac{d^3y(t)}{dt^3} + 10\frac{d^2y(t)}{dt^2} + 8\frac{dy(t)}{dt} + 5y(t) = 13\frac{dx(t)}{dt} + 7x(t).$$

For what input will the steady-state output be $y(t) = \sin t$?

9-26 Restate Kirchhoff's current law and Kirchhoff's voltage law for a linear time-invariant network in the sinusoidal steady-state where the sources are all sinusoidal with the same frequency. Use phasors.

9-27 Large amounts of electrical energy are usually transmitted by three-phase power networks. The energy is usually converted from other forms into electrical energy where the final stage of the conversion system is a rotating machine called a three-phase generator. Three sinusoidal voltages with the same frequency and the same peak amplitude are produced by the generator. The three voltages are

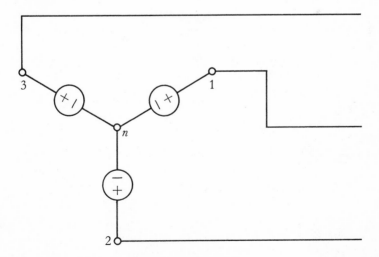

Figure Problem 9-27

120° out of phase with respect to each other. The voltage sources are usually internally connected in a Y-configuration as in Figure Problem 9-27. In the figure, if v_{2n} lags v_{1n} and if v_{3n} lags v_{2n}, we say that the phase sequence is 1–2–3. Otherwise, the phase sequence is said to be 1–3–2. Suppose that $v_{1n}(t) = \sqrt{2}(V) \cos [2\pi(60)t]$, where V is a positive constant, and the phase sequence is 1–2–3. Using the phasor $\sqrt{2}V \; \underline{/0°}$ for representing $v_{1n}(t)$, draw the phasors V_{1n}, V_{2n}, and V_{3n}. On the same phasor diagram, draw V_{12}, V_{23}, and V_{31}. From the phasor diagram, determine $v_{12}(t)$, $v_{23}(t)$, and $v_{31}(t)$.

The Impedance Concept

and Network Functions **10**

10.1 Impedance for sinusoidal signals

In the previous chapter, it was demonstrated that for a linear time-invariant network, the steady-state response to a sinusoid is another sinusoid of the same frequency, provided that the complementary solution eventually reduces to zero. The most convenient procedure for carrying out analysis is to obtain the response to a hypothetical input $e^{j\omega t}$. The response to a sinusoid is then easily obtained from the real or imaginary part.

Consider a 1-port linear time-invariant network which may be a portion of a larger network as shown in Figure 10.1. Applying Kirchhoff's laws and the branch constraints characterizing the linear time-invariant network, a single differential equation relating v and i may be obtained. The differential equation would be linear with constant coefficients of the type considered in the previous chapter. It is assumed that the linear 1-port network contains no independent sources. The quantities i and v are not identically zero because of sources outside the 1-port network. Suppose that i or v is sinusoidal. Then in the steady-state, v or i will also be sinusoidal

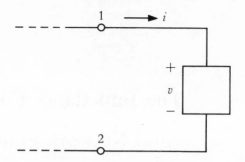

Figure 10.1   Reference conventions for *i* and *v* in defining impedance for a linear time-invariant network.

with the same frequency. Suppose that

$$i = \text{Re}[Ie^{j\omega t}], \tag{10.1}$$

where I is a complex number $|I|e^{j\theta}$ and

$$v = \text{Re}[Ve^{j\omega t}], \tag{10.2}$$

where V is also a complex number $|V|e^{j\phi}$. Suppose that $i = |I|\cos(\omega t + \theta)$ and $v = |V|\cos(\omega t + \phi)$ satisfy the differential equation. Then so will the complex time functions $i = Ie^{j\omega t}$ and $v = Ve^{j\omega t}$. Conversely, if the complex hypothetical signals satisfy the differential equation, so will the real parts of the signals. The ratio of the voltage rotating phasor $Ve^{j\omega t}$ to the current rotating phasor $Ie^{j\omega t}$ is defined as *impedance Z*:

$$Z = \frac{Ve^{j\omega t}}{Ie^{j\omega t}} = \frac{V}{I}. \tag{10.3}$$

Note that because the network is linear and time-invariant, scaling I by any amount will result in a scale of V by the same amount, and time shifting i will result in a time shift of v by the same amount. This means that Z does not depend on the magnitude of I nor the angle of I. It does depend on the *ratio* of the magnitudes of V and I and the *difference* in the angles between V and I. The reciprocal of impedance also finds frequent use and it is known as *admittance Y*:

$$Y = \frac{1}{Z} = \frac{I}{V}. \tag{10.4}$$

Equations 10.3 and 10.4 are frequently written in Ohm's law form as

$$V = ZI \tag{10.5}$$

and

$$I = YV. \tag{10.6}$$

Steinmetz first used the words "apparent resistance" in describing what we now call impedance.† The motivation in introducing this and like terms just before the turn of the century was to make the analysis of networks with sinusoidal signals similar to the analysis of resistive networks with time-invariant (dc) signals. Impedance is intended to be the means of relating a voltage to a current when both are sinusoidal. Note that for the generalized Ohm's law of Equation 10.5, the current-reference direction through the 1-port network is from the positive terminal to the negative terminal of the voltage reference. Otherwise, the equation would be $V = -ZI$. The following example will illustrate how impedance may be used in relating sinusoidal voltage and current.

EXAMPLE 10.1-1.   The impedance of a given element in a network is $10e^{j30°}$. If the current is $i(t) = 10 \sin(\omega t + 45°)$, find the voltage related to this current by the given impedance. We first represent the current by the phasor $I = 10e^{j45°}$ (or $10\ \underline{/45°}$). Then the voltage phasor is

$$V = ZI = (10e^{j30°})(10e^{j45°}) = 100e^{j75°}. \tag{10.7}$$

Then the voltage $v(t)$ corresponding to this phasor is

$$v(t) = 100 \sin(\omega t + 75°). \qquad \square \tag{10.8}$$

The impedance and admittance in Equations 10.5 and 10.6 may be written in rectangular form. These complex numbers have real and imaginary parts which are identified by specific names. Thus, in the equation

$$Z = R + jX \text{ ohms,} \tag{10.9}$$

R is the *resistance* and X is the *reactance*, while in

$$Y = G + jB \text{ mhos,} \tag{10.10}$$

G is the *conductance* and B the *susceptance*, where R, X, G, and B are real numbers. Since $Z = 1/Y$, we see that R and X may be expressed in terms of G and B as follows:

$$R + jX = \frac{1}{G + jB} = \frac{G - jB}{G^2 + B^2}. \tag{10.11}$$

Equating real and imaginary parts, we have

$$R = \frac{G}{G^2 + B^2} \quad \text{and} \quad X = \frac{-B}{G^2 + B^2}. \tag{10.12}$$

---

† A. E. Kennelly, "Impedance," *Trans. AIEE*, **10** (1893), 175-216; C. P. Steinmetz and F. Bedell, "Reactance," *Trans. AIEE*, **11** (1894), 640-648.

● **EXERCISES**

10.1-1   Given a voltage and current related by the admittance function
$Y = 1 + j1$. If $v(t) = 5 \sin (3t - 30°)$, determine the associated $i(t)$.
Assume that v and i have the reference directions as in Figure
10.1.

10.1-2   Write expressions similar to Equations 10.12, expressing G and B
in terms of R and X.

10.1-3   Write expressions for G and B in terms of $|Z|$ and θ.

10.2   Impedance of R, L, and C elements

We next make use of the definition of impedance given in the last section
to determine expressions for Z and Y for the three linear time-invariant
passive elements: R, L, and C. For the resistor, the voltage and current
are related by Ohm's law

$$v_R(t) = Ri_R(t), \tag{10.13}$$

where v_R and i_R are identified in Table 10.1. To find impedance, we let
the current be $i_R(t) = I \sin \omega t$, so that $v_R(t) = RI \sin \omega t$. To use the phasor
definition of impedance, we see that $I_R = Ie^{j0}$ and $V_R = Rie^{j0}$. Thus we have

$$Z_R = \frac{V_R}{I_R} = R \text{ ohms.} \tag{10.14}$$

While the use of the phasor definition for impedance is not necessary for
this particular derivation, its use in analyzing the resistor sets the pattern
we will follow in finding the impedance expression for L and C.

For the inductor, we again assume that the current is the reference
quantity, written $i_L(t) = I_L \sin \omega t$. Then the voltage is

$$v_L(t) = L\frac{di_L}{dt} = \omega LI_L \sin (\omega t + \pi/2). \tag{10.15}$$

The corresponding current and voltage phasors are

$$I_L = I_L e^{j0} \quad \text{and} \quad V_L = \omega LI_L e^{j\pi/2}. \tag{10.16}$$

Then the impedance for the inductor is

$$Z_L = \frac{V_L}{I_L} = \omega Le^{j\pi/2} = j\omega L. \tag{10.17}$$

From this expression, we see that the impedance for the inductor is reactive; if $Z_L = R_L + jX_L$, then we have

$$R_L = 0 \quad \text{and} \quad X_L = \omega L. \tag{10.18}$$

Table 10.1

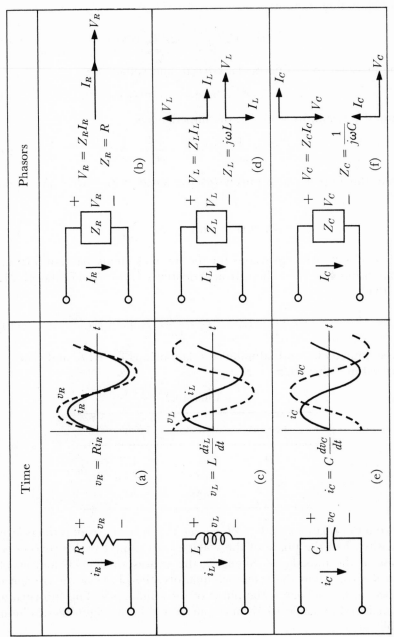

Similarly for the capacitor, we let $v_C(t) = V_C \sin \omega t$ and then find the corresponding current:

$$i_C(t) = C \frac{dv_C(t)}{dt} = \omega C V_C \cos \omega t. \tag{10.19}$$

The phasors for this particular current and voltage are

$$V_C = V_C e^{j0} \quad \text{and} \quad I_C = \omega C V_C e^{j\pi/2}. \tag{10.20}$$

From this result, we find that the impedance is

$$Z_C = \frac{1}{\omega C} e^{-j\pi/2} = -j \frac{1}{\omega C} = \frac{1}{j\omega C}. \tag{10.21}$$

Again this impedance is purely reactive since, if $Z_C = R_C + jX_C$, then we have

$$R_C = 0 \quad \text{and} \quad X_C = \frac{-1}{\omega C}. \tag{10.22}$$

The admittance expressions for the three elements are found from the relationship $Y = 1/Z$. Then, from Equations 10.14, 10.17, and 10.21, we see that

$$Y_R = \frac{1}{R} = G, \quad Y_L = \frac{-j}{\omega L}, \quad Y_C = j\omega C. \tag{10.23}$$

These impedance and admittance relationships for R, L, and C are summarized in Table 10.2.

Table 10.2

Element	Impedance	Admittance
R	R	$1/R$
L	$j\omega L$	$-j/\omega L$
C	$-j/\omega C$	$j\omega C$

From the relationship $V = ZI$, we see that if the current is the reference quantity, then the phase of the voltage with respect to this current is the phase of the impedance. Similarly, the expression $I = YV$ indicates that with the voltage as the reference quantity, the phase of the current with respect to the voltage is the phase of the admittance. This information is summarized in Table 10.3† and is illustrated in the right-hand column of Table 10.1.

† Table 10.3 is summarized by the mnemonic, "ELI, the ICE man," where E represents voltage and I current. Thus we read ELI as "Voltage leads current in an inductor," and ICE as "Current leads voltage in a capacitor."

Table 10.3

Element	Phase of $v(t)$ in relationship to $i(t)$	Phase of $i(t)$ in relationship to $v(t)$
R	0°	0°
L	90°	−90°
C	−90°	90°

When considered singly, the capacitor and inductor elements may have nonzero arbitrary constants for complementary functions associated with the responses. For instance, if there is an initial charge on a capacitor and if the excitation is current, even if i is sinusoidal, the voltage will be a sinusoid plus a constant. We are assuming that the initial condition is such that the response is simply a sinusoid. Alternatively, we take the point of view that even if the storage elements have nonzero initial conditions, when the element is combined with others to form a network, the complementary function for the network response eventually decays to zero for t approaching infinity.

● EXERCISES

10.2-1   Figure Exercise 10.2-1 shows the sinusoidal voltage and current for a constant network element. What is the element? What is its value in ohms, henrys, or farads?

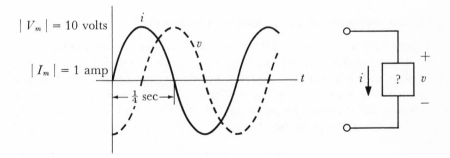

Figure Exercise 10.2-1

10.2-2   With the references for voltage and current indicated in Figure Exercise 10.2-2 together with the waveforms shown, find the kind of element and its value in ohms, henrys, or farads.

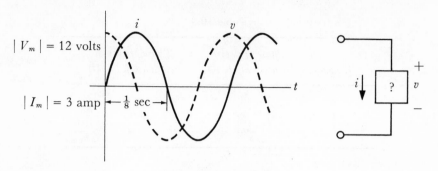

$|V_m| = 12$ volts

$|I_m| = 3$ amp $\quad\vdash\frac{1}{8}$ sec $\dashv$

Figure Exercise 10.2-2

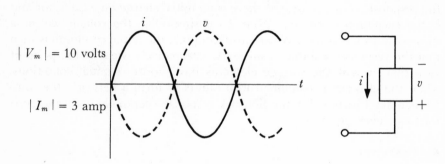

$|V_m| = 10$ volts

$|I_m| = 3$ amp

Figure Exercise 10.2-3

10.2-3 Repeat Exercise 10.2-1 for the waveforms of Figure Exercise 10.2-3.

10.3 The impedance of series-parallel networks

Figure 10.2 shows a series *RLC* network connected to a sinusoidal source of voltage. For this network, we will consider two problems: (a) given $i(t)$, find $v(t)$; and (b) given $v(t)$, find $i(t)$. For the first problem, we will assume that we are at liberty to select $i(t)$ as the reference quantity by which we mean that we will select its phase angle to be zero. The Kirchhoff voltage law tells us that (see Exercise 10.3-1)

$$V_R + V_L + V_C = V \qquad (10.24)$$

or

$$Z_R I + Z_L I + Z_C I = V. \qquad (10.25)$$

If we next divide through the equation by the phasor I and define the phasor ratio V/I to be the total impedance of the network, Z_t, then we have

$$Z_t = Z_R + Z_L + Z_C. \qquad (10.26)$$

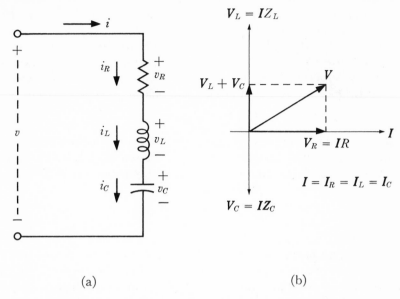

(a)   (b)

Figure 10.2 (a) Series *RLC* network. (b) the phasor diagram showing the relationship of voltages and currents.

This expression may be generalized for any number of elements in series as

$$Z_t = \sum_{i=1}^{n} Z_i. \tag{10.27}$$

If we substitute appropriate quantities from Table 10.2 into Equation 10.26, we find that Z_t in Equation 10.27 has the form

$$Z_t = R + j\left(\omega L - \frac{1}{\omega C}\right). \tag{10.28}$$

The magnitude and phase of the total impedance Z_t are

$$|Z_t| = \sqrt{R^2 + (\omega L - 1/\omega C)^2} \tag{10.29}$$

and

$$Z_t = \tan^{-1}\frac{\omega L - 1/\omega C}{R}. \tag{10.30}$$

From these values, we may write an expression for the voltage $v(t)$; if

$$i(t) = |I| \sin \omega t, \tag{10.31}$$

then the voltage $v(t)$ is

$$v(t) = \sqrt{R^2 + (\omega L - 1/\omega C)^2}\, |I| \sin\left(\omega t + \tan^{-1}\frac{\omega L - 1/\omega C}{R}\right). \tag{10.32}$$

These operations are illustrated by the phasor diagram of Figure 10.2. This diagram can be constructed by observing that $I = I_R = I_L = I_C$ because of the series connection. These quantities are represented on the diagram as the reference phasor. The phasors V_R, V_L, and V_C are located on this diagram by superimposing the individual phasor diagrams shown in Table 10.1. Once this is accomplished, the phasor V is found from

$$V = V_R + V_L + V_C. \tag{10.33}$$

Directly from the figure, we see that the phase of V with respect to I is that angle described by Equation 10.30. We also see that V has a magnitude which is equal to the magnitude of Z_t times the magnitude of I. Observe that

$$|V_R| + |V_L| + |V_C| \neq |V|. \tag{10.34}$$

For this particular figure, both $|V_L|$ and $|V_C|$ are larger than $|V|$.

For the second problem, given $v(t)$ and required to find $i(t)$, we assume that $v(t)$ is the reference quantity. This does not necessarily imply that the phase of $v(t)$ is zero, but rather that other quantities will be expressed in terms of the $v(t)$ reference. Let the voltage $v(t)$ be given by

$$v(t) = |V| \sin(\omega t + \phi) = \operatorname{Im}[|V|e^{j(\omega t + \phi)}]. \tag{10.35}$$

For convenience, choose the real quantity $|V|$ for the V phasor:

$$V = |V|. \tag{10.36}$$

The phasor current is related to V by

$$I = Y_t V = \frac{1}{Z_t} V. \tag{10.37}$$

Now the phase and magnitude of Z_t are given by Equations 10.29 and 10.30, and we see that

$$I = \frac{V}{\sqrt{R^2 + (\omega L - 1/\omega C)}} \exp\left[j\left(-\tan^{-1}\frac{\omega L - 1/\omega C}{R}\right)\right]. \tag{10.38}$$

But from the choice of the reference phasor V in Equation 10.36 and from the relationship of $v(t)$ to V in Equation 10.35, we see that

$$i(t) = \operatorname{Im}[Ie^{j(\omega t + \phi)}]. \tag{10.39}$$

Hence we have

$$i(t) = \frac{|V|}{|Z_t|} \sin\left(\omega t + \phi - \tan^{-1}\frac{\omega L - 1/\omega C}{R}\right), \tag{10.40}$$

which is the desired current.

In Equation 10.27, it is shown that the impedance of a number of ele-

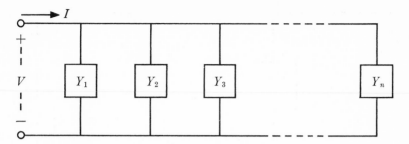

Figure 10.3 Representation of elements connected in parallel, with each one characterized by its admittance.

ments connected in series is the sum of the impedances of the individual elements. The analysis of the representation of a number of elements connected in parallel shown in Figure 10.3 requires that we recognize that the same voltage is applied to all of the parallel elements (or combinations of elements within any one box in the figure). The total current is the summation of the individual currents to the elements by Kirchhoff's current law, so that (see Exercise 10.3-2) we have

$$I = I_1 + I_2 + I_3 + \cdots + I_n. \tag{10.41}$$

Now each of the phasor currents is related to the phasor voltage V by the appropriate admittance, so that we obtain

$$I = Y_1 V + Y_2 V + Y_3 V + \cdots + Y_n V. \tag{10.42}$$

Again dividing through by V and defining the ratio of I to V to be the total admittance of the network, we have

$$Y_t = Y_1 + Y_2 + Y_3 + \cdots + Y_n. \tag{10.43}$$

The impedance of the network of Figure 10.3 is

$$Z_t = \frac{1}{Y_t} = \frac{1}{Y_1 + Y_2 + \cdots + Y_n}. \tag{10.44}$$

A special case of this equation for $n = 2$ is

$$Z_t = \frac{Z_1 Z_2}{Z_1 + Z_2}, \tag{10.45}$$

for which the pattern "product over sum" of impedances is easily remembered. In this equation, $Z_1 = 1/Y_1$ and $Z_2 = 1/Y_2$.

Two 1-port networks are said to be *equivalent* if they have the same impedance at the port terminals called the *driving-point* terminals. The two networks of Figure 10.4 are equivalent *for sinusoidal signals* when

$$Z = Z_1 + Z_2. \tag{10.46}$$

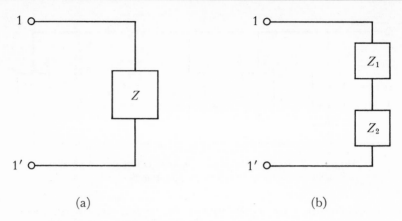

(a)   (b)

Figure 10.4   The two networks are equivalent for sinusoidal
signals (in the steady state) when $Z = Z_1 + Z_2$.

Note that this definition for equivalence of 1-port networks is for sinusoidal
steady-state only. More general cases will be given later. The same conclusions apply to the parallel connection shown in Figure 10.5 when

$$Y = \frac{1}{Z} = Y_1 + Y_2. \tag{10.47}$$

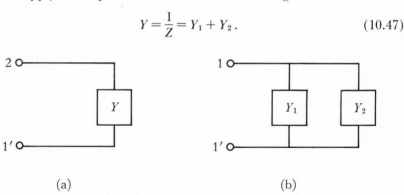

(a)   (b)

Figure 10.5   Two equivalent networks for sinusoidal signals when $Y = 1/Z = Y_1 + Y_2$.

The pattern suggested by these two simple examples may be used suc-
cessively to find the equivalent impedance for series–parallel networks of
the form shown in Figure 10.6(a). (Non-series–parallel networks formed
by the bridging of nodes will be considered in a later chapter.) Reduction
for this network starts at the "far end" of the network where we recognize
that $Z_a = Z_3 + Z_4$ as in (b). The impedance Z_b is found from the parallel
combination of Z_2 and Z_a from Equation 10.45. Thus we have

$$Z_b = \frac{Z_2 Z_a}{Z_2 + Z_a}. \tag{10.48}$$

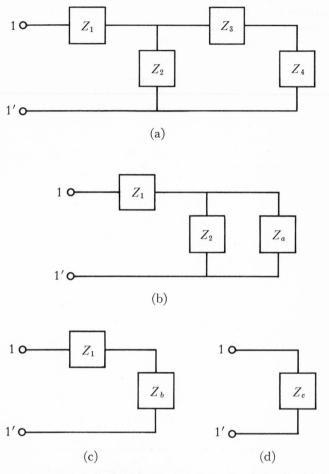

Figure 10.6 Steps in finding an equivalent network by successive series and parallel combinations of impedances for sinusoidal signals.

Finally, we see that the total impedance of the network at terminals 1 and 1' is the sum of Z_1 and Z_b. Thus we have

$$Z_t = Z_c = Z_1 + \frac{Z_2(Z_3 + Z_4)}{Z_2 + Z_3 + Z_4}.$$ (10.49)

● **EXERCISES**

10.3-1   Verify Equation 10.24, starting from

$$v_R(t) + v_L(t) + v_C(t) = v(t)$$

as given by Kirchhoff's voltage law and writing each of the

sinusoidal voltages as the imaginary part of appropriate rotating phasors.

10.3-2   Verify Equation 10.41. Use hint similar to that in Exercise 10.3-1.

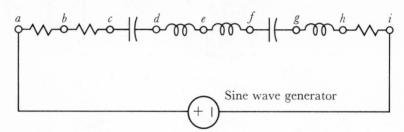

Figure Exercise 10.3-3

10.3-3   For the network in Figure Exercise 10.3-3, an rms-reading voltmeter records the following values:

Voltmeter terminals at	Voltage (volts)
a and b	1
b and c	3
c and d	2
d and e	2
e and f	1
f and g	2
g and h	3
h and i	2

What will the voltmeter read when connected from a to i? From c to g?

10.3-4   In the network of Figure Exercise 10.3-4, $R_1 = 4$ ohms, $R_2 = 6$ ohms, and $R_3 = 2$ ohms. The reactance of L has a magnitude of 3 ohms and that of C a magnitude of 8 ohms. If $|V_1| = 100$ volts, find $|V_2|$.

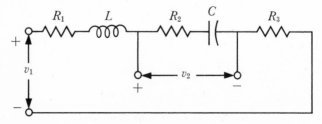

Figure Exercise 10.3-4

10.3-5   In the series RLC network of Figure Exercise 10.3-5, $i(t)$ lags $v(t)$ by 45°. If $|V| = 1$ volt, $|I| = 1$ ampere, $L = 1$ henry, and $\omega = 2$ radians/sec, find the magnitude of the voltage across each of the elements: $|V_L|$, $|V_C|$, and $|V_R|$.

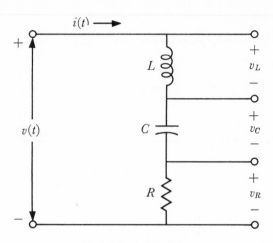

Figure Exercise 10.3-5

10.3-6   The following voltmeter readings are made on the series RLC network given in Figure Exercise 10.3-6 where the subscripts refer to the voltmeter connections:

$$|V_{ac}| = 20 \text{ volts}, \qquad |V_{bd}| = 9 \text{ volts}, \qquad |V_{ad}| = 15 \text{ volts}.$$

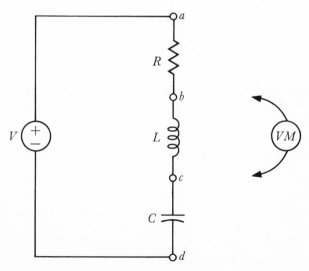

Figure Exercise 10.3-6

Find the voltmeter readings across each of the three elements under these conditions. [*Answers:* 12, 16, and 7 or 25 volts.]

10.3-7　Find the impedance of the network shown in Figure Exercise 10.3-7(a) when $\omega = 1$ radian/sec. Repeat for $\omega = 2$ radians/sec.

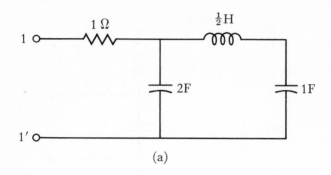

(a)

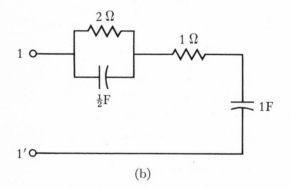

(b)

Figure Exercise 10.3-7

10.3-8　Determine the impedance of the network of Figure Exercise 10.3-7(b) at terminals 1 and 1′ for $\omega = 2$ radians/sec.

10.3-9　In Exercise 10.3-4, if $|V_2| = 100$ volts, find $|V_1|$.

10.4　Analysis with phasor diagrams

The *phasor diagram* of Figure 10.2(b) shows important phase and magnitude relationships for the voltages and currents in the series *RLC* network of Figure 10.2(a). It shows at a glance that the phasor voltage V_L leads the phasor current I by 90°, that the phasor sum of $V_L + V_C$ and V_R is equal to the phasor voltage V. We also see at a glance that the current lags the applied voltage by an angle between 0° and 90°. If we wish to find the voltage across the resistor and inductor, it may be done routinely by adding the phasors V_L and V_R. Phasor diagrams of this type find frequent use for the analysis of networks with sinusoidal signals, not often for detailed computation but instead for a "rough check" to guide computations and analysis.

The *reference angle* or *reference* of a phasor diagram is the line $\theta = 0$. It is not really necessary that any voltage or current coincide with the reference, although analysis is often more convenient when a given voltage or current phasor is the reference. Different phasors of Figure 10.2(b) may be made to be the reference simply by rotating the entire phasor diagram in either the clockwise or counterclockwise direction. For example, when all phasors are rotated in the clockwise direction, the phasor V may be made to coincide with the reference angle $\theta = 0$.

The selection of the reference quantity to be used in the construction of a phasor diagram turns out to be an important matter. In the series *RLC* network of Figure 10.2(a), the current common to the three elements turned out to be a good choice as a reference. Try working the problem

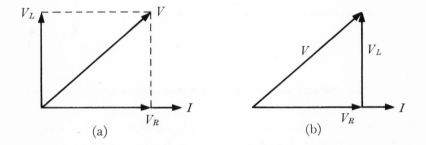

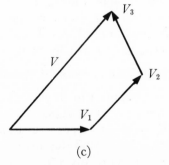

Figure 10.7 (a) A polar phasor diagram. (b) A phasor diagram in polygon form. (c) Another polygon phasor diagram.

with V as the reference to prove that it is possible to make a poor choice. When several elements are in parallel, then the voltage common to these elements is a good choice as a reference. No firm rule applies to all situations. A number of examples will be given to indicate the choice of the reference quantity.

The phasor diagram may be drawn in a number of ways such as in the form of a *polar* (or ray) diagram with all phasors originating at the origin, or in the form of a *polygon* with one phasor located at the end of another. These two forms of phasor diagrams are illustrated by the examples of Figure 10.7.

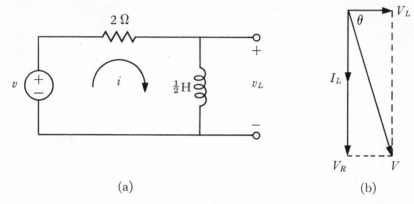

(a)   (b)

Figure 10.8 Network and corresponding phasor diagram for Example 10.4-1.

EXAMPLE 10.4-1.   For the network in Figure 10.8, it is given that $v_L(t) =$ $\sin t$ and it is required that we find $v(t)$. The phasor diagram is constructed with $V_L = 1$ as the reference. We know that the current in the inductor lags the voltage by 90°. Since this current must also be the current of the resistor, we see that V_R will be in phase with I_L. Finally, as shown in Figure 10.8(b), $V = V_L + V_R$, and from this phasor voltage $v(t)$ may be written. With the numerical values given: $V_L = 1$, $I_L = V_L/Z_L = -j2$, $V_R = RI_L = -j4$, and $V = 1 - j4$ or $V = \sqrt{17}\ \underline{/-\tan^{-1}4}$. Finally we have

$$v(t) = \sqrt{17} \sin (t - \tan^{-1}4) \text{ volts.} \quad \square \qquad (10.50)$$

EXAMPLE 10.4-2.   We are required to draw a phasor diagram for the voltages and currents of the network in Figure 10.9(a). We select the two voltage phasors V_R and V_C as the reference as shown in Figure 10.9(b). We know that I_R is in phase with V_R and that I_C leads V_C by 90°. By KCL, $I_L = I_C + I_R$, and the construction of this phasor is shown by the broken lines. Now we also know that V_L leads I_L by 90°, which fixes the position

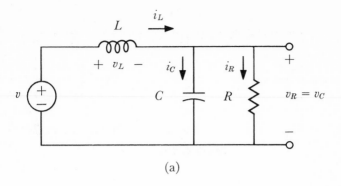

(a)

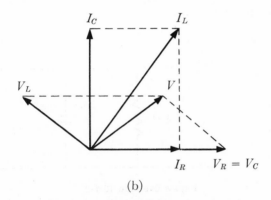

(b)

Figure 10.9 A series-parallel network and a complete
phasor diagram showing all voltages and currents.

of V_L. Finally, from KVL, $V_L + V_C$ and again broken lines indicate the construction that determines the position of V. This phasor diagram was
constructed without knowledge of element values or frequency of the
sinusoidal signal, and it is clear that the actual phasor diagram for a
specific network may differ in detail (magnitudes and angles) from that
shown. If $v_R(t) = |V_R| \cos(\omega t + \phi)$, then $v(t) = \mathrm{Re}[V e^{j(\omega t + \phi)}]$, where V is
the phasor obtained from the phasor diagram. $\square$

● EXERCISES

10.4-1 In the network of Figure Exercise 10.4-1, it is given that $v_L(t) =$
$2\sqrt{2} \sin(t - 30°)$. Find $v(t)$, using phasors and show each step on
a phasor diagram. [*Answer:* $2 \sin(t - 75°)$.]

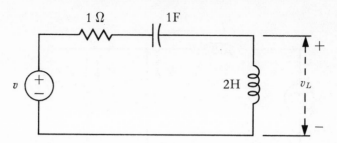

Figure Exercise 10.4-1

10.4-2   In the network of Figure Exercise 10.4-2, $v_2(t) = 2 \sin (2t - \pi/4)$ for all t. (a) Find $v_1(t)$, using phasors. (b) Draw a phasor diagram showing all voltages and currents.

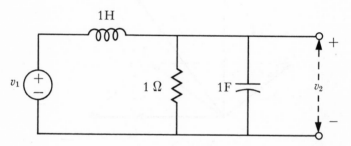

Figure Exercise 10.4-2

10.4-3   For the *RC* network of Figure Exercise 10.4-3, $v_2(t) = \sqrt{2} \sin t$. (a) Draw a phasor diagram (approximately to scale) showing all voltages in the network. (b) From the phasor diagram, show that $v_1(t) = 3\sqrt{2} \sin (t - 90°)$ volts. (c) What value will an rms meter record for the voltage $v_1(t)$?

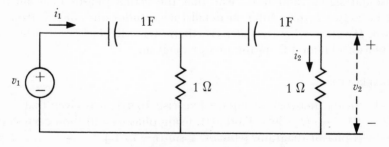

Figure Exercise 10.4-3

Table 10.4

No.	Network 1	Network 2	V_m	ω	ϕ
a	$R = 1$	$C = 2$	2	1/2	−30°
b	$R = 2$	$C = 1$	$2\sqrt{2}$	2	45°
c	$R = 20$	$C = 1/2$	1	0.1	0°
d	$R = 2$	$L = 2$	2	1/2	30°
e	$L = 1/2$	$R = 1$	$2\sqrt{2}$	1/2	0°
f	$C = 2$	$R = 2$	3	1	45°
g	$L = 3$	$C = 1$	$5\sqrt{2}$	1/2	−45°
h	$C = 1$	$L = 1/2$	1	2	0°
i	$R = 2$	$L = 1/2$	$2\sqrt{2}$	4	37.5°
j	$L = 3$	$R = 4$	$120\sqrt{2}$	1	−37.5°
k	$C = 4$	$R = 3$	1	1/16	20°
l	$L = 1$	$C = 2$	2	1/2	120°
m	$C = 3$	$L = 4$	1	1	240°
n	$R = 3$	$R = 4$	$2\sqrt{2}$	27	713°
o	$R = 5$	$C = 1$	$2\sqrt{3}$	1/4	0°
p	$R = 1, \quad C = 1$	$L = 2$	1	1/2	−45°
q	$R = 2, \quad C = 2$	$L = 1$	3	1	30°
r	$R = 1, \quad L = 2$	$C = 1/2$	$3\sqrt{2}$	1	45°
s	$R = 1/2, \quad L = 1$	$C = 2$	1	2	120°
t	$L = 1, \quad C = 2$	$R = 1$	$3\sqrt{2}$	1/2	25°
u	$R = 1, \quad C = 1$	$R = 1, \quad L = 1$	$4\sqrt{2}$	1	0°
v	$R = 2, \quad C = 2$	$R = 2, \quad L = 1$	1	1/2	90°
w	$L = 1/2, \quad C = 1$	$R = 1, \quad C = 1$	120	1	−90°
x	$R = 3, \quad L = 2$	$R = 1, \quad C = 1/2$	1	1/2	0°
y	$L = 1, \quad C = 2$	$L = 2, \quad C = 1$	$5\sqrt{2}$	1	−90°

10.4-4   This exercise is intended to provide practice in drawing and inter-
preting phasor diagrams. In Table 10.4, the network of Figure
Exercise 10.4-4 is described as well as the voltage $v_2(t) = V_m$

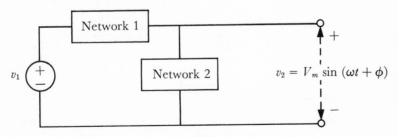

Figure Exercise 10.4-4

$\sin(\omega t + \phi)$. For each row, you are to determine $v_1(t)$ and draw a phasor diagram used in finding this voltage. (A double entry in the Network 1 and Network 2 columns implies a series connection of two elements.)

10.5   Generalization of impedance: network functions

In Example 10.4-1, we let $V_L = 1$ and found that $V = 1 - j4$ or $V = \sqrt{17}\, e^{-j\,\tan^{-1}4}$. The quotient of these two phasor is

$$\frac{V_L}{V} = \frac{1}{\sqrt{17}}\, e^{j\,\tan^{-1}4}. \tag{10.51}$$

By this example, we see that the quotient of two voltage phasors is itself a phasor similar to impedance. Furthermore, this ratio may be used in exactly the same way as impedance. Thus, if $v(t) = 2\sin t$ and the associated phasor is $V = 2$, then we have

$$V_L = \frac{1}{\sqrt{17}}\, e^{j\,\tan^{-1}4}V. \tag{10.52}$$

From this, we see that

$$v_L(t) = \frac{2}{\sqrt{17}}\sin(t + \tan^{-1}4). \tag{10.53}$$

Now the ratio of V_L and V is not impedance according to our definition. Phasor ratios of this kind are given the name *network functions*. Impedance is one member of the family of network functions. Before introducing you to the other members of this family, we will distinguish between driving-point and transfer functions. When the voltage and current are identified with one pair of terminals, as in Figure 10.10(a), then the network function which is the quotient of the phasors V and I or its reciprocal is known as a *driving-point function*. The network is being driven by a voltage source or current source at these terminals; in this sense, these terminals are the

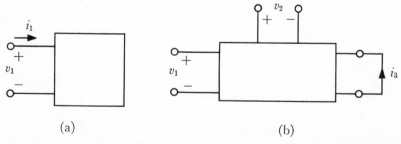

(a)   (b)

Figure 10.10   Network described by (a) driving-point functions and (b) transfer functions.

driving points. In the situation depicted in Figure 10.10(b), other pairs of terminals are involved. When the phasors of a network function are identified with two different pairs of terminals, the network function is said to be *transfer* in nature. Knowing the transfer network function, and one phasor for one pair of terminals, we may compute a phasor for another pair of terminals and in this sense transfer from one terminal pair to another.

Driving-point functions may be written without subscript identification if there is only one port. Thus

$$Z = \frac{V_1}{I_1} \quad \text{and} \quad Y = \frac{I_1}{V_1} \tag{10.54}$$

are the *driving-point impedance* and *admittance* functions at terminal pair 1. Transfer functions, on the other hand, are written with double subscripts identifying the pairs of terminals involved. If the two terminal pairs are identified as 1 and 2 (the terminals themselves are ordinarily marked 1 and 1′, 2 and 2′), then

$$Z_{21} = \frac{V_2}{I_1} \tag{10.55}$$

is the transfer impedance function, while

$$Y_{21} = \frac{I_2}{V_1} \tag{10.56}$$

is the *transfer admittance*. Voltage ratios are denoted by G (from gain of similar amplifying devices), so that

$$G_{21} = \frac{V_2}{V_1} \tag{10.57}$$

is the *voltage-ratio transfer function*. The current ratio

$$\alpha_{21} = \frac{I_2}{I_1} \tag{10.58}$$

is similarly transfer in nature and is known as the *current-ratio transfer function*. Transfer functions are conventionally defined as ratios of output phasors to input phasors.

EXAMPLE 10.5-1.   In Exercise 10.4-3, it was shown that when $v_2(t) = \sqrt{2} \sin t$, then $v_1(t) = 3\sqrt{2} \sin (t - 90°)$. This information may be summarized by a voltage-ratio transfer function; thus, from $V_2 = \sqrt{2}\, e^{j0}$ and $V_1 = 3\sqrt{2}\, e^{-j\pi/2}$, we have

$$G_{21} = \frac{V_2}{V_1} = \frac{1}{3} e^{j\pi/2} \tag{10.59}$$

in polar form, or in rectangular form we have

$$G_{21} = 0 + j\tfrac{1}{3}. \tag{10.60}$$

Now suppose that we change the magnitude and phase of $v_1(t)$, not changing ω, of course, since G_{21} is a function of ω. Then we may find the corresponding $v_2(t)$ from the transfer function we have computed. For example, if $v_1(t) = 10 \sin (t - 30°)$, then using the corresponding phasor $V_1 = 10e^{-j\pi/6}$, we have

$$V_2 = G_{21}V_1 = \tfrac{1}{3} e^{j\pi/2} 10 e^{-j\pi/6} = 3.33 e^{j\pi/3}. \tag{10.61}$$

Finally, from this phasor we construct the time function $v_2(t)$ as

$$v_2(t) = 3.33 \sin (t + 60°). \tag{10.62}$$

The network functions of these examples have been complex numbers. In many cases, we need the network functions expressed in terms of ω. In the network of Figure 10.11, for example, we see that

$$I_L = V_2 Y_L = \frac{V_2}{j\omega L}. \tag{10.63}$$

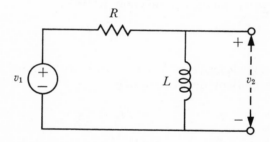

Figure 10.11   Network with voltage ratio transfer function given by Equation 10.65.

The driving-voltage phasor is

$$V_1 = I_L R + V_2 = \left(\frac{R}{j\omega L} + 1 \right) V_2. \tag{10.64}$$

Finally, we see that

$$\frac{V_2}{V_1} = \frac{j\omega L}{R + j\omega L}. \tag{10.65}$$

From this general expression, the voltage-ratio transfer function may be found for given values of R, L, and ω. $\square$

● EXERCISES

10.5-1   (a) For the network of Figure Exercise 10.3-4 and the element values of Exercise 10.3-4, find the voltage-ratio transfer function, $G_{21} = V_2/V_1$. Assume that for the given reactance data, the frequency is 1,000 radians per second. (b) If $v_1(t) = 10 \sin (\omega t + 45°)$, use the transfer function of (a) to find $v_2(t)$.

10.5-2   Using the network of Figure Exercise 10.4-2, determine $G_{21} = V_2/V_1$ as a function of frequency, ω. Express your results in polar form.

10.5-3   For the network of Figure Exercise 10.4-3 with $\omega = 1$ radian/sec, find: (a) $Z_{21} = V_2/I_1$; (b) $Y_{21} = I_2/V_1$; (c) Does $Y_{21} = 1/Z_{21}$? Discuss your conclusion.

10.5-4   For the network of Figure Exercise 10.4-3 with $\omega = 1$, find the current-ratio transfer function, $\alpha_{21} = I_2/I_1$.

10.5-5   For the network of Figure Exercise 10.4-3, determine an expression for $G_{21} = V_2/V_1$ as a function of frequency, ω. To simplify notation, let $j\omega = s$, and express your solution in the form of a quotient of polynomials in s.

10.5-6   Repeat Exercise 10.5-5 for $I_2/I_1 = \alpha_{21}$.

10.6   Network functions for signals of the form Ke^{st}

The same philosophy of impedance and other network functions just developed for sinusoidal signals may be applied to signals of the form Ke^{st}. For this type of input signals, the particular solution to the differential equation relating the input and output also has the form $K_1 e^{st}$, where K_1 is not a function of time but may depend on s. For example, consider the series RLC network in Figure 10.2. Applying Kirchhoff's voltage law, we have

$$v(t) = L\frac{di(t)}{dt} + Ri(t) + \frac{1}{C} \int i(t)\ dt, \qquad (10.66)$$

and differentiating once, we obtain the second-order differential equation

$$L\frac{d^2i(t)}{dt^2} + R\frac{di(t)}{dt} + \frac{1}{C}i(t) = \frac{dv(t)}{dt}. \qquad (10.67)$$

Suppose the hypothetical input signal (not necessarily physically realizable) is $v(t) = Ve^{st}$. Then we wish to verify that $i(t) = Ie^{st}$ satisfies Equation 10.67 for an appropriate choice of I, provided that s is not equal to a characteristic root. For $v(t) = Ve^{st}$, the right-hand side of Equation 10.67 is sVe^{st}, and for $i(t) = Ie^{st}$, the left-hand side is equal to $(Ls^2e^{st} + Rse^{st} + 1/C\ e^{st})I$.

In order for the two sides to be equal, the complex quantity I must be

$$I = \frac{sVe^{st}}{Ls^2e^{st} + Rse^{st} + 1/C\, e^{st}} = \frac{sV}{Ls^2 + Rs + 1/C}. \tag{10.68}$$

We define the ratio V/I as the *impedance function* $Z(s)$. In this example, it is

$$Z(s) = \frac{Ls^2 + Rs + 1/C}{s} = Ls + R + \frac{1}{Cs}. \tag{10.69}$$

Note that this impedance expression yields the same answer for the rotating phasor $e^{j\omega t}$ if we simply replace s by $j\omega$. Thus, for an ideal constant inductor, the impedance expression is Ls, for a constant resistor it is R, and for a constant capacitor it is $1/Cs$.

The procedures developed for finding the impedance of series-parallel combinations of elements for the signal $e^{j\omega t}$ also apply when the signal is e^{st}. The apparent difference is that the term $j\omega$ is replaced by s. Thus the network functions $Z(j\omega)$, $Y(j\omega)$, $G(j\omega)$, $\alpha(j\omega)$ which are functions of $j\omega$ become $Z(s)$, $Y(s)$, $G(s)$, and $\alpha(s)$ which are functions of s. The parameter s is a generalized frequency which is conventionally called *complex frequency*. The complex frequency s may have real and imaginary parts,

$$s = \sigma + j\omega, \tag{10.70}$$

where σ and ω are real. The signal e^{st} may be written

$$e^{st} = e^{\sigma t}e^{j\omega t}. \tag{10.71}$$

This form may be considered as a *damped or growing rotating phasor* depending on whether σ is negative or positive as shown in Figure 10.12(a) and Figure 10.12(b), respectively. Aside from the minor algebraic simplification that results when $j\omega$ is replaced by s, the major significance in the use of a complex s is in the representation of general signals as sums or integrals of complex exponentials, as mentioned in Chapter 8.

From Equation 10.69, it is apparent that there will be some values of s such that $Z(s)$ becomes zero. When

$$Ls^2 + Rs + \frac{1}{C} = 0, \tag{10.72}$$

which is the case when

$$\left.\begin{array}{r} s_1 \\ s_2 \end{array}\right\} = \frac{-R}{2L} \pm \sqrt{(R/2L)^2 - 1/LC}, \tag{10.73}$$

where s_1 and s_2 are roots of Equation 10.72, then $Z(s_1) = Z(s_2) = 0$. These values of s for which $Z(s)$ becomes zero are called *zeros* of the function $Z(s)$. Likewise, in the expression for $Z(s)$ which is a ratio of polynomials in s, there are values of s, for which $1/Z(s)$ becomes zero. These are the values

Complex plane

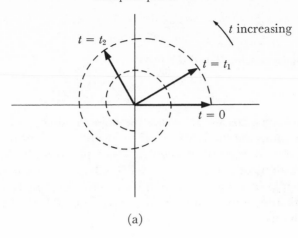

(a)

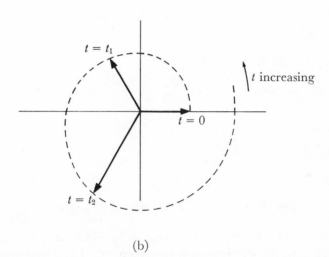

(b)

Figure 10.12   (a) A damped or shrinking rotating phasor. (b) A growing or expanding rotating phasor. The magnitude of the rotating phasor $e^{j\omega t}$ is scaled by $e^{\sigma t}$. In (a), σ is negative and in (b), σ is positive.

of s for which the denominator of $Z(s)$ becomes zero. For example, in Equation 10.69, the denominator is zero when $s = 0$. Those values of s which make $1/Z(s)$ take zero value are called *poles* of $Z(s)$. Remember that we are talking about linear time-invariant lumped networks which give rise to ordinary linear differential equations with constant coefficients. For such networks, the impedance $Z(s)$ is always a ratio of polynomials. A ratio of two polynomials is called a *rational function*. That is, in general, we have

$$Z(s) = \frac{b_m s^m + b_{m-1} s^{m-1} + \cdots + b_0}{a_n s^n + a_{n-1} s^{n-1} + \cdots + a_0}. \tag{10.74}$$

The polynomials may be factored so that

$$Z(s) = \frac{b_m}{a_n} \frac{(s - z_1)(s - z_2) \cdots (s - z_m)}{(s - p_1)(s - p_2) \cdots (s - p_n)}, \tag{10.75}$$

where the z_j are the zeros and the p_j are the poles. Thus $Z(s)$ may be specified by determining the locations of the zeros, the locations of the poles, and the value of a constant scale factor (in this case, b_m/a_n). In the complex *s-plane*, the locations of zeros are marked by $\bigcirc$ and the location of poles by $\times$. An example of a *pole-zero* configuration is shown in Figure 10.13. Other network functions such as $Y(s)$, $G(s)$, and $\alpha(s)$ are treated in a similar way; that is, they have zeros and poles too.

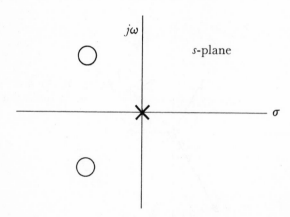

Figure 10.13   Example of a pole-zero plot in the *s*-plane.

EXAMPLE 10.6-1.   Consider the network in Figure Exercise 10.3-7(b). Let us determine the driving-point impedance $Z(s)$ at terminals 1 and 1'. The impedance of the parallel combination is the reciprocal of $\frac{1}{2} s + \frac{1}{2}$. Hence

$$Z(s) = \frac{1}{\frac{1}{2} s + \frac{1}{2}} + 1 + \frac{1}{s} = \frac{(s + 1)^2 + 2s}{s(s + 1)}. \tag{10.76}$$

This function has poles at $s + 1 = 0$ and $s = 0$, or

$$s = -1 \quad \text{and} \quad s = 0. \tag{10.77}$$

The zeros are the roots of

$$(s + 1)^2 + 2s = 0. \tag{10.78}$$

Since

$$(s+1)^2 + 2s = s^2 + 4s + 1 = 0, \tag{10.79}$$

then

$$(s+2)^2 - 3 = 0 \tag{10.80}$$

and

$$s = -2 \pm \sqrt{3} \tag{10.81}$$

Thus $s_1 = -2 + \sqrt{3}$ and $s_2 = -2 - \sqrt{3}$ are the two zero locations of $Z(s)$.   □

EXAMPLE 10.6-2. The voltage transfer function for a linear time-invariant network has a double zero at the origin and poles at $s = -1$ and

$$s = -\frac{1}{2} \pm j\frac{\sqrt{3}}{2}.$$

The constant scale factor for the transfer function is 5. The problem is to determine the steady-state response when the input voltage is $10 \cos t$. From the given data,

$$G_{21}(s) = \frac{5s^2}{\left(s + \frac{1}{2} - j\frac{\sqrt{3}}{2}\right)\left(s + \frac{1}{2} + j\frac{\sqrt{3}}{2}\right)}$$

$$= \frac{5s^2}{\left(s + \frac{1}{2}\right)^2 + \frac{3}{4}} = \frac{5s^2}{s^2 + s + 1}. \tag{10.82}$$

The response due to e^{st} is $G_{21}(s)e^{st}$. In particular, the response due to e^{jt} is $G_{21}(j1)e^{jt}$. Hence the response due to $10 \cos t$ which is $10 \, \text{Re}\{e^{jt}\}$ is

$$y(t) = 10 \, \text{Re}\{G_{21}(j1)e^{jt}\}$$

$$= 10 \, \text{Re}\left\{\frac{5(-1)}{-1 + j1 + 1}e^{jt}\right\} \tag{10.83}$$

$$= 10 \, \text{Re}\{j5e^{jt}\}$$

$$= 50 \, \text{Re}\{e^{(jt + \pi/2)}\} = 50 \cos(t + \pi/2). \quad \square$$

● EXERCISES

10.6-1   A network is composed of constant R, L, and C connected in parallel and is driven by a current source $i(t)$. For this network, show that

$$Y(s) = \frac{1}{R} + Cs + \frac{1}{Ls}.$$

10.6-2 For the network of Figure Exercise 10.4-3, find: (a) $Z_{21}(s)$, (b) $Y_{21}(s)$, (c) $G_{21}(s)$, and (d) $\alpha_{21}(s)$. Find numerical values for each of these functions with $s = -1$.

10.6-3 Find $G_{21}(s) = V_L(s)/V(s)$ for the network of Figure Exercise 10.4-1.

10.6-4 Find $G_{21}(s)$ for the network of Figure Exercise 10.4-2. If $v_1(t) = 10e^{3t}$, find $v_2(t)$ using this transfer function.

Problems

10-1 In the series RLC network shown in the figure, the current is known to be $i(t) = 2 \sin (10t - 30°)$. It is given that $R = 3$ ohms, $C = 0.05$ farad, and $L = 0.6$ henry. Determine the following quantities: (Let $\sin 10t$ correspond to $1 \angle 0°$.) (a) I, (b) V_R, V_L, and V_C, (c) V, (d) the impedance $Z = V/I$, (e) the admittance, $Y = 1/Z$, (f) R and X in $Z = R + jX$, (g) G and B in $Y = G + jB$, (h) $v(t)$, $v_r(t)$, $v_L(t)$, and $v_C(t)$, and (i) the rms value of $v(t)$.

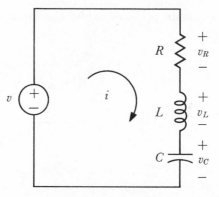

Figure Problem 10-1

10-2 For the two-terminal network shown in the figure, it is given that $v(t) = 100 \sin (100t + 25°)$ volts and $i(t) = 2 \sin (100t + 65°)$ amperes.

(a) Determine the equivalent series resistance of the impedance at the input terminals of the network. Is the network capacitive or inductive?

(b) Compute the average power into the network by taking the average of the instantaneous power.

(c) Compute the average power into the network by taking the average of the instantaneous $i^2 R_{eq}$, and compare with the answer in (b). Is the average of $i^2 R_{eq}$ equal to $I_{rms}^2 R_{eq}$, where I_{rms} is the rms value of i?

(d) Show that for this example, average power $P_{av} = V_{rms} I_{rms} \cos \theta$, where V_{rms} and I_{rms} are rms values of the instantaneous v and i,

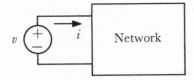

Figure Problem 10-2

respectively, and θ is the difference in the phase angles of v and i. (e) Let V_{rms} be $1/\sqrt{2}$ times the phasor V of v and let I_{rms} be $1/\sqrt{2}$ times the phasor I of i. Form $V_{\text{rms}} I_{\text{rms}}^*$, where I_{rms}^* is the complex conjugate of I_{rms}. Show that for this example, the average power into the network is equal to the real part of $V_{\text{rms}} I_{\text{rms}}^*$.

10-3 In the given network, $C = 1$ farad, $L = 1$ henry, and $M = \frac{1}{2}$ henry. Find the impedance of the network at terminals 1–2 when $\omega = 1$ radian/sec.

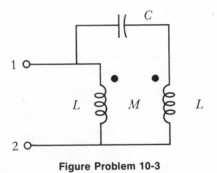

Figure Problem 10-3

10-4 The source in the network of the figure is sinusoidal. An rms-reading voltmeter is used to measure the following: $V_{ab} = 10$ volts

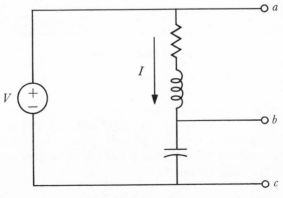

Figure Problem 10-4

and $V_{bc} = 15$ volts. Using I as the reference, draw a phasor diagram showing V_{bc}, V_{ab}, and V. Is your phasor diagram unique?

10-5   The network of the figure is excited by a sinusoidal source and is in the steady-state. Using V_2 as the reference, draw a neat phasor diagram showing I_C, I_L, I_R, I and V_1.

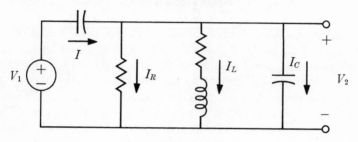

Figure Problem 10-5

10-6   The network of the figure is excited by a sinusoidal source and is in the steady-state. Use the phasor I_2 as the reference and draw a complete phasor diagram showing all voltage and current phasors.

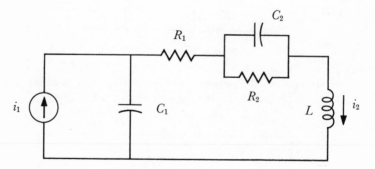

Figure Problem 10-6

10-7   The network shown is a model for a resistor in series with a lossy coil. With the system operating in the sinusoidal steady-state, the rms voltage of the source is 15 volts, that of the coil is 13 volts, and for the resistor 5 volts. If R is known to be 10 ohms, and $\omega = 1$ radian/sec, find R_L and L.

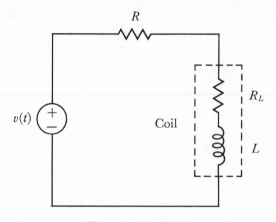

Figure Problem 10-7

10-8   In the network of the figure, $i(t) = \sqrt{2}\, \sin t$. Find $v_2(t)$.

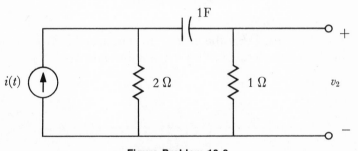

Figure Problem 10-8

10-9   For the given network, find $v_a(t)$ if $v_1(t) = \sqrt{2}\, \cos 2t$ and the system is in the steady-state. Draw a complete phasor diagram showing all voltage and current phasors.

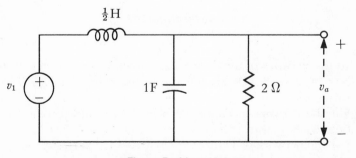

Figure Problem 10-9

10-10 Determine the transfer function $V_2(s)/I(s)$ for the network in Figure Problem 10-8.

10-11 Determine the transfer function $V_a(s)/V_1(s)$ for the network in Figure Problem 10-9.

10-12 In the network of the figure, $v_2(t) = 2 \sin 2t$. Determine $v_1(t)$ in the form $K_1 \sin (2t + \theta)$.

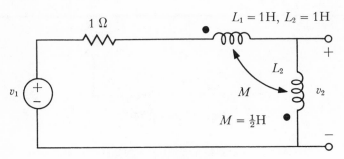

Figure Problem 10-12

10-13 It is determined that the current in the capacitor, $i_a(t)$, is $i_a(t) = \frac{1}{2} \sin t$. For this network, find the phasor ratio $Z_{21} = V_2/I_1 = a + jb$.

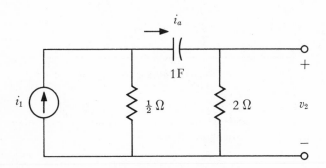

Figure Problem 10-13

10-14 In the network of the figure, it is known from an oscillograph that $v_3(t) = 2 \sin 2t$. Determine the transfer function V_2/V_1 in polar form.

10-15 For the network in Figure Problem 10-12, find the transfer function, $G_{21} = V_2/V_1$.

10-16 For the network of Figure Problem 10-14, determine the following voltage-ratio transfer functions: (a) V_3/V_1, (b) V_2/V_1.

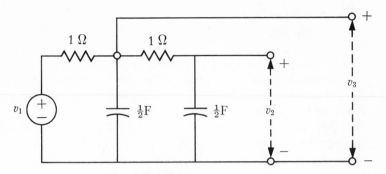

Figure Problem 10-14

10-17 In the network of the figure, it is given that $R = 10$ ohms, $1/\omega_0 C = 10$ ohms, and $i(t) = 10 \sin \omega_0 t$. We are required to find the source voltage, $v(t)$. The following solution is proposed:

$$v(t) = \left(R + \frac{1}{j\omega_0 C}\right) 10 \sin \omega_0 t$$

$$= (10 - j10)\, 10 \sin \omega_0 t$$

$$= 100 \sin \omega_0 t - j100 \sin \omega_0 t = 100\sqrt{2} \sin (\omega_0 t - 45°).$$

Is this solution correct? Comment on the method of solution and the justification of each of the steps.

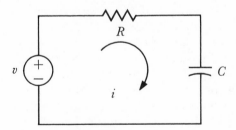

Figure Problem 10-17

10-18 Repeat Problem 10-1 but let $\cos 10t$ correspond to $1 \,/\underline{0°}$. Are the answers to (d), (e), (f), (g), (h), and (i) affected by the choice of reference phasor?

10-19 Repeat Problem 10-18 but let $\sin (10t - 30°)$ correspond to $1 \,/\underline{0°}$.

10-20 Repeat Problem 10-1 but for $i(t) = 5 \cos (10t - 45°)$. Are the answers to (d), (e), (f), and (g) affected by this change? Why or why not?

10-21   Repeat Problem 10-1, but for $i(t) = 2 \sin (20t - 30°)$. Are the answers to (d), (e), (f), and (g) affected by this change? Why or why not?

10-22   For the network in Figure Problem 10-14, $v_1(t) = 2 \sin 2t$. Use phasors to compute $v_2(t)$. [*Hint:* Make use of linearity.]

10-23   Repeat Problem 10-13 but for $i_a(t) = 10 \cos (t + \pi/6)$. Is the answer the same as that of Problem 10-13? Why or why not?

10-24   For the network in Figure Exercise 10.3-7(a), does the resistive component of Z (real part of Z) depend on the value of ω? How about the real part of Y?

10-25   Determine the driving point impedance $Z(s)$ for the networks in Figure Exercise 10.3-7 and plot the pole-zero configuration for $Z(s)$.

10-26   Plot the pole-zero configuration for $Y(s)$ for the same networks in Problem 10-25.

10-27   Determine the voltage transfer function $G(s) = V_L(s)/V(s)$ for the network in Figure Exercise 10.4-1.

10-28   Determine the voltage transfer function $G(s) = V_2(s)/V_1(s)$ for the network in Figure Exercise 10.4-2 and plot the pole-zero configuration of $G(s)$.

10-29   Repeat Problem 10-28 for the network of Figure Exercise 10.4-3.

10-30   Determine the transfer impedance $Z_{21}(s)$ for the network in Figure Problem 10-8.

10-31   Repeat Problem 10-30 for Figure Problem 10-13.

10-32   Restate Thevenin's theorem for linear time-invariant networks with sinusoidal sources of the same frequency, if only the steady-state is of interest. Use phasors.

10-33   Restate Norton's theorem for linear time-invariant networks in the sinusoidal steady-state where the sources are all sinusoidal with the same frequency. Use phasors.

10-34   Restate the principle of superposition for linear time-invariant networks in the sinusoidal steady-state where the sources are all sinusoidal with the same frequency. Use phasors.

10-35   A sinusoidal voltage source is in series with a linear time-invariant network, forming a composite two-terminal network. Assuming sinusoidal steady-state conditions, determine an equivalent composite two-terminal network consisting of a sinusoidal current source in parallel with a linear time-invariant network. Denote the driving point impedance of the original network by Z, and use phasors.

10-36   Find the Thevenin equivalent for the linear time-invariant network in the figure, where v is $V_0 e^{st}$.

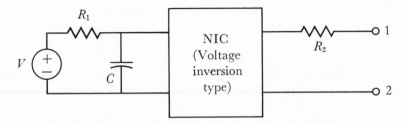

Figure Problem 10-36

10-37 The network consists of a voltage-controlled voltage source connected to an arbitrary linear time-invariant network with driving point impedance $Z(j\omega)$. Determine the Thevenin equivalent from terminals 1 and 2. How does the controlled source compare with an *NIC*? (Find relations between the phasors V_1 and V_2, and between the phasors I_1 and I_2.)

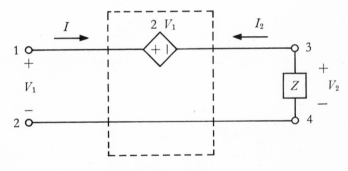

Figure Problem 10-37

10-38 Let the driving-point impedance of a linear time-invariant one-port network be denoted by $Z(j\omega)$. Express the average power into the network for a sinusoidal excitation of frequency ω in terms of Z, and the phasors for v and i.

10-39 A model for a sinusoidal signal generator consists of sinusoidal voltage source in series with an impedance $Z_s = R_s + jX_s$. The source is connected to a load $Z_L = R_L + jX_L$. If R_L and X_L are independently adjustable, determine values of R_L and X_L such that the power delivered to Z_L is maximized. It is given that $R_s > 0$.

10-40 Repeat Problem 10-39 if $|Z_L|$ is adjustable but X_L/R_L is fixed.

10-41 Repeat Problem 10-39 if X_L is fixed but R_L is adjustable.

10-42   Suppose that for the network in Problem 10-39, R_s and X_s are adjustable, but R_L and X_L are fixed. Determine R_s and X_s so that the power delivered to Z_L is maximized. It is also required that $R_s \geq 0$.

10-43   The maximum power delivered to Z_L in Problem 10-39 is called the *available power* of the source. Determine the available power for the source in Problem 10-39. Note that the available power is the most power that can be extracted from a given practical source whose model includes an impedance.

10-44   Restate Tellegen's theorem for linear time-invariant networks in the sinusoidal steady-state where the sources are all sinusoidal with the same frequency. Use phasors.

10-45   Restate the formula for the average power flow into an n-terminal linear time-invariant network in the sinusoidal steady-state where the sources are all sinusoidal with the same frequency. Use phasors. See Problem 6-8 (p. 142) and Figure 6.10 (p. 128).

Resonance and Signal Filtering **11**

11.1 Filtering

The word *filter* usually connotes something that separates one thing from a mixture of things. For instance, a sieve may let liquid and small particles pass through but solid particles larger than the mesh size of the sieve are obstructed from passing through. Likewise, an electric signal filter seeks to extract one electric signal from a mixture of electric signals. We may have a signal composed of the summation of various sinusoids (or exponentials) of different frequencies. This signal may be the input to a filter which yields as an output a single sinusoid. This is of course an idealization. In an actual practical case, the undesired components are not completely suppressed. Let us examine a simple example involving the network in Figure 11.1.

Suppose the input to the network is a sinusoid of frequency ω. Then, if $v_{in}(t) = V_{in} \sin \omega t$ is represented by the phasor $V_{in}e^{j0}$, then the output phasor is

$$V_0 = \left(\frac{1/j\omega c}{R + (1/j\omega c)}\right)V_{in} = \frac{V_{in}}{1 + j\omega RC}. \tag{11.1}$$

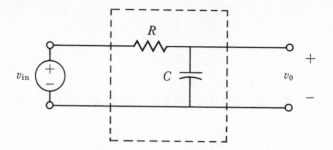

Figure 11.1 A simple low-pass filter.

This means that the function $v_0(t)$ is

$$v_0(t) = \frac{V_{\text{in}}}{\sqrt{1 + (\omega RC)^2}} \sin (\omega t - \tan^{-1} \omega RC). \qquad (11.2)$$

If $R = 1000$ ohms, $C = .001 \ \mu\text{F}$, and $\omega = 1000$ radians/sec, then we have

$$v_0(t) = \frac{V_{\text{in}}}{\sqrt{1 + [(1000)(1000)(10^{-3})(10^{-6})]^2}} \sin (1000t - \tan^{-1} 10^{-3})$$

$$\approx V_{\text{in}} \sin (1000t). \qquad (11.3)$$

If instead of $\omega = 1000$ we have $\omega = 10^7$ radians/sec with the same R and C, the output voltage becomes

$$v_0(t) = \frac{V_{\text{in}}}{\sqrt{1 + [(10^7)(10^3)(10^{-9})]^2}} \sin (10^7t - \tan^{-1} 10)$$

$$= 0.099 V_{\text{in}} \sin (10^7t - 88.5°). \qquad (11.4)$$

Suppose that the input voltage now consists of two sinusoids

$$v_{\text{in}}(t) = V_1 \sin 1000t + V_2 \sin 10^7t. \qquad (11.5)$$

Since the network is linear, we may use the principle of superposition. From the previous calculations of Equations 11.3 and 11.4, the output due to the input of Equation 11.5 is

$$v_0(t) = V_1 \sin 10^3t + 0.099 V_2 \sin (10^7t - 88.5°). \qquad (11.6)$$

Notice that peak values of the two sinusoids comprising the input are V_1 and V_2, whereas the output of the network has the peak value of the higher-frequency sinusoid relatively suppressed. By examining Equation 11.2, we see that the higher the frequency ω, the less the magnitude of the output. The ratio of the magnitudes of V_0 to V_{in} is

$$\frac{V_0}{V_{\text{in}}} = \frac{1}{\sqrt{1 + (\omega RC)^2}}. \qquad (11.7)$$

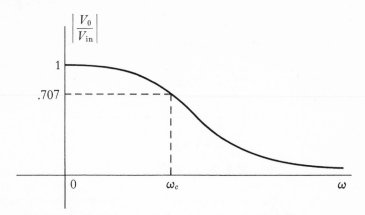

Figure 11.2 Frequency characteristic of the low-pass filter of Figure 11.1.

The variation with respect to ω is shown in Figure 11.2. Because of the shape of the curve, this network is called a *low-pass filter*. It is low-pass in the sense that high-frequency signals are attenuated much more than those of low frequency. By convention, the range of frequencies for which the relative frequency response or characteristic is at least .707 is called the *passband*. In Figure 11.2, the passband is the band of frequencies from $\omega = 0$ to $\omega = \omega_c$. The passband is also called the *bandwidth*. The band of frequencies for which the relative frequency characteristic or response is less than $1/\sqrt{2}$ is referred to as the *stopband*.† In Figure 11.2, the stopband is the range of frequencies from $\omega = \omega_c$ up to infinity. The *ideal* low-pass response is a constant characteristic of 1 from $\omega = 0$ to $\omega = \omega_c$ and zero characteristic or response for $\omega > \omega_c$. Such a characteristic is not physically realizable (meaning that it can not be built) but it is still a useful reference for comparing actual low-pass responses. With more network elements, it is possible to design more elaborate filters which have a response nearly equal to one in the passband, and closer to zero in the stopband than the one for the simple RC network we have considered.

Another simple filter is shown in Figure 11.3. It is called a *high-pass filter* because it attenuates low-frequency signals much more than it does the high-frequency ones. An examination of the network reveals immediately that if $\omega = 0$, then there is no output voltage because there is no current through the capacitor and hence no current through R. For low frequencies, the impedance of C, which is $1/j\omega C$, is relatively high. The impedance of the resistor is R, a constant. The voltage-divider effect of these two

---

† If the voltage is $1/\sqrt{2}$ of the largest possible voltage, then assuming that we have a resistive load, the power is proportional to V^2. Hence, the power is one half of the largest possible power. Although a figure other than $\frac{1}{2}$ could be arbitrarily chosen, $\frac{1}{2}$ is frequently used.

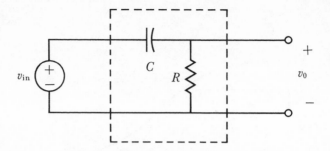

Figure 11.3 A simple high-pass filter.

impedances is such that the output voltage is relatively low. However, when ω is very large, then the magnitude of the impedance $1/j\omega C$ is small and the voltage drop across C is also very small. Consequently, for large ω, the magnitude of the voltage at the output is almost equal to that of the input. The voltage transfer function is

$$\frac{V_0}{V_{in}} = \frac{R}{R + (1/j\omega C)} = \frac{j\omega RC}{1 + j\omega RC}. \tag{11.8}$$

Hence the magnitude is

$$\left|\frac{V_0}{V_{in}}\right| = \frac{\omega RC}{\sqrt{1 + (\omega RC)^2}}, \tag{11.9}$$

which is plotted in Figure 11.4. From our definition of the passband, this high-pass filter has a passband corresponding to the range of frequencies from ω_c to infinity. Again ω_c, the *cut-off frequency*, corresponds to the point where the magnitude of the transfer function is 0.707 times maximum possible magnitude. The stopband is the frequency range from 0 to ω_c. For more elaborate networks, the response can be made more nearly constant in the passband and more nearly zero in the stopband.

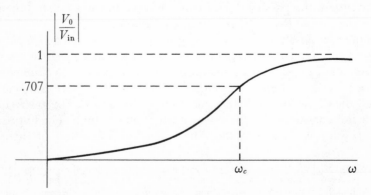

Figure 11.4 Frequency characteristic of the high-pass filter of Figure 11.3.

● EXERCISES

11.1-1 For the network of Figure 11.1, what is the cut-off frequency ω_c in terms of R and C? What is the *time constant* of the network? How is the time constant related to the bandwidth?

11.1-2 Suppose the network of Figure 11.1 has $R = 1000$ ohms and $C = 100 \ \mu F$. The input voltage is $v_{in}(t) = 100 - 20 \cos \left[2\pi (60)t \right]$. Determine $v_0(t)$. Sketch $v_{in}(t)$ and $v_0(t)$ for t from zero to 0.1 sec.

11.1-3 Repeat Exercise 11.1-2 for Figure 11.3.

11.1-4 Determine an expression for the phase angle of the voltage-transfer function as a function of ω for the low-pass filter of Figure 11.1. What is the phase angle at the cut-off frequency?

11.1-5 Repeat Exercise 11.1-4 for the high-pass filter of Figure 11.3.

11.2 Series resonance

A simple circuit which exhibits another type of signal filtering is shown in Figure 11.5. Suppose that the source voltage is sinusoidal and that we are interested in how the current magnitude depends on the frequency ω. By inspection of the series RLC circuit, we observe that for very low frequencies the impedance of the capacitor, $1/j\omega C$, has a relatively large magnitude. This means that the current magnitude is low. In fact, for $\omega = 0$, there is zero current. Likewise, for very large frequency, the impedance of the inductor, $j\omega L$, has a large magnitude resulting in a small magnitude of current. It turns out that for some intermediate value of ω, the current magnitude attains its largest value. Let us determine this critical frequency.

Let the voltage be

$$v(t) = V_{in} \sin (\omega t + \theta). \tag{11.10}$$

Since the impedance is

$$Z = R + j\omega L + \frac{1}{j\omega C} = R + j\left(\omega L - \frac{1}{\omega C} \right), \tag{11.11}$$

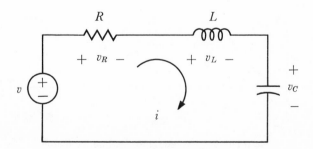

Figure 11.5 A series *RLC* circuit.

then the current is

$$i(t) = I_m \sin(\omega t + \theta - \phi), \tag{11.12}$$

where the phase angle ϕ is

$$\phi = \tan^{-1}\left[\frac{\omega L - (1/\omega C)}{R}\right], \tag{11.13}$$

and I_m, the peak value of the sinusoidal current, is

$$I_m = \frac{V_m}{\sqrt{R^2 + [\omega L - (1/\omega C)]^2}}. \tag{11.14}$$

For a given set of R, L, C, and V_m which are constants, I_m and ϕ depend only on the frequency ω. We see that I_m is largest if the value of ω is such that the denominator of the right-hand side of Equation 11.14 is the smallest. This occurs when $[\omega L - (1/\omega C)]^2$ is smallest. Clearly, this occurs when

$$\omega L - \frac{1}{\omega C} = 0 \tag{11.15}$$

or

$$\omega = \frac{1}{\sqrt{LC}}. \tag{11.16}$$

From Equation 11.13, we have $\phi = 0$ if Equation 11.15 is satisfied. For a series *RLC* circuit, the condition which obtains when $\phi = 0$ is called *resonance*. The corresponding value of ω is called *resonant frequency*, usually

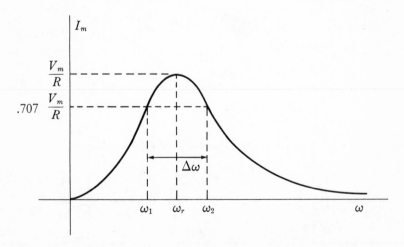

Figure 11.6 I_m versus ω for *RLC* series circuit.

denoted by ω_r. Figure 11.6 shows a typical plot of I_m vs. ω. From Equation 11.14, we see that the largest value of I_m is V_m/R. The bandwidth is $\Delta\omega = \omega_2 - \omega_1$, which is the range of frequencies for which I_m is at least $1/\sqrt{2}$ of its largest value.

Let us derive the bandwidth $\Delta\omega$ in terms of the parameters of the circuit. To calculate ω_1 and ω_2, we solve for the frequencies which satisfy

$$I_m = \frac{V_m}{\sqrt{R^2 + [\omega L - (1/\omega C)]^2}} = \frac{1}{\sqrt{2}}\frac{V_m}{R}. \tag{11.17}$$

These points are indicated on Figure 11.6.

Simplifying Equation 11.17 we have

$$\left(\omega L - \frac{1}{\omega C}\right)^2 = R^2 \quad \text{or} \quad \left(\omega L - \frac{1}{\omega C}\right) = \pm R. \tag{11.18}$$

Taking the positive sign first and simplifying, we have

$$LC\omega^2 - RC\omega - 1 = 0 \tag{11.19}$$

or

$$\omega = \frac{RC \pm \sqrt{(RC)^2 + 4LC}}{2LC}. \tag{11.20}$$

Since we are considering positive ω's only, we discard the negative solution; and the positive solution in Equation 11.20 is either ω_1 or ω_2. Taking the negative sign in Equation 11.18 and simplifying, we have

$$LC\omega^2 + RC\omega - 1 = 0 \tag{11.21}$$

or

$$\omega = \frac{-RC \pm \sqrt{(RC)^2 + 4LC}}{2LC}. \tag{11.22}$$

Again, the positive solution in Equation 11.22 is either ω_1 or ω_2, and since we are assuming ω_2 to be larger than ω_1, then we have

$$\omega_1 = \frac{\sqrt{(RC)^2 + 4LC} - RC}{2LC} \tag{11.23}$$

and

$$\omega_2 = \frac{\sqrt{(RC)^2 + 4LC} + RC}{2LC}. \tag{11.24}$$

Then from Equations 11.23 and 11.24, it follows that

$$\Delta\omega \equiv \omega_2 - \omega_1 = \frac{R}{L}. \tag{11.25}$$

and

$$\omega_1\omega_2 = \frac{1}{LC} = \omega_r^2,\qquad(11.26)$$

where ω_r is the resonant frequency.

Equation 11.25 indicates that in order to have a narrow bandwidth, the ratio of R to L must be small. Now R is the total series resistance of the circuit. In practical circuits, the components are not ideal and have loss. The coil component is represented by the model with an inductor in series with a small resistor. In the series circuit of Figure 11.5, R includes the resistance of the coil. The bandwidth as given in Equation 11.25 can not be made arbitrarily small because of this resistance. If we make L larger by using more turns in the coil, we use more wire and the resistance of the coil also increases.

Equation 11.26 also shows that the resonant frequency is the geometric mean of the cut-off frequencies ω_1 and ω_2. The formula is useful for calculating the resonant frequency from the cut-off frequencies and also for calculating one cut-off frequency in terms of the resonant frequency and the other cut-off frequency.

In an ideal resonant circuit, there is no dissipation. Energy is simply stored in the associated magnetic field of the inductor and the associated electric field of the capacitor. In a practical circuit with nonzero resistance, part of the energy is dissipated. A useful figure of merit for resonant circuits is based on the ratio of total stored energy at the resonant frequency to energy dissipated per cycle. Let us first find expressions for energy stored and energy dissipated per cycle before we define this figure of merit precisely. Let the current through the circuit be

$$i(t) = I_m \sin (\omega t + \alpha).\qquad(11.27)$$

Then the energy stored in the inductor at any time t is

$$W_L(t) = \tfrac{1}{2} Li^2 = \tfrac{1}{2} LI_m^2 \sin^2 (\omega t + \alpha).\qquad(11.28)$$

The voltage $v_C(t)$ with polarity reference as shown in Figure 11.5 lags the current by $90°$, and it is

$$v_C(t) = \frac{I_m}{\omega C} \sin (\omega t + \alpha - 90°) = -\frac{I_m}{\omega C} \cos (\omega t + \alpha).\qquad(11.29)$$

The energy stored in the capacitor at any time t is

$$W_C(t) = \frac{1}{2} Cv_C^2 = \frac{1}{2} C\left(\frac{I_m^2}{\omega^2 C^2}\right) \cos^2 (\omega t + \alpha)$$

$$= \frac{I_m^2}{2\omega^2 C} \cos^2 (\omega t + \alpha).\qquad(11.30)$$

The total stored energy at any instant of time is then

$$W_T(t) = W_L(t) + W_C(t) = \frac{1}{2} I_m^2 [L \sin^2(\omega t + \alpha) + \frac{1}{\omega^2 C} \cos^2(\omega t + \alpha)].$$

(11.31)

At resonance, $\omega^2 = 1/LC$ so that $1/\omega^2 C = L$ and Equation 11.31 becomes

$$W_T(t) = \frac{1}{2} I_m^2 L [\sin^2(\omega t + \alpha) + \cos^2(\omega t + \alpha)] = \frac{1}{2} L I_m^2 = \text{const.} \quad (11.32)$$

We note that at resonance, although the current and voltages in the series *RLC* circuit are sinusoidal, the total *instantaneous* stored energy is a *constant*. For frequencies other than ω_r, the instantaneous stored energy as given by Equation 11.31 fluctuates with time. The energy dissipated at resonant frequency in one cycle is

$$W_d = \text{Average power} \times \text{period} = I_{\text{rms}}^2 R \times T = \frac{I_m^2 R}{2} \times T. \quad (11.33)$$

We now *define* a figure of merit or quality factor Q as

$$Q = 2\pi \frac{\text{total energy stored at resonant frequency}}{\text{energy dissipated per cycle at resonant frequency}}. \quad (11.34a)$$

Since one cycle corresponds to 2π radians, then the energy dissipated per cycle at resonant frequency divided by 2π is the average energy dissipated per radian at resonant frequency. Hence, the definition of Q in Equation 11.34a may be written

$$Q = \frac{\text{total energy stored at resonant frequency}}{\text{average energy dissipated per radian at resonant frequency}}. \quad (11.34b)$$

For the series circuit of Figure 11.5, Q is

$$Q = 2\pi \frac{\frac{1}{2} L I_m^2}{\frac{1}{2} R I_m^2 T} = \frac{2\pi}{T} \frac{L}{R} = \frac{\omega_r L}{R}. \quad (11.35)$$

The energy definition of Q of Equation 11.34a is quite universal and applies to parallel resonance to be described later as well as to more complicated resonant networks. In fact, it is used in describing resonant mechanical networks, resonant acoustical devices and resonant microwave cavities. For series *RLC* circuits, it reduces to the expression in Equation 11.35. Another figure of merit which is used to characterize resonant systems is *selectivity S* which is defined as

$$S = \frac{\text{resonant frequency}}{\text{bandwidth}} = \frac{\omega_r}{\Delta \omega}. \quad (11.36)$$

We can verify that for the series circuit, since $\Delta \omega = R/L$, $S = \omega_r L/R$, which is equal to the Q factor as in Equation 11.35. Note that R in Equation 11.35 is the total resistance in the circuit. In general, Q and S are different. A quality factor for the practical inductor alone is defined as

$$Q_{\text{coil}} = \frac{\omega_r L}{R_L},$$ (11.37)

which is the same as the expression in Equation 11.35 except that total resistance R is replaced by R_L, the resistance of the practical inductor.

Figure 11.7 shows the relative responses for different values of S. For the *same resonant frequency* ω_r, the higher the selectivity the narrower the bandwidth. Similarly, for the *same S*, the higher the resonant frequency ω_r, the larger the bandwidth in accordance with Equation 11.36.

Thus far, we have considered the current as the output variable for the network in Figure 11.5. Other possible quantities we may consider are the voltages across each of the elements. The variation of voltage magnitude as a function of ω is found by multiplying the magnitude of the current by the magnitude of the impedance. That is, we have

$$V_{Rm} = RI_m = \frac{V_m R}{\sqrt{R^2 + [\omega L - (1/\omega C)]^2}},$$ (11.38)

$$V_{Cm} = \frac{1}{\omega C} I_m = \frac{V_m}{\omega C \sqrt{R^2 + [\omega L - (1/\omega C)]^2}},$$ (11.39)

and

$$V_{Lm} = \omega L I_m = \frac{\omega L V_m}{\sqrt{R^2 + [\omega L - (1/\omega C)]^2}}.$$ (11.40)

These expressions give the peak values of the corresponding sinusoidal

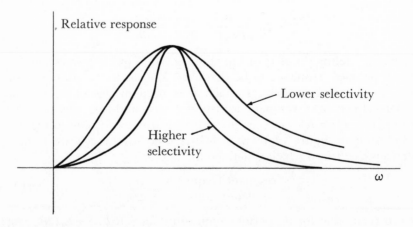

Figure 11.7 Effect of selectivity on resonance curve or frequency-characteristic curve.

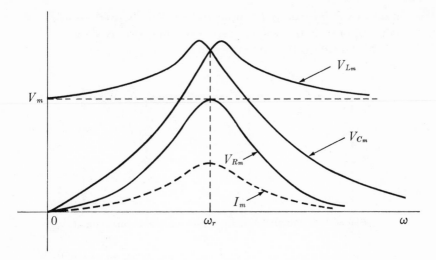

Figure 11.8 Plots of V_{R_m}, V_{L_m}, and V_{C_m} versus ω for a series *RLC* circuit.

voltages. Typical plots of these magnitudes vs. ω are shown in Figure 11.8. Observe that V_{Rm}, the peak value of v_R, and I_m have the same variation with frequency, but that the peak values V_{Cm} and V_{Lm} plotted as a function of ω each have their own characteristic shape. The largest value of V_{Cm} and V_{Lm} occur at frequencies slightly different from resonant frequency (see Problem 11.5).

● **EXERCISES**

11.2-1   Show that the Q of a series *RLC* circuit is equal to (a) $Q = 1/\omega_r RC$, (b) $Q = (1/R)\sqrt{L/C}$.

11.2-2   Show that $V_{Cm} = V_{Lm}$ when $\omega = \omega_r$ as shown in Figure 11.8 for the series *RLC* circuit.

11.2-3   Show that V_L approaches V_m asymptotically as ω approaches infinite value, as shown in Figure 11.8 for the *RLC* circuit.

11.2-4   Determine an expression for the magnitude of the admittance of the series *RLC* circuit of Figure 11.5. Compare your expression to that for I_m in Equation 11.14. From this expression, we see that series resonance corresponds to the frequency for which the magnitude of the admittance is a maximum.

11.2-5   Show that the selectivity of a series *RLC* circuit is equal to the expressions in Exercise 11.2-1.

11.3 Parallel resonance

In the preceding section, we have considered a series *RLC* circuit where a voltage source is the excitation and current is the response of interest.

We will now examine another simple and commonly used network where the usual response is the voltage across the network as shown in Figure 11.9 and the excitation is a current source.

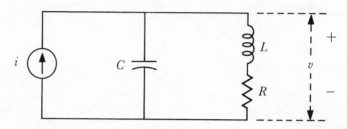

Figure 11.9   A parallel network with a current-source input.

As before, we are interested in the dependence of the response on the frequency of the source, ω. Suppose the input current is

$$i(t) = I_m \sin (\omega t + \theta) \tag{11.41}$$

with a corresponding phasor

$$I = I_m e^{j\theta}. \tag{11.42}$$

Then the phasor voltage is

$$V = IZ, \tag{11.43}$$

where Z is the total complex impedance

$$Z = \cfrac{1}{j\omega C + \cfrac{1}{R + j\omega L}}$$

$$= \cfrac{1}{j\omega C + \cfrac{R}{R^2 + (\omega L)^2} + \cfrac{-j\omega L}{R^2 + (\omega L)^2}}. \tag{11.44}$$

At resonance, $v(t)$ and $i(t)$ must be in phase by definition. This requires that ω have a value such that Z is real at that frequency. The impedance Z is real provided the denominator in Equation 11.44 is real, that is,

$$\omega C - \frac{\omega L}{R^2 + (\omega L)^2} = 0. \tag{11.45}$$

This is satisfied when either $\omega = 0$ or

$$\omega = \frac{1}{\sqrt{LC}} \sqrt{1 - (R^2 C / L)}. \tag{11.46}$$

Equation 11.46 assumes that

$$\frac{R^2 C}{L} \le 1. \tag{11.47}$$

If $R^2 C/L > 1$, then there is no nonzero frequency for which $v(t)$ and $i(t)$ are in phase.

Examining Equation 11.46, it is clear that if $R = 0$, then the formula for resonant frequency is the same as that of Equation 11.16 for series resonance. However, for practical coil components, a pure inductance model is not satisfactory for many purposes. Hence, the R in Figure 11.8 is meant to represent the coil resistance.

For a constant current source, the magnitude of the voltage response is proportional to the magnitude of the complex Z as given in Equation 11.44. For a given set of R, L, and C, we may plot $|Z|$ as a function of ω and graphically determine the value of ω for which $|Z|$ is largest. We may also determine the range of frequencies for which the response is at least $1/\sqrt{2}$ of the largest $|Z|$. If an exact analytical expression is sought for the bandwidth $\Delta\omega$ and the peak frequency, the resulting equations are quite unwieldy. For this reason, let us consider a special case for which an approximation can be made. Suppose that in the frequency range of interest, such as in the bandwidth range $\Delta\omega$, R is small compared to ωL. Then in Equation 11.44, $R^2 + (\omega L)^2 \approx (\omega L)^2$, and Equation 11.44 can be approximated by

$$Z \approx \frac{1}{j\omega C + \dfrac{R}{(\omega L)^2} + \dfrac{-j\omega L}{(\omega L)^2}} = \frac{1}{\dfrac{R}{(\omega L)^2} + j\left(\omega C - \dfrac{1}{\omega L}\right)}. \tag{11.48}$$

Hence we have

$$|Z| \approx \frac{1}{\sqrt{[R/(\omega L)^2]^2 + [\omega C - (1/\omega L)]^2}}. \tag{11.49}$$

Assuming that the selectivity of the circuit is high, then for ω inside the range of $\Delta\omega$ the value of ω is approximately equal to the value of ω for which $|Z|$ is maximum. Then $R/(\omega L)^2$ is approximately constant in the bandwidth $\Delta\omega$. If $R/(\omega L)^2$ is considered constant in the range of $\Delta\omega$ in Equation 11.49, then the problem of determining $\Delta\omega$ approximately is simplified. First, we notice from Equation 11.49 that $|Z|$ is approximately maximum when

$$\omega C - \frac{1}{\omega L} = 0$$

or

$$\omega = \frac{1}{\sqrt{LC}}. \tag{11.50}$$

That is, the peak in the response curve occurs in the vicinity of $\omega = 1/\sqrt{LC}$, which is also in the vicinity of resonance as given by Equation 11.46. Next, we notice that the dependence of $|Z|$ on ω, for the range of ω in $\Delta\omega$, is similar to that of I_m for series resonance as given in Equation 11.14. Comparing Equation 11.14 and 11.49, we see that R in Equation 11.14 corresponds to $R/(\omega L)^2$ in Equation 11.49, L and C in Equation 11.14 correspond to C and L, respectively, in Equation 11.49. The mathematical problem of determining $\Delta\omega$ is the same for both. Since we have done it already for Equation 11.14, we need not repeat. We simply look at the result in Equation 11.26 and make appropriate substitutions in symbols. Thus in Equation 11.26, we replace R by $R/(\omega L)^2$ and L by C. We note also that $\omega \approx \omega_r$. The approximate bandwidth for the parallel circuit of Figure 11.9 is then

$$\Delta\omega \approx \frac{R/(\omega L)^2}{C} \approx \frac{R}{\omega_r^2 L^2 C}. \tag{11.51}$$

Since $\omega_r^2 = 1/LC$, this reduces further to

$$\Delta\omega \approx \frac{R}{L}, \tag{11.52}$$

which is the same for the series case. The approximate selectivity S is

$$S = \frac{\omega_r}{\Delta\omega} \approx \frac{\omega_r L}{R}. \tag{11.53}$$

To arrive at Equations 11.52 and 11.53, we assumed that $R \ll \omega L$ and that S is high. The two conditions turn out to be equivalent. In order for our

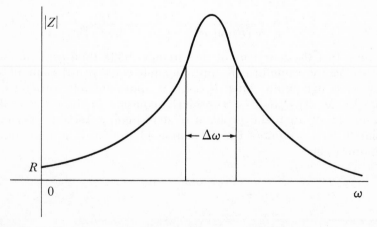

Figure 11.10 Typical response curve for the circuit of Figure 11.9 when *R* is small.

approximations to be justified, the resulting value of S should be high. They should not be used for S less than 10. To determine the general shape of the response curve, we note, by examining Figure 11.9, that the higher the frequency, the lower the impedance of the capacitor. For extremely large ω, the capacitor is essentially a short circuit. Hence, as ω approaches infinity, $|Z|$ approaches zero. Likewise for very low frequencies, the capacitor becomes almost an open circuit and the inductor acts like a short circuit. The net impedance is low but not zero. As ω approaches zero, $|Z|$ approaches R. A typical response curve is shown in Figure 11.10. Thus for high values of S, the parallel circuit of Figure 11.9 has approximately the same equations for bandwidth, Q, and peak frequency.

● **EXERCISES**

11.3-1 Suppose for the network in Figure 11.9, $C = 100$ picofarad (pF) (1 pF $= 10^{-12}$ F), $L = .01$ henry, $R = 1000$ ohms. What is the approximate resonant frequency? What is the selectivity S? What is the bandwidth? What is the Q?

11.3-2 For the network in Exercise 11.3-1, what is the approximate magnitude of the impedance at resonance? Calculate $|Z|$ at the following additional values of ω: $\omega = 0$, $\omega = \frac{1}{2}\omega_r$, $\omega = \omega_r - \frac{1}{4}\Delta\omega$, $\omega = \omega_r + \frac{1}{4}\Delta\omega$, $\omega = 2\omega_r$, $\omega = \infty$. Sketch the variation of $|Z|$ as a function of ω.

11.3-3 Suppose the current $i(t)$ in Figure 11.9 is $i(t) = 0.1 \cos \omega_r t + 0.1 \cos 2\omega_r t$, where $\omega_r = 1/\sqrt{LC}$. Determine $v(t)$ if the network parameters are as given in Exercise 11.3-1. Is there a filtering effect?

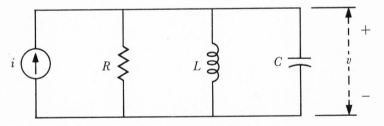

Figure Exercise 11.3-4

11.3-4 The parallel RLC network of Figure Exercise 11.3-4 is connected to a sinusoidal current source of fixed maximum value but adjustable frequency. All measurements are made when the system is in the steady-state. We define resonance as occurring when $v(t)$ and $i(t)$ are in phase. Determine the frequency of resonance, ω_r, in terms of the R, L, and C of the network.

11.3-5   Defining bandwidth as the range of frequencies over which V_m is at least 0.707 of the largest V_m, determine the bandwidth for the network of Figure Exercise 11.3-4. Calculate the Q and S of the resonant network and compare the answer with that given for the series RLC network.

11.3-6   Plot the magnitude of the impedance of a parallel LC network as a function of ω. The frequency at which the circuit appears to be an open circuit is defined as the resonant frequency. What is this frequency in terms of L and C?

11.4 Locus diagrams

Suppose that we plot the current phasor I in the series RLC circuit for various values of ω. Then we will obtain a set of phasors as in Figure 11.11. If we connect the tips of the arrows of the phasors, we obtain a curve known as the *locus* of I with ω as a parameter. For the RLC series circuit, the locus turns out to be a circle as shown in Figure 11.12. That this is true may be seen by the following consideration. The phasor voltage V_R is always 90° out of phase with the phasor voltage V_x across the LC combination. The phasor sum, however, is equal to V, the phasor voltage corresponding to the source. No matter what the current is

$$V = V_R + V_x = \text{const.} \qquad (11.54)$$

A typical phasor diagram is shown in Figure 11.13. Since the V_R and V_x phasors are always perpendicular and the sum is constant, the locus of the right-angle corner will be a circle. Hence, the locus of V_R is a circle. Since $V_R = IR$ and since R is constant, the locus of I is also a circle. It is clear that

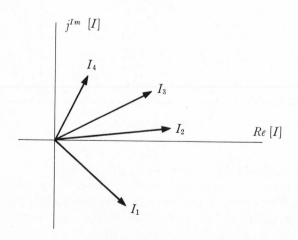

Figure 11.11 Current phasors for various values of ω.

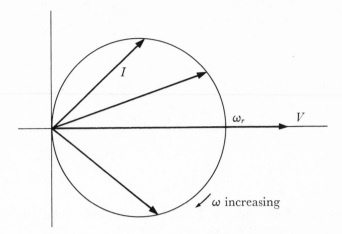

Figure 11.12 Locus for the *I* phasor with ω as parameter.

V_R is largest when $V_x = 0$ and the corresponding *I* is $|V|/R$, which is the diameter of the circle of the *I* locus. Note that we are using *V* as a reference phasor (on the horizontal axis) and that *I* lagging corresponds to

$$\omega L - \frac{1}{\omega C} > 0$$

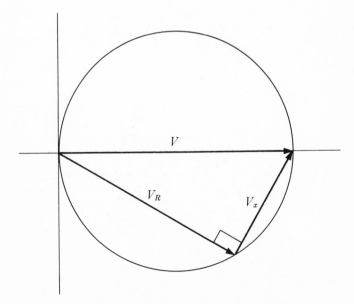

Figure 11.13 Typical phasor diagram for a series *RLC* circuit.

or

$$\omega > \frac{1}{\sqrt{LC}}, \tag{11.55}$$

and I leading corresponds to

$$\omega L - \frac{1}{\omega C} < 0,$$

or

$$\omega < \frac{1}{\sqrt{LC}}. \tag{11.56}$$

At the resonant frequency ω_r, I and V are in phase. From the locus it is seen that $|I|$ is largest at $\omega = \omega_r$.

Instead of plotting I for various values of ω, we may investigate the dependence of I on L or C at a fixed value of ω. For example, we may allow L to be adjustable from zero to very large values. For the sake of drawing locus diagrams, let L be adjustable from zero to infinity. The reactance $\omega L - 1/\omega C$ will vary between $-1/\omega C$ and infinity. Thus, when $L = 0$, I leads V. As L increases, the angle of lead decreases and eventually I becomes a lagging current. Finally, as L approaches infinity, the lag angle will approach $-90°$, but the magnitude of I approaches zero at the same time. If the tips of the I phasor for various values of L are connected, we obtain the *locus* of I with L as a parameter, and we obtain a *part* of a circle as shown in Figure 11.14. For I to be in phase with V, L must be such that

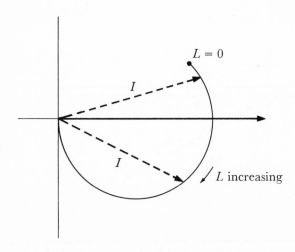

Figure 11.14   Locus of I in an *RLC* series circuit with L as parameter.

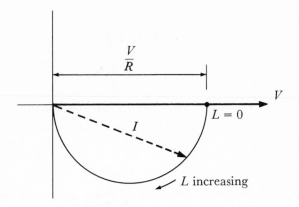

Figure 11.15	Locus of *I* in an *RL* series circuit with *L* as a parameter.

$\omega L - 1/\omega C = 0$ or

$$L_r = \frac{1}{\omega^2 C}. \tag{11.57}$$

If C is short-circuited in the RLC series circuit, i.e., if we have an RL circuit only, then the locus of I as L is adjusted will be a semicircle as shown in Figure 11.15. The reason for the exclusion of portions of the circle in Figures 11.14 and 11.15 is that we are not allowing L to be negative. Recall that the complete circle in Figure 11.12 corresponds to the variation of the reactance $\omega L - 1/\omega C$ from $-\infty$ to $+\infty$. In Figure 11.14, the reactance varies from $-1/\omega C$ to $+\infty$, and in Figure 11.15, from 0 to $+\infty$. Similarly, if we have an adjustable C in an RLC series circuit, the reactance varies between $-\infty$ to ωL, and the locus of I with C as a parameter is shown in Figure 11.16. For an RC circuit with an adjustable C, the reactance varies between $-\infty$ and 0, and the locus of I is shown in Figure 11.17.

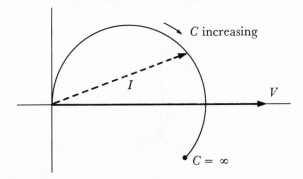

Figure 11.16	Locus of *I* in an *RLC* series circuit with *C* as a parameter.

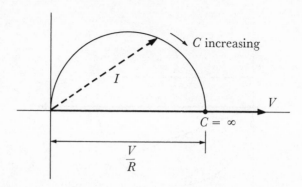

Figure 11.17   Locus of *I* in an *RC* circuit with *C* as a parameter.

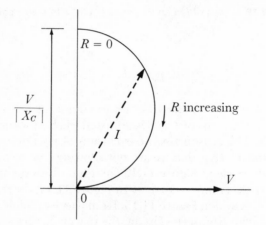

Figure 11.18   Locus of *I* in an *RC* circuit with *R* as a parameter.

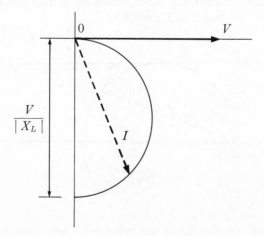

Figure 11.19   Locus of *I* in an *RL* circuit with *R* as a parameter.

The locus of I with R as a parameter in an RC series circuit is as shown in Figure 11.18.† For an RL series circuit with an adjustable R, the locus of I is also a semicircle as shown in Figure 11.19.

● **EXERCISES**

11.4-1   From the locus diagram of I in an RLC series circuit, with ω as a parameter, show that when $|I|$ is $1/\sqrt{2}$ of its maximum value, V and I are out of phase by 45°.

11.4-2   For a series RLC circuit, verify the locus of I with C as a parameter by calculating I for several values of C. Assume $V_{rms} = 10$ volts, $R = 1$ ohm, $L = 1$ henry, $\omega = 1$ radian/sec and take C to be 0, 1, 10, and 100.

11.4-3   For a series RLC circuit with adjustable C, draw the locus of I if $v(t) = 10 \sin 100t$, $R = 10$ ohms, and $L = 0.1$ henry. Draw the I phasor corresponding to $C = 10^3 \ \mu F$.

11.4-4   The voltage source in Figure Exercise 11.4-4 has a given peak value V_m and a given ω and all the network parameters are given except C. Assuming that V is the reference phasor, complete the following: (a) draw I_L; (b) draw the locus of I_C with C as a parameter; (c) draw the locus of I with C as parameter.

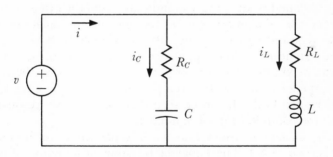

Figure Exercise 11.4-4

11.4-5   Suppose that in the network of Figure Exercise 11.4-4, L instead of C is adjustable. Draw a locus of I with L as a parameter.

11.5 Resonance in other networks

As in series resonance, resonance in the network of Figure Exercise 11.4-4 occurs when the sinusoidal $v(t)$ and $i(t)$ are in phase. For an adjustable C, the locus for I is shown in Figure 11.20. Note that there are two possible values of I_C which cause I to be in phase with V. If the radius of

† For a derivation, see M. B. Reed, *Alternating Current Circuit Theory*, 2nd ed. (New York: Harper and Bros., 1956).

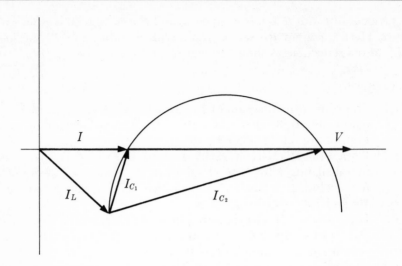

Figure 11.20   Locus for *I* of the network in Figure Exercise 11.4-4, with *C* as a parameter.

the semicircle is just equal to the vertical component of I_L, then there is only one resonance point, but if the radius is less than the vertical component of I_L, resonance is not possible. The minimum magnitude of I may be simply obtained by drawing a straight line from the origin to the center of the semicircle. The intersection of the line and the semicircle gives the tip of the required I phasor. Since $v(t)$ is assumed to have a fixed peak value, the magnitude of the impedance Z is largest when $|I|$ is minimum. Hence, the maximum value of $|Z|$ does not coincide with the resonance. If $R_C = 0$, the locus of I_C with C as a parameter is simply a vertical line as shown in Figure 11.21. It can be seen that for this case, resonance coincides with the condition for minimum $|I|$.

Similarly, we may consider L as the free parameter in the network of Figure Exercise 11.4-4. There may be two, one, or no points of resonance depending on the relative magnitudes of the radius of the semicircle and the vertical component of I_C. A typical case where there are two points of resonance is shown in Figure 11.22. At resonance, the vertical component of I_L is equal in magnitude to the vertical component of I_C. This leads to an equation relating the unknown L with the other network parameters.

EXAMPLE 11.5-1.   Suppose that in the network of Figure Exercise 11.4-4, $R_L = R_C = 5$ ohms, $\omega L = 12$ ohms, $\omega = 1000$ radians/sec, and $V_{\text{rms}} = 100$ volts. It is desired to calculate the value or values of C which will produce resonance. Let V be the reference, that is, $V = 100 + j0$. The impedance of the RL branch is $5 + j12$, so that I_L is

$$I_L = \frac{100}{5 + j12} = \frac{100}{169}(5 - j12). \tag{11.58}$$

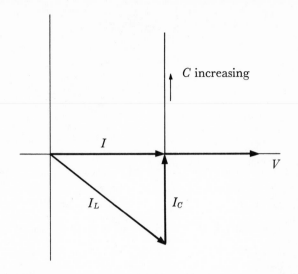

Figure 11.21   Locus for *I* if $R_C = 0$ with *C* as a parameter for the network in Figure Exercise 11.4-4.

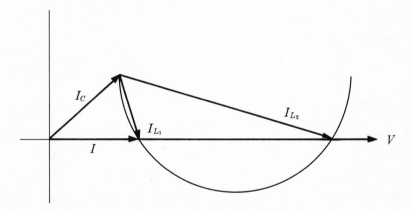

Figure 11.22   Typical *I* locus for the network of Figure Exercise 11.4-4, with *L* as a parameter.

The vertical component of I_L is $100(-12)/169$. Since the radius of the semicircle in Figure 11.19 is $100/10$ and $100/10 > |-100(12)/169|$, there will be two points of resonance. The current I_C is

$$I_C = \frac{100}{5 + jX_C} = \frac{100}{5^2 + X_C^2}(5 - jX_C), \qquad (11.59)$$

where $X_C = -1/\omega C$. At resonance, $I_L + I_C$ is in phase with V so that since V is real, the imaginary component of $I_L + I_C$ is zero. Thus we have

$$100\left[-\frac{12}{169} - \frac{X_C}{25 + X_C^2}\right] = 0 \tag{11.60}$$

or

$$-\frac{12}{169} + \frac{1/\omega C}{25 + (1/(\omega C)^2)} = -\frac{12}{169} + \frac{\omega C}{25(\omega C)^2 + 1} = 0. \tag{11.61}$$

Simplifying, we obtain

$$(\omega C)^2 + .5633(\omega C) + .04 = 0, \tag{11.62}$$

$$(\omega C) = \frac{.5633 \pm \sqrt{(.5633)^2 - 4(.04)}}{2} = .0887 \quad \text{or} \quad .480, \tag{11.63}$$

and, finally we have

$$C = .0887 \times 10^{-3} \quad \text{or} \quad .480 \times 10^{-3} \text{ farad.} \tag{11.64}$$

These two values of C make $i(t)$ in phase with $v(t)$.   □

EXAMPLE 11.5-2. Suppose that for the same network as in Example 11.5-1, it is desired to calculate the smallest possible value of $|I|$. The corresponding phasor will be colinear with the ray passing through the origin and the center of the semicircle. The I phasor starts from the origin and terminates on the semicircle. The phasor from the origin to the center of the semicircle in Figure 11.19 is

$$I_L + \frac{V}{2R_C} = \frac{100}{169}(5 - j12) + \frac{100}{10} = \left(\frac{500}{169} + 10\right) - j\frac{100(12)}{169}. \tag{11.65}$$

The length of $I_{\min}$ is then

$$I_{\min} = \sqrt{\left(\frac{500}{169} + 10\right)^2 + \left(\frac{1200}{169}\right)^2} - \frac{100}{10} = 14.78 - 10 = 4.78. \quad \square \tag{11.66}$$

● EXERCISES

11.5-1   Solve the problem in Example 11.5-2 by scaling from an accurately drawn locus diagram. What is the value of the maximum $|Z|$?

11.5-2   From the locus diagram of Exercise 11.5-1, scale the values of I_C at resonance and then calculate the corresponding capacitances. Compare your results with those given in Example 11.5-1.

11.5-3   For the parallel network in Figure Exercise 11.4-4, the following parameters are given: $V_{rms} = 100$ volts, $R_C = R_L = 5$ ohms, $1/\omega C = 12$ ohms, $\omega = 1000$ radians/sec, and L is a free parameter. Draw an accurate locus diagram for I with L as a parameter. What is the angle of lead of I with respect to V when $|I|$ is minimum? Using a graphical calculation, find values of L which cause resonance.

11.5-4   Suppose that in the network of Figure Exercise 11.4-4 $R_C = 0$ and C is adjustable. (a) Calculate the maximum $|Z|$. (b) Calculate the nonzero value of C such that $|I| = |I_L|$. It is given that $R_L = 5$ ohms, $\omega L = 12$ ohms, and $\omega = 1000$ radians/sec.

11.5-5   The locus diagrams we have discussed so far are diagrams of I with a parameter adjustable and V fixed. Since V is usually assumed to be the reference (on the positive real axis), I/V, which is the admittance, will have the same form as I. The condition for resonance, for example, corresponds to the case when the admittance is purely conductive. From the locus diagram in Exercise 11.5-1, find the admittance Y at several points of the locus and calculate the corresponding complex Z. Plot the complex values of Z. Do the points lie on a circle? Note that minimum $|Y|$ corresponds to maximum $|Z|$. Also, note that the resonant points will be zero reactance.

11.5-6   A popular dictionary gives the following definition of resonance: "In electricity, the condition of adjustment of a circuit that allows the greatest flow of current of a certain frequency." Do you agree with this definition? Discuss.

11.6   Magnitude and phase functions from pole-zero diagrams

From previous chapters, we have seen that if we apply an exponential signal e^{st} as input to a linear time-invariant system or network, the particular integral is of the form $H(s)e^{st}$, where $H(s)$ is the system or network transfer function. That is, if $x(t)$ is the input and $y(t)$ the particular integral component of the zero-state output, we have

$$H(s) = \frac{y(t)}{x(t)}\bigg|_{x\,=\,e^{st}}.$$
(11.67)

For example, for the series RLC circuit, if $i(t) = e^{st}$,

$$v(t) = \left(R + Ls + \frac{1}{Cs}\right)e^{st},$$

and the impedance is

$$Z(s) = R + Ls + \frac{1}{Cs} = \frac{LCs^2 + RCs + 1}{Cs} = L\frac{s^2 + (R/L)s + (1/LC)}{s}.$$
(11.68)

This function $Z(s)$ has a pole at $s = 0$ and two zeros at the roots of the equation

$$s^2 + \frac{R}{L}s + \frac{1}{LC} = 0.$$
(11.69)

Suppose $L = 0.1$ henry, $C = 10\mu F$, $R = 100$ ohms. Then the zeros are

$$s_1, s_2 = -500 \pm j500\sqrt{3}.$$
(11.70)

The pole-zero configuration for the impedance is shown in Figure 11.23.

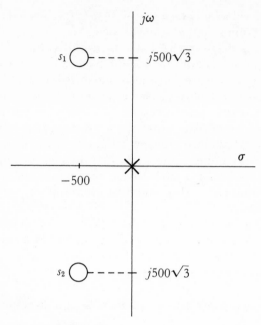

Figure 11.23 Pole-zero configuration for the impedance of an *RLC* series circuit with *R* = 100 ohms, *L* = 0.1 H, *C* = 10 μF.

Note that s_1 and s_2 are conjugates of each other. We may write this impedance function as

$$Z(s) = 0.1 \frac{(s - s_1)(s - s_2)}{s}$$

$$= \frac{0.1(s + 500 - j500\sqrt{3})(s + 500 + j500\sqrt{3})}{s}.$$

(11.71)

If we wish to evaluate $Z(s)$ at some value of s, we simply substitute that value of s in Equation 11.71. In particular, we are usually interested in $s = j\omega$. It is expedient in many cases to do (or at least visualize) the calculation graphically. First we note that the complex number s minus the complex number s_1 is equal to another complex number $s - s_1$. The length and angle of the complex number $s - s_1$ are indicated in Figure 11.24. That is, l is the distance between the points s and s_1, and θ is the angle made by the ray directed from s_1 to s and the positive real axis. Applying this idea to the calculation of $Z(j\omega_1)$, we see from Figure 11.25 that

$$Z(j\omega_1) = (0.1) \frac{(j\omega_1 - s_1)(j\omega_1 - s_2)}{j\omega_1} = 0.1 \frac{l_1 \, \underline{/\theta_1} \, l_2 \, \underline{/\theta_2}}{l_3 \, \underline{/\theta_3}}$$

$$= (0.1) \left(\frac{l_1 l_2}{l_3} \right) \underline{/\theta_1 + \theta_2 - \theta_3}.$$

(11.72)

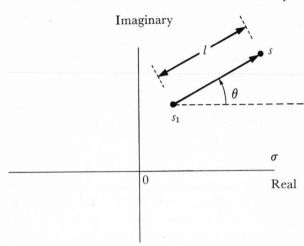

Figure 11.24   Graphical illustration of $s - s_1$.

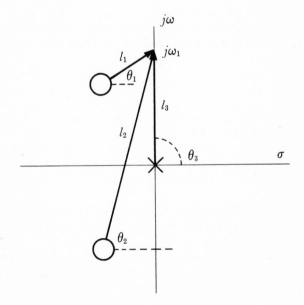

Figure 11.25   Calculation of $Z(j\omega_1)$.

The quantities l_1, l_2, l_3, θ_1, θ_2, and θ_3 can be measured by a ruler and protractor if the pole and zero locations are accurately plotted to scale. To compute $Z(j\omega)$ for several values of ω, the procedure in Figure 11.25 is repeated for various values of ω. This technique may be applied to any rational function

$$H(s) = K \frac{(s - z_1)(s - z_2) \cdots (s - z_m)}{(s - p_1)(s - p_2) \cdots (s - p_n)}.$$ (11.73)

To calculate $H(s)$ at some value $s = j\omega_1$, we plot the pole-zero configuration and draw phasors from the zero locations and the pole locations to the point $s = j\omega_1$. Then the magnitude of $H(j\omega_1)$ is K times the product of the lengths of the phasors from the zeros to $j\omega_1$ divided by the product of the lengths of the phasors from the poles to $j\omega_1$. If some zeros and poles are multiple, i.e., two or more are located at the same point, then care should be taken to consider the multiplicity. For example, if there is a double zero at a point Z_1, then we imagine that there are two phasors drawn from Z_1 to $j\omega_1$. Thus we square the length and double the angle. After some practice, the graphical technique described above enables one to sketch the magnitude and phase response vs. frequency rapidly. Furthermore, certain properties of the response may be determined by simply looking at the pole-zero plot. For instance, in Figure 11.25 we note that the magnitude curve vs. frequency becomes very large for small ω because the length of the phasors from the pole at the origin is very small. Likewise, for extremely large ω, we have very large l_1, l_2, and l_3. Since they are about the same order of magnitude, the magnitude of Z is of the order of $0.1l$. We also guess that somewhere in the neighborhood of the resonant frequency near the largest zero, l_1 will be very short and $|Z(j\omega)|$ will be smallest.

● **EXERCISES**

11.6-1   Plot the pole-zero diagram for the admittance $Y(s)$ of an *RLC*-series network whose impedance is described in Figure 11.23. Use the graphical procedure described in this section to evaluate $|Y(j\omega)|$ and $\underline{/Y}(j\omega)$ for several values of ω and plot these functions of ω.

11.6-2   Do Exercise 11.3-2 using a graphical procedure.

11.6-3   Plot the pole-zero configurations for the voltage-transfer functions of the networks in Figures 11.1 and 11.3.

11.6-4   Plot the pole-zero configuration of the impedance of the network in Figure Exercise 11.3-4. There are three cases, depending on the relative values of R, L, and C.

Problems

11-1   The series *RLC* network of the figure is in resonance. The voltage V_1 has an rms value of 1 volt, and V_2 across R and C is 5 volts (rms). If $\omega = 1$ radian/sec, what is the value of L? [*Answer:* 2H.]

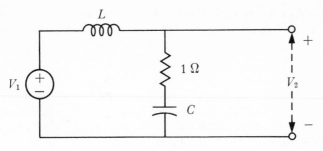

Figure Problem 11-1

11-2 The Q of a series RLC network at resonance is 10. The magnitude of the current at resonance is 1 ampere when the applied voltage is 10 volts. If $L = 0.1$ henry, find the value of C in microfarads. Assume that all voltage and currents are sinusoidal.

11-3 A 5-volt (rms) sinusoidal voltage source is connected to a series RLC network. When $C = \frac{1}{5}$ farad, $|I| = 1$ ampere (rms) and the average power is $P = |I|^2R = 3$ watts. With the same voltage source connected to the network but with the capacitor changed such that $C = 1/45$ farad, the magnitude of the current and the power are the same. Find the value of L in henrys.

11-4 A coil under test is connected in series with a calibrated capacitor as shown in the figure. A sine-wave generator of 10 volts rms at a frequency $\omega = 1000$ radians/sec is connected to the network. The capacitor is adjusted and it is found that the current is a maximum when $C = 10.0$ μF. Further, when $C = 12.5$ μF, the current is 0.707 of the maximum value. Find the Q of the coil at $\omega = 1000$ radians/sec.

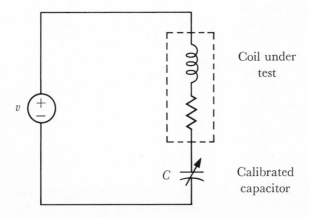

Coil under test

Calibrated capacitor

Figure Problem 11-4

11-5   As frequency is varied, the voltages $|V_L|$ and $|V_C|$ of a series *RLC* network vary as shown in Figure Exercise 11.2-2. Show that

$$\left|V_{Cm}\right|_{\max} = \left|V_{Lm}\right|_{\max}.$$

11-6   The capacitor *C* is varied from zero to infinity in the series-parallel network of the figure. If $R_C = 5$ ohms, $R_L = 10$ ohms, and $X_L = 20$ ohms, how many conditions of resonance will be observed as *C* is adjusted?

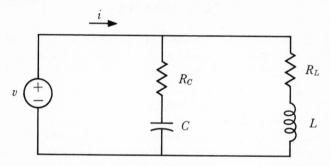

Figure Problem 11-6

The following problems refer to the network of Figure Problem 11.6. In each case, draw a locus diagram showing the variation of *I* as the parameter is varied; determine the number of values of the parameter that will cause resonance; and plot $|I|$ and the phase angle of *I* as functions of the element value. For each problem, $\omega = 1$ radian/sec.

Problem	R_C (ohms)	C (farads)	R_L (ohms)	L (henrys)
11-7	variable	1	1	1
11-8	variable	2	1	1
11-9	variable	1	1/2	1/2
11-10	0.06	variable	1/4	1/3
11-11	1	variable	2	2
11-12	0	variable	1	1
11-13	1/3	4	variable	25/4
11-14	1/2	2	variable	1
11-15	1/3	4	variable	0.8
11-16	1/3	4	1	variable
11-17	1/2	2	1/2	variable
11-18	1	1	1/4	variable

11-19   The network of the figure is driven by a current source which is sinusoidal and the frequency is such that $|X_C| = |X_L|$. Determine the locus of the voltage phasor V_R as *R* is varied from zero to infinity.

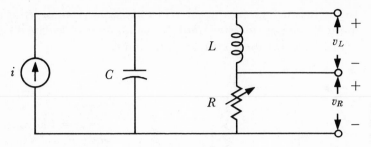

Figure Problem 11-19

11-20 In the network of the figure, the generator voltage is sinusoidal and has an rms value of 10 volts. Also $R = 2$ ohms, L and ω are constant, but C is varied. (a) Draw a locus diagram of I with V as the reference. Label important points on the locus. (b) If I leads V by 60°, what must be the value of $|I|$?

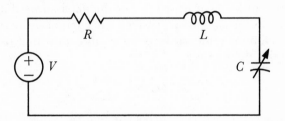

Figure Problem 11-20

11-21 For the network shown, draw a locus diagram for the voltage V_1 as R_L varies from zero to infinite value. Use I_0 as the reference.

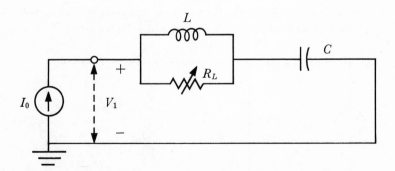

Figure Problem 11-21

11-22   In the network given, the value of C_1 is adjusted until $|I_1|$ is minimum. Then C_2 is adjusted until $|I_2|$ is minimum. Calculate the value of $|I_2|$ (rms) for these settings of C_1 and C_2.

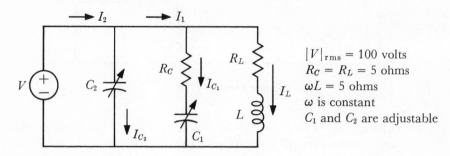

$|V|_{\text{rms}} = 100$ volts
$R_C = R_L = 5$ ohms
$\omega L = 5$ ohms
ω is constant
C_1 and C_2 are adjustable

Figure Problem 11-22

11-23   The derivation of Section 11.2 found the bandwidth $\Delta\omega$ defined by the current being at least $1/\sqrt{2}$ of the maximum value. Repeat the derivation for ω_1 and ω_2 at which the current is the fraction $1/k$ of the maximum value (at resonance) and show that the bandwidth using this definition is

$$\Delta\omega = \frac{R\sqrt{k^2 - 1}}{L}.$$

11-24   The capacitor in the network of Figure Problem 11-6 is varied from zero to infinity and the following observations are made: resonance occurs at only one value of C; and the value of capacitance at resonance is C_r. Show that L is given by the expression

$$L = \frac{1 \pm \sqrt{1 - C_r^2 R_L^2 \omega^2}}{\omega^2 C_r}.$$

11-25   For the network of the figure, how many values of L will cause resonance and what are these values of L (a) for $\omega = 1$, (b) for $\omega = \frac{1}{2}$.

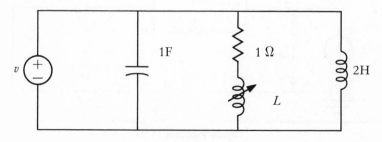

Figure Problem 11-25

11-26 For the network shown, draw a locus diagram for the voltage V_1 as R_L varies from zero to infinity, using I_0 as the reference.

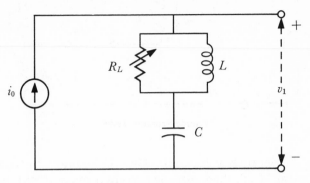

Figure Problem 11-26

11-27 Draw a locus diagram for V_1 as R_C varies from zero to infinity with I_0 as a reference for the given network. Repeat for L varying from zero to infinity.

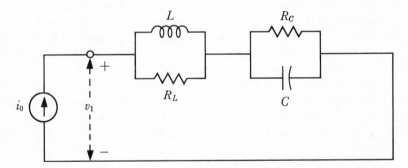

Figure Problem 11-27

11-28 The voltage source in the network of the figure is sinusoidal and the network is operating in the steady-state. Show that if the elements are adjusted such that

$$R_L = R_C = \sqrt{L/C} \equiv R,$$

then the impedance of the network at the driving-point terminals is

$$Z = \frac{V_1}{I_1} = R$$

for all values of ω. In other words, show that the impedance of this network is independent of ω.

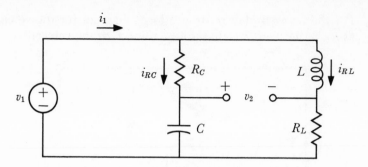

Figure Problem 11-28

11-29   For the network of Figure Problem 11-28 under the conditions of
        Problem 11-28, show that the current through the *RC* branch and
        the voltage across the inductor are in phase for all frequencies.

11-30   For the conditions of Problem 11-28, it is clear that the voltage V_1
        must be in phase with the current I_1 for all values of ω. It is interest-
        ing to study how the various voltages and currents in the network
        adjust so that this is always the case. For the given network com-
        plete the following: (a) draw a complete phasor diagram for the
        condition $|V_L| = |V_{RC}|$; (b) let the frequency for the condition of
        part (a) be ω_1. Draw a phasor diagram to approximately the same
        scale as in (a) for a frequency ω_2 larger than ω_1. (c) Repeat part (b)
        for a frequency ω_3 smaller than ω_1.

11-31   For the network of Figure Problem 11-28, let frequency ω_y be the
        frequency at which $v_1(t)$ and $v_2(t)$ are 90° out of phase. Determine
        an expression for ω_y and simplify. Does v_2 lead or lag v_1?

11-32   For the network of Figure Problem 11-28, let ω_z be the frequency
        at which $|V_1| = |V_2|$. Determine the value of ω_z and simplify your
        expression. Is there only one value?

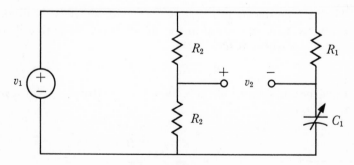

Figure Problem 11-33

11-33 In the network of the figure, $v_1(t)$ is sinusoidal and the network is in the steady-state. The capacitor C_1 is varied from zero to infinity. (a) Show that the phase of $v_2(t)$ with respect to $v_1(t)$ may be varied from 0 to 180°. It is suggested that this be done by a phasor diagram. (b) For this part of the problem, the limits of the capacitor are such that it varies from the value for which $1/\omega C_1 = 0.1R_1$ to that for which $1/\omega C_1 = 10R_1$. Determine the range of the phase angle between $v_1(t)$ and $v_2(t)$ which is possible with these limits on C_1.

11-34 In the network of Figure Problem 11-33, the capacitor C_1 is replaced by an inductor L_1. Repeat parts (a) and (b) of Problem 11-33 with the quantity ωL_1 replacing $1/\omega C_1$ in part (b).

11-35 It is desired to design a simple low-pass filter as in Figure 11.1, such that signal components with frequencies of 60 Hertz or higher are attenuated by at least 100 to 1 compared to dc (or $\omega = 0$) signals. Select practical and satisfactory values for R and C. Is your answer unique?

11-36 It is usually convenient to normalize the resonance curve so that the maximum value is unity. For the series RLC circuit, we define a normalized response as I/I_{max}, where I is the phasor current and I_{max} is the largest value for the magnitude of I. Show that

$$\frac{I}{I_{max}} = \frac{1}{1 + j\left(\dfrac{\omega L}{R} - \dfrac{1}{\omega CR}\right)} = \frac{1}{1 + jQ\left(\dfrac{\omega}{\omega_r} - \dfrac{\omega_r}{\omega}\right)}.$$

11-37 The network in Figure Problem 11-37 is commonly used to measure Q of coils with relatively high Q's. The procedure is to use a voltage signal generator with an adjustable frequency and provision for making the peak value remain the same. The signal generator is adjusted at the desired frequency and the capacitor is adjusted until the voltmeter reads maximum. For a high Q cir-

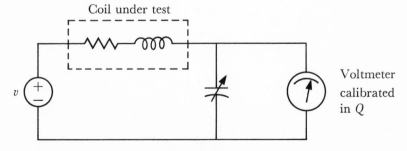

Figure Problem 11-37

cuit, this value of C is approximately the value to set the circuit in resonance. Assuming that the circuit is thus adjusted to resonance, show that $V_C = QV$, where V_C is the rms voltage across C, and V is the rms voltage across the source. Thus, if $V = 1$, V_C reads directly in Q.

11-38   For the circuit of Figure Problem 11-37, derive an exact formula for the value of C which causes the voltmeter to read the largest. Compare this C with C_r, the value needed for resonance.

11-39   Derive an expression for the voltage-transfer function of the network. Assume that $R_L \ll \omega_r L$ and $R \approx R_L$. Plot the pole-zero configuration.

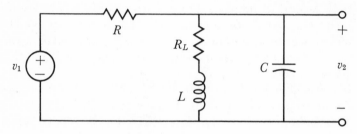

Figure Problem 11-39

11-40   For the parallel network of Figure 11.9 and assuming $R \ll \omega_r L$ at the resonant frequency ω_r, apply the energy definition for Q to derive an approximate expression for Q. [*Hint:* Assume that the voltage across L is approximately equal to the voltage across the RL combination.]

11-41   For the network in Figure 11.5, let V_x be the phasor corresponding to the voltage across the LC combination. Assume that R, L, and C are given constants and v is a sinusoidal source with the peak value given. Using the frequency ω as a parameter, show that the locus of the V_x phasor is a semicircle.

Linear Independence of

Topological Equations 12

12.1 Linearly independent variables and equations

In our development of network analysis, there are two sets of fundamental postulates. One set is the assumption of voltage-current relationships in the various branches of the network. These branch characteristics or branch constraints may be considered as the set of generalized Ohm's-law equations governing the terminal behavior of the elements. These equations, as discussed in Chapter 4, may be nonlinear differential equations. The other set of fundamental postulates is the assumption of Kirchhoff's current law and Kirchhoff's voltage law. These laws may be reduced to simple linear algebraic equations.

The approach we have used thus far is to consider only very simple networks with few variables. We have also developed analysis concepts which were applicable only if the branch constraints are linear and time-invariant. To facilitate the understanding of these concepts, only simple networks were treated. In this chapter, we finally face the question of what to do when we have a network with a large number of variables or when we have a complex topological configuration.

In analyzing a network with b branches, we have b branch voltages and b branch currents. The branch constraints provide us with b equations. On the other hand, there are more than b loops and nodes, so that the application of KCL and KVL to all nodes and loops will give us more than b equations. Since there are only $2b$ variables, some of these equations must be redundant. In order to develop a general method for writing a set of as many nonredundant equations as there are variables or unknowns, we must have a procedure for systematically choosing the loops and nodes to which we apply KVL and KCL. First, let us illustrate that the application of KVL and KCL may yield redundant equations.

EXAMPLE 12.1-1.   Consider the network in Figure 12.1(a). Applying KVL to loops *abefa*, *bcdeb*, and *abcdefa*, we have

$$v_{ab} + v_{be} + v_{ef} + v_{fa} = 0, \qquad (12.1)$$

$$v_{bc} + v_{cd} + v_{de} + v_{eb} = 0, \qquad (12.2)$$

and

$$v_{ab} + v_{bc} + v_{cd} + v_{de} + v_{ef} + v_{fa} = 0. \qquad (12.3)$$

We note that since f, e, and d are the same node, we have $v_{de} = v_{ef} = 0$. We also note that if we add Equations 12.1 and 12.2 we obtain Equation 12.3. Hence the application of KVL to loop *abcdefa* is redundant if KVL has been applied already to loops *abefa* and *bcdeb*. Thus, in the network of Figure 12.1(a) where there are six branch voltages, although it is possible to write six equations by applying KVL to six different loops, some of the equations are redundant. Similarly, some variables may be redundant. For example, in Figure 12.1(a) again, consider the variables v_{ab}, v_{bc} and v_{ac}. If we are given the three values for v_{ab}, v_{bc}, and v_{ac}, one specification is really redundant since it is always true that

$$v_{ac} = v_{ab} + v_{bc}. \qquad (12.4)$$

Thus, knowing two voltages automatically specifies the third. For the same network, the set of voltages v_{ae}, v_{be}, and v_{ab} also constitute a redundant set because, from KVL, we have

$$v_{ab} + v_{be} - v_{ae} = 0, \qquad (12.5)$$

and knowing two of the voltages automatically fixes the value of the third.   □

Redundancy in a set of equations is now defined. Consider a set of p algebraic equations in n variables. Hence we have

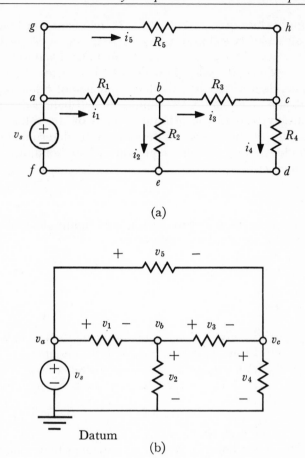

Figure 12.1   Networks for Example 12.1-1.

$$f_1(x_1, x_2, \ldots, x_n) = 0,$$
$$f_2(x_1, x_2, \ldots, x_n) = 0,$$
$$\vdots \tag{12.6}$$
$$f_p(x_1, x_2, \ldots, x_n) = 0,$$

where the f_k functions may be linear or nonlinear in the arguments $x_1, x_2, \ldots, x_n$. The *set* of p equations in Equation 12.6 is said to be *linearly dependent* if there exist constants $c_1, c_2, \ldots, c_p$, at least one of which is not zero, such that

$$c_1 f_1(x_1, x_2, \ldots, x_n) + c_2 f_2(x_1, x_2, \ldots, x_n)$$
$$+ \cdots + c_p f_p(x_1, x_2, \ldots, x_n) \equiv 0 \tag{12.7}$$

for all arbitrary values of $x_1, x_2, \ldots, x_n$. If the identity in Equation 12.7 which is for all arbitrary values of $x_1, x_2, \ldots, x_n$ cannot be satisfied except for $c_1 = c_2 = \cdots = c_p = 0$, then the set of equations is said to be *linearly independent*. For instance, the set of Equations 12.1, 12.2, and 12.3 constitutes a linearly dependent set because the left-hand side of Equation 12.1 plus the left-hand side of Equation 12.2 minus the left-hand side of Equation 12.3 is identically zero for all arbitrary values of the voltage variables.

The remainder of the chapter is devoted to the determination of a set of linearly independent network equations whose solutions completely characterize the network.

● EXERCISES

12.1-1   For the network in Figure 12.1(a), determine which of the following sets of variables are redundant.

(a) v_{ab}, v_{ac}, v_{be}

(b) $v_{be}, v_{cd}, v_{ab}, v_{gh}$

(c) i_1, i_2, i_4

(d) i_1, i_2, i_3

(e) i_2, i_3, i_4

12.1-2   Apply KCL to nodes $a, b, c,$ and e of the network in Figure 12.1(a). Is the set of four equations linearly independent?

12.1-3   Write six KVL equations involving the six voltage variables for the network in Figure 12.1(b). Are these six equations linearly independent?

12.1-4   For the network in Figure 12.1, express the branch voltages in terms of the node voltages $v_a, v_b,$ and v_c.

12.1-5   For the network in Figure 12.1, investigate whether all the branch currents can be expressed in terms of $i_1, i_3,$ and i_5.

12.2   Network topology

In Chapter 5, we introduced the notions of *branches, nodes, paths,* and *loops.* The structural relationship among the elements or branches, or the manner in which they are interconnected, has nothing to do with the type of elements in the branches; it does not matter whether the branch is a resistor, capacitor, inductor, voltage source, or current source. The skeleton that remains when all elements are replaced by lines is known as a *linear graph* of the network. The graph portrays the topological relationship of the elements and nodes in the network. Thus two graphs may be topologically identical even though they contain different kinds of elements in corresponding branches.

EXAMPLE 12.2-1.   Consider the network in Figure 12.2. Replacing the

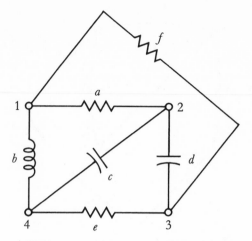

Figure 12.2   Network for Example 12.2-1.

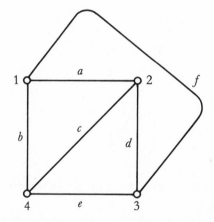

Figure 12.3   Graph for the network in Figure 12.2.

element symbols by lines, we get the graph in Figure 12.3. The graph in Figure 12.4 also represents the network in Figure 12.2. A little checking of the connecting lines in the graph of Figure 12.5 shows that it is no different from those in Figures 12.3 and 12.4. It also represents the network in Figure 12.2. The example shows that identical graphs may have different geometrical shapes. Also different networks may be represented by the same graph. The network in Figure 12.6, for example, also has a graph shown in Figure 12.3. Again, the graphs of Figures 12.4 and 12.5 are equivalent representations.   □

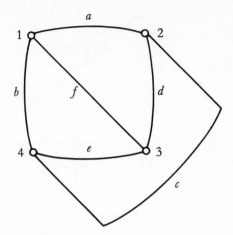

Figure 12.4   A different version of the graph for the network in Figure 12.2.

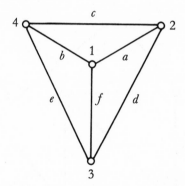

Figure 12.5   A third version of the graph for the network in Figure 12.2.

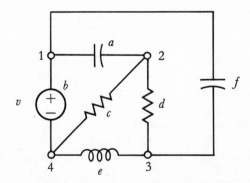

Figure 12.6   Another network for Example 12.2-1.

The definitions of *branches* and *nodes* for networks have counterparts in linear graphs. A network *branch* corresponds to an *edge* of a graph. Thus in Figure 12.5, *a*, *b*, *c*, *d*, *e*, and *f* are edges. On the other hand, *ab* is not an edge. A network node corresponds to a *vertex* of a graph. Thus in Figure 12.5, 1, 2, 3, and 4 are vertices.

In a graph, a *path* is a specified train of edges which becomes a *closed path* or a *loop* when the starting vertex and ending vertex are the same. Thus in Figure 12.5, *cd* is a path, *ade* is also a path, *bf* is a path, and *e* is a path. These paths are shown in Figure 12.7. Note that the intermediate vertices in the paths connect exactly two edges. On the other hand, the end or terminal vertices in the paths connect only one edge. A path is defined so that it may consist of only one edge.

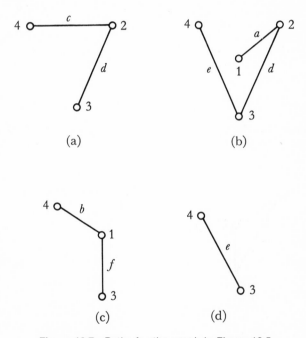

Figure 12.7   Paths for the graph in Figure 12.5.

Figure 12.8 shows more examples of paths in a graph. These are all the paths between vertices 4 and 1 in the graph of Figure 12.5.

Another entity which we encountered in Chapter 5 which applies here is the *closed loop* or simply the *loop*. Examples for some loops in the graph of Figure 12.5 are shown in Figure 12.9.

The entities mentioned above—edges, vertices, path, and loops—are portions of a graph. They may be classified under the heading *subgraphs*.

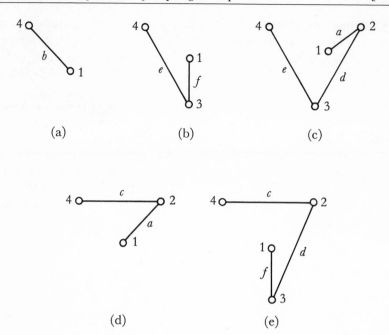

Figure 12.8   Paths between 4 and 1 for the graph in Figure 12.5.

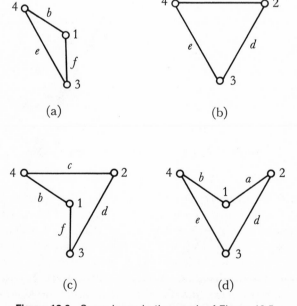

Figure 12.9   Some loops in the graph of Figure 12.5.

Another kind of subgraph which is very fundamental in the study of graphs is the *tree*, a name first used by Kirchhoff in 1846. A tree is a subgraph containing all the vertices of the graph but not containing any loop. Furthermore, the tree must be a *connected* subgraph in the sense that a path should exist between any two vertices.

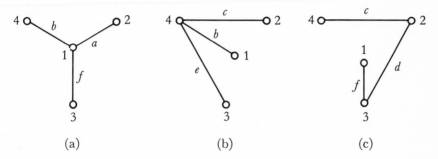

Figure 12.10 Some trees for the graph in Figure 12.5.

EXAMPLE 12.2-2.   Figure 12.10 shows some of the trees for the graph in Figure 12.5. We observe that in a tree there must be only one path between any two vertices. If there were two or more, then a loop would be present and this would violate our definition for a tree. In Figure 12.10(a), edges *a*, *b*, and *f* together constitute a tree. Similarly, from Figures 12.10(b) and 12.10(c), branches *b*, *c*, and *e* constitute another tree, and *c*, *d*, and *f* constitute still a third tree. Figure 12.11 shows some subgraphs which, although containing all the nodes, are *not* trees. Figure 12.11(a) and 12.11(b) violate the condition that there must be a path between any two nodes. For example, in Figure 12.11(a) there is no path between 4 and 2. Similarly, in Figure 12.11(b), there is no path between 2 and 1. In Figure 12.11(c), the condition violated is that there must be no loops in the subgraph, because *adf* constitutes a loop.   □

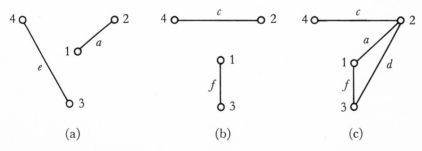

Figure 12.11 Some subgraphs which are not trees (although all the nodes are included) for the graph of Figure 12.5.

The edges of a graph belonging to a particular tree are called *tree edges*. For instance, edges a, b, and f are tree edges for the tree in Figure 12.10(a). After a tree is extracted from a graph, the edges that remain are called *chords* or *links*.

EXAMPLE 12.2-3.   The chords for the graph in Figure 12.5 corresponding to the tree in Figure 12.10(a) are c, e, and d. The chords for the tree in Figure 12.10(b) are a, f, and d. For the tree in Figure 12.10(c), the chords are b, a, and e.   □

Observe next that if one chord is restored in a tree, the chord closes a loop in the graph. For instance, if chord c is added to the tree in Figure 12.10(a), loop abc is produced. Similarly, the chord d added to the tree in Figure 12.10(a) produces loop afd. For this reason, chords are sometimes called *links* because they provide the "missing link" to produce loops.

Let b be the number of edges in a connected graph, and let n be the number of vertices. Then the number of tree edges in a given tree is clearly $n - 1$. If there are two vertices in a graph, only one edge is needed to connect them. If there are three vertices, two tree edges are involved. For example, in the graph of Figure 12.5 there are six edges, four vertices, and the trees shown in Figure 12.10 have three edges each. In general, for a graph with n nodes, $n - 1$ tree edges are needed to connect them. To get the number of chords corresponding to a tree, we can simply subtract the number of tree edges from the total number of edges. Hence, the number of chords is

$$l = b - (n - 1) = b - n + 1. \tag{12.8}$$

The loops generated by the chords of a tree are called chord-set loops.

● EXERCISES

12.2-1   Find trees other than those given in Figure 12.10 for the graph in Figure 12.5.

12.2-2   Draw chord-set loops for the trees in Exercise 12.2-1.

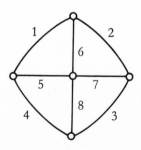

Figure Exercise 12.2-4

12.2-3   Find all the paths connecting nodes 2 and 4 in the graph of Figure 12.3.

12.2-4   For the graph in Figure Exercise 12.2-4, which of the following are trees of the graph: 1234, 1576, 1673, 5678, 5724, 1683, 1237, 1238, 1235, 2347, 2456, and 1268?

12.2-5   Draw chord-set loops for the trees in Exercise 12.2-4.

12.3   Number of independent topological constraints

We shall now establish the maxima for the number of linear independent topological equations based on KCL and KVL. First let us recapitulate Kirchhoff's laws: (a) The voltage law (KVL) states that if any loop of a network is traced in one direction (say clockwise), the sum of voltages with like reference direction minus the sum of voltages with the opposite reference location is zero. (b) The current law (KCL) states that the sum of the currents entering any vertex in a network minus the sum of currents leaving the same vertex is zero. KCL may be generalized by adding appropriate sets of KCL equations. Thus, if we stretch a network so as to expose n wires as in Figure 12.12, the net current flowing through a hypothetical plane across the wires is zero. This may be derived by simply adding the KCL equations for all the nodes in N_1. The set of edges cut by the plane is called a *cut set*.

From the previous section, given a connected network with b branches and n nodes, we see that any tree of the network has exactly $n - 1$ tree branches and $b - n + 1$ chords. We also recall that for a given tree, every time we replace a chord, one and only one loop is formed. Hence, we can find $b - n + 1$ loops, each one of which contains an edge not contained in any other loop. Hence, if we apply KVL to these chosen loops, each equa-

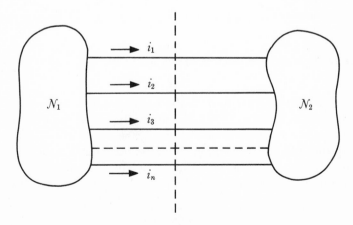

Figure 12.12   The net current flowing from N_1 to N_2 is zero.

tion would contain a voltage variable not contained in any other KVL equation. We conclude that there must be *at least* $b - n + 1$ linearly independent KVL equations.

If we *assume* that a nontrivial solution exists, then since there are $2b$ unknowns, there must be exactly $2b$ linearly independent equations. This means that we are assuming that it is possible to obtain answers (values for v and i), at least one of which is not zero. These answers satisfy KCL, KVL, and the differential equations defining the various network elements.

The equations which relate the branch currents to the branch voltages must be linearly independent. This is the case because each differential equation contains at least one variable not contained in any other. Since there are b branches, there are b such equations.† Hence, there must be exactly $2b - b$ linearly independent topological constraint equations. But we have established that there are at least $b - n + 1$ linearly independent KVL equations. Therefore, there must be *at most* $b - (b - n + 1) = n - 1$ linearly independent KCL equations.

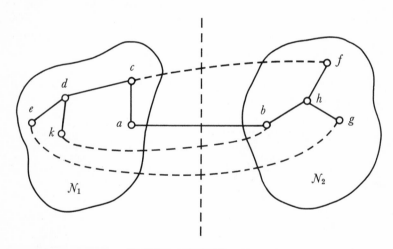

Figure 12.13 Applying KCL across a plane intersecting exactly one tree branch.

Let us now turn our attention to the particular tree from which we obtained the $b - n + 1$ chords above. Consider a typical tree as shown in solid lines in Figure 12.13 and a typical tree edge *ab* as labeled in Figure 12.13. We group the subnetwork containing all the tree edges connected to node *a* (imagine the branch *ab* to be temporarily cut) and call it N_1. Likewise, we group the subnetwork containing all tree branches connected to node *b*

---

† If a branch is a voltage source (or current source) the branch equation becomes degenerate in that it simply specifies the branch voltage (or current).

and call it N_2. The dotted lines in the figure are the chords corresponding to the tree being used. Now we apply KCL across the hypothetical plane separating N_1 and N_2. The cut-set equation we obtain will contain exactly one tree-branch current and some chord currents. We repeat this procedure for all other tree branches. Since we have $n - 1$ tree branches, we obtain $n - 1$ KCL cut-set equations. Since each equation contains a tree-branch current variable not appearing in any of the other equations, these $n - 1$ equations must be linearly independent. Since we do not know whether there may be more, we conclude that there must be *at least* $n - 1$ linearly independent KCL equations.

Recall that from a previous argument we also concluded that there must be *at most* $n - 1$ linearly independent equations. The only way we can have both conditions satisfied is to have exactly $n - 1$ linearly independent KCL equations. Since the number of linearly independent KCL equations plus the number of linearly independent KVL equations equals b, there must be exactly $b - (n - 1) = b - n + 1$ linearly independent KVL equations. Thus, we have shown that if we assume that for any given network a unique nontrivial solution exists, then there are exactly

$$N_c = n - 1 \tag{12.9}$$

linearly independent KCL equations and exactly

$$N_v = b - n + 1 \tag{12.10}$$

linearly independent KVL equations.†

In the above development, we have assumed that the graph of the network is *connected*. In case the graph is disconnected, then the above equations apply to the separate subgraphs. For instance, suppose that a graph has two separate parts with b_1 branches and n_1 nodes in one part and b_2 branches and n_2 nodes in another part. Then $N_{c_1} = n_1 - 1$, $N_{c_2} = n_2 - 1$, $N_{v_1} = b_1 - n_1 + 1$, and $N_{v_2} = b_2 - n_2 + 1$. In other words, the total number of N_c is $N_c = N_{c_1} + N_{c_2} = (n_1 + n_2) - 2$, and $N_v = N_{v_1} + N_{v_2} = (b_1 + b_2) - (n_1 + n_2) + 2$. In general, for a network with s separate or disconnected parts, we have

$$N_c = n - s \tag{12.11}$$

and

$$N_v = b - n + s, \tag{12.12}$$

where n is the *total* number of nodes and b is the *total* number of branches.

---

† In advanced treatments, it is possible to prove the same results without assuming the existence of nontrivial solutions. However, the proof is not as simple as we have presented here. See S. Seshu and M. B. Reed, *Linear Graphs and Electrical Networks* (Reading, Mass.: Addison-Wesley Publishing Co., Inc., 1961).

●   EXERCISES

12.3-1   For the graph of Figure 12.5, what is the maximum number of linearly independent KCL equations that can be written? How about KVL?

12.3-2   Repeat Exercise 12.3-1 for Figure 12.6.

12.3-3   Repeat Exercise 12.3-1 for Figure Exercise 12.2-4.

12.3-4   Repeat Exercise 12.3-1 for Figure Exercise 12.3-4.

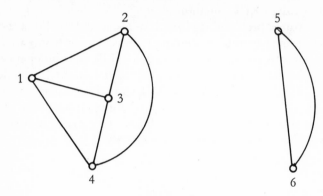

Figure Exercise 12.3-4

12.3-5   For the graph of Figure 12.13 and the tree indicated, apply KCL in such a way that each equation contains a tree-edge current not contained in any of the other equations.

12.3-6   For the graph of Figure 12.13, apply KVL such that each equation contains a voltage variable not contained in any of the other equations.

12.4   Choosing independent equilibrium equations

In the preceding section, we have proved that there are $n - s$ linearly independent KCL equations and $b - n + s$ linearly independent KVL equations. In arriving at these results, we have demonstrated a method for obtaining $n - s$ linearly independent KCL equations and another method for obtaining $b - n + s$ linearly independent KVL equations. We may pick a tree and since each link forms exactly one loop with the tree edges, we use the $b - n + s$ loops as the loops to which we apply KVL. The equations are guaranteed to be independent. For KCL, we also pick a tree and apply KCL to cut sets in such a way that each equation contains a tree-edge current not contained in any other equation, as illustrated in Figure 12.13.

Again, the $n - s$ KCL equations are guaranteed to be independent. Of course for a graph with s separate parts, we pick a tree in each separate part. Since a graph does not have a unique tree, we see that there are several ways of obtaining the maximum number of equilibrium equations. As a matter of fact, there are other ways of systematically choosing linearly independent sets of equations without using trees. We shall now describe two such commonly used procedures. In most cases, especially simple ones, these choices are easier to apply.

Node Method. In any connected graph with n nodes, the application of KCL to any $n - 1$ of the n nodes results in $n - 1$ linearly independent equations. If the graph has s separate parts, then if n_K is the number of nodes in the Kth part, we apply KCL to any $n_K - 1$ nodes of the Kth part to obtain $n_K - 1$ linearly independent equations. Since there are s separate parts, we have $(n_1 - 1) + (n_2 - 1) + \cdots + (n_s - 1) = n - s$ linearly independent KCL equations. To prove the validity of this method, it is sufficient to consider only one separate part, that is, a connected graph. We shall carry out the proof by contradiction. Thus, we shall suppose that the theorem is not true. We shall then show that this assumption always leads to a contradiction. This implies that the theorem must be true because if it is not, we always get a contradiction.

So suppose the theorem is not true; that is, suppose that after applying KCL to any $n - 1$ of the n nodes of a network, we find that one of the equations can be expressed as a linear combination of the remaining $n - 2$ equations. Since we may label the nodes arbitrarily, there is no loss of generality if we assume that the first equation obtained from node 1 is a linear combination of Equation No. 2 from node 2, Equation No. 3 from node 3, and so on up to Equation $n - 1$ from node $n - 1$. Let $y_1 = 0$ denote Equation 1 and $y_2 = 0$ denote Equation 2, and so on. Note that y_K is a sum of currents at the Kth node. Then we have

$$y_1 = c_2 y_2 + c_3 y_3 + \cdots + c_{n-1} y_{n-1}, \tag{12.13}$$

where the c's are constants, not all of which are zero. Suppose r of these constants are not zero where $1 \leq r \leq n - 2$. Again, we may relabel the nodes and their corresponding equations for convenience and without loss of generality say that

$$c_K \neq 0, \qquad 2 \leq K \leq r + 1,$$
$$c_K = 0, \qquad r + 1 < K \leq n - 1.$$

That is, we have

$$y_1 = c_2 y_2 + c_3 y_3 + \cdots + c_{r+1} y_{r+1}, \tag{12.14}$$

so that it is assumed that the first equation depends on r of the other $n - 2$

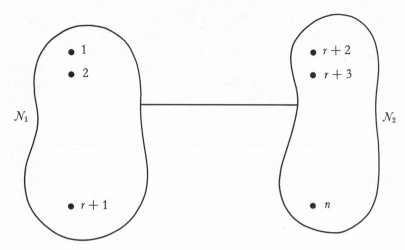

Figure 12.14 Establishing the node method.

equations. Draw the network in such a way that nodes 1 to $r + 1$ are on one side and nodes $r + 2$ to n are on another, as shown in Figure 12.14.

The portion N_2 in Figure 12.14 contains *at least* one node, namely node n. If some of the c's are zero, then N_2 contains two or more nodes, and if all the c's are nonzero, then N_2 contains just node n. Since we are considering a connected network (or a connected part of a network with s separate parts), then there must be at least one branch joining N_1 to N_2, carrying the current i_x, for instance. If i_x goes to node 1, then Equation 1 will contain i_x, but it will be absent from Equations $2, 3, \ldots, r + 1$. Therefore, Equation 12.14 can not be satisfied. Likewise if i_x goes to either node 2, $3, \ldots$ or $r + 1$, say node K, then it will be contained in Equation K but not in any other. Since $c_K \neq 0$, then Equation 12.14 cannot be satisfied either. Since these are all the possibilities which all imply that Equation 12.14 cannot be satisfied, and since we assumed at the start of the proof that such an equation is satisfied, we arrive at a contradiction. Hence the theorem is true.

In summary, given any connected network with n nodes, we may choose any $n - 1$ of the n nodes at which we apply KCL. The resulting $n - 1$ equations are guaranteed to be linearly independent. Furthermore, from the results of the previous section, this is the maximum number of linearly independent KCL equations that may be written.

Mesh Method. For writing linearly independent KVL equations, the mesh method which we will describe shortly is useful for a class of networks called *planar networks*. A planar network is one which has a planar graph. A *planar graph* is a type of graph which can be laid flat on a plane surface without any of its edges crossing each other. If it is not possible to rearrange the positions of the vertices and edges such that there is no cross-ing of edges, then the graph is called *nonplanar*.

EXAMPLE 12.4-1.　The graph in Figure 12.5 is planar because no lines cross. The graph shown in Figure 12.15(a) is also planar because it can be redrawn as shown in Figure 12.15(b) where no edges cross. Figure 12.16 shows an example of a nonplanar graph. A special kind of loop defined for planar graphs is the *mesh* or *window*. If a planar graph is drawn in planar form as in Figure 12.15(b), then a *mesh* of the graph is a loop such that no

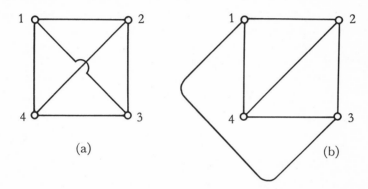

(a)　　　　　　　　　　　　　　　　(b)

Figure 12.15　Example of a planar graph.

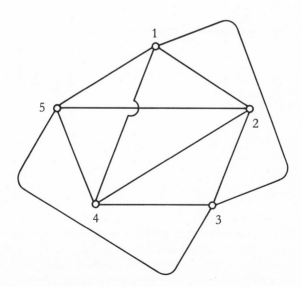

Figure 12.16　Example of a nonplanar graph.

other loop of the network is inside it. In Figure 12.15(b), the loop 2342 is an example of a mesh. It is analogous to the mesh of a fishing net. If we draw a planar graph in planar form on a piece of paper and cut along the edges, then the boundaries of the resulting small pieces of paper represent the meshes. Note that there is no unique way of drawing a planar network in planar form. As we have mentioned previously, the graphs in Figures 12.3, 12.4, and 12.5 represent the same network. Hence, for a given planar network, the set of meshes is not unique. ☐

The mesh method depends on two key theorems. These theorems pertain to connected planar graphs drawn in planar form and are as follows:

(1) *For every planar form, there are exactly $b - n + 1$ meshes.*

(2) *The set of equations resulting from the application of KVL around each of the $b - n + 1$ meshes is linearly independent.*

These two theorems enable us to write precisely $b - n + 1$ linearly independent KVL equations. The first theorem is illustrated in Example 12.4-2.

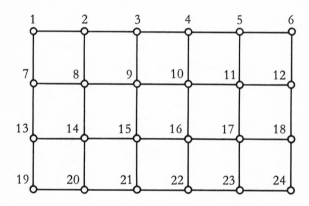

Figure 12.17   Graph for illustrating number of meshes $= b - n + 1$.

EXAMPLE 12.4-2. Consider the planar network in Figure 12.17. By inspection, there are 15 meshes or windows. We also note that there are 24 nodes and 38 branches. Hence we have $b - n + 1 = 38 - 24 + 1 = 15$, which is the correct number of meshes. ☐

Let us prove the first theorem. Suppose we have a connected planar graph with b edges and n vertices. We shall show that if we draw any planar graph in planar form, we always have $b - n + 1$ meshes.

Consider retracing the graph. First, trace a tree. Since the planar graph is assumed to be drawn in planar form, the tree is also in planar form, containing exactly $n-1$ edges and all the n vertices. We now have $b-(n-1)=b-n+1$ untraced edges left. Any edge retraced at this stage will produce one loop. Geometrically, this produces a polygon. Each additional edge retraced will increase the number of polygons that are not contained in other polygons by exactly one. Since there are $b-n+1$ such edges, $b-n+1$ such polygons will be generated. These polygons are the meshes for the planar form.†

In terms of our paper cutting model, we first cut along the tree edges. Then the first additional edge cut will generate a polygon. The second additional edge cut will either generate an entirely separate polygon or else split the first polygon into two polygons. In either case, we now have two polygons. Similarly, the third additional edge cut will either generate a separate polygon or split one of the previous two polygons, giving a total of three polygons. The end result for making the additional $b-n+1$ cuts is to partition the planar form into $b-n+1$ polygons which are identified with $b-n+1$ meshes.

To prove the second theorem, we will use the method of contradiction. That is, we suppose that the theorem is false. Then the mesh equations are linearly dependent, so that we have

$$c_1 y_1 + c_2 y_2 + \cdots + c_{b-n+1} y_{b-n+1} = 0, \qquad (12.15)$$

where not all the c's are zero, and y_K is the left-hand side of the Kth mesh equation. Suppose there are r nonzero coefficients in Equation 12.15. Without loss of generality, we may assume that these are the first r coefficients, since the node labeling is arbitrary. Then we have

$$c_1 y_1 + c_2 y_2 + \cdots + c_r y_r = 0. \qquad (12.16)$$

That is, mesh equation 1 is dependent on mesh equations $2, 3, \ldots, r$. Suppose we remove the edges of the planar form not involved in the first r meshes. Then in the resulting graph there will be at least one *boundary* edge. A boundary edge is an edge which belongs to only one mesh. Hence, one of the y's contains a term not present in other terms of Equation 12.16. This means that these r equations can not be linearly dependent which contradicts Equation 12.16. We conclude that the $b-n+1$ mesh equations are linearly independent.‡

† A more elegant proof using a mapping of the graph onto a sphere is used in advanced treatises. See for example, S. Seshu and M. B. Reed, *Linear Graphs and Electrical Networks* (Reading, Mass.: Addison-Wesley Publishing Co., Inc., 1961), 39-45.

‡ Consider our paper model again. We draw our planar graph in planar form on a piece of paper and color the first r meshes in question. Then we cut out the colored portion of the paper. Obviously, the colored cutout will have at least one edge or boundary. This edge corresponds to an edge in a mesh not found in any of the other $r-1$ meshes.

We note that from Section 12.3 the maximum number of linearly independent KVL equations that can be written for a connected graph with b edges and n vertices is $b - n + 1$. Hence the set of $b - n + 1$ mesh equations represents one such set of a maximum number of linearly independent KVL equations.

● EXERCISES

12.4-1   Determine the meshes in Figure 12.3. The graph of Figure 12.4 represents the same network as that of the graph of Figure 12.3. Trace the meshes of Figure 12.3 on the graph of Figure 12.4. Likewise, trace the meshes of Figure 12.3 on the graph of Figure 12.5.

12.4-2   Repeat Exercise 12.4-1 for the meshes of the graph on Figure 12.4 and trace on the graphs of Figures 12.3 and 12.5.

12.4-3   Write a set of linearly independent node equations for the graph in Figure 12.3, using the maximum number of linearly independent equations.

12.4-4   Write a set of linearly independent mesh equations for the graph in Figure 12.3, using the maximum number of linearly independent equations.

12.4-5   Repeat Exercise 12.4-3 for the graph in Figure 12.16.

12.4-6   Is the mesh method applicable to the graph in Figure 12.16? How about that in Figure 12.15(a)? Explain.

12.5   Choosing network variables

From what has been described in this chapter so far, given any network with b branches, we can always write $2b$ linearly independent equations in b voltage variables and b current variables. However, these equations may be readily reduced to $n - 1$ linearly independent equations in $n - 1$ voltage variables. Once these voltage variables are found, the other $b - n + 1$ voltage variables can be obtained very easily. Furthermore, once the branch voltages are known, the branch currents are known. We will also show that it is always possible to write $b - n + 1$ linearly independent equations in $b - n + 1$ current variables. Then, once these variables are determined, all the other variables can be determined readily.

Voltage Variables. We have seen from the previous section that there are $b - n + 1$ linearly independent KVL equations. This means that we have $b - n + 1$ independent equations relating the b branch voltage variables. From these equations it is possible to solve for each of $b - n + 1$ branch voltage variables in terms of the remaining $n - 1$ branch voltage variables. If we can determine the values of these $n - 1$ voltage variables from some other considerations, then the other $b - n + 1$ voltage variables follow. Thus of the b branch voltage variables, it is sufficient to first solve for $n - 1$ of them. The set of $n - 1$ voltages which completely specifies all the voltages in a network is not unique. There may be several such sets which will do. But not any set of $n - 1$ voltages may work.

The problem is to determine a method which will guarantee that our choice of $n - 1$ voltages is sufficient to subsequently determine the other $b - n + 1$ voltages.

One way is to pick a tree and *choose the $n - 1$ tree-edge voltages* as the set to use. The remaining edges are links of the tree. We may apply KVL around each loop formed by a chord. This enables us to solve for each link voltage in terms of the tree-edge voltages. Hence, if we know the tree-edge voltages, we know all the branch voltages of the network.

Another way which is the commonly used one is to pick a node (any node) and call it the datum or reference node. Then we define the voltage between any node, say node K, and the reference node as the node voltage at node K. We then have $n - 1$ node voltages. Note that every node voltage can be expressed as a linear combination of some tree-edge voltages. Likewise every tree-edge voltage for any tree can be expressed as the difference between the node voltages for the two nodes of the branch. That is, the set of node voltages uniquely determines a set of tree-edge voltages and vice versa. Hence, if we know the node voltages, we automatically know all the branch voltages.

EXAMPLE 12.5-1.   For the graph of Figure 12.5, some trees are shown on Figure 12.10. The tree-edge voltages in Figure 12.10(a) are v_{14}, v_{12}, and v_{13}. The three other edge voltages which are the chord voltages are determined from these three tree-edge voltages. We have

$$v_{42} = v_{41} + v_{12} = -v_{14} + v_{12},$$

$$v_{23} = v_{21} + v_{13} = -v_{12} + v_{13}, \tag{12.17}$$

$$v_{34} = v_{31} + v_{14} = -v_{13} + v_{14}.$$

Hence the tree-branch voltages v_{14}, v_{12}, and v_{13} are sufficient to determine all branch voltages.   □

EXAMPLE 12.5-2.   In Figure 12.5 again, suppose we assign vertex 3 as the reference vertex. Let v_1, v_2 and v_4 be the voltages with respect to vertex 3 of vertices 1, 2, and 4, respectively. Then the edge voltages are expressible in terms of the vertex node voltages. Thus we have

$$v_{42} = v_4 - v_2, \qquad v_{43} = v_4, \qquad v_{23} = v_2,$$
$$v_{41} = v_4 - v_1, \qquad v_{21} = v_2 - v_1, \qquad v_{13} = v_1. \tag{12.18}$$

We conclude that v_1, v_2, and v_4 are sufficient to determine all the branch voltages of the corresponding network.   □

We now have a method for choosing $n - 1$ voltage variables which completely determine all other network voltages. Recall from the previous section that there are $n - 1$ linearly independent KCL equations. We therefore write these KCL equations in terms of these $n - 1$ voltage variables. Note that the current through any branch is related to the difference between the node voltages of the nodes touching the branch, by means of the branch constraint equations. Similarly, tree-branch voltage variables may be employed. The full development of the details in writing these equations is carried out in the next chapter.

Current Variables. For a connected network with b branches and n nodes, we have b branch currents. Recall that we have $n - 1$ linearly independent KCL equations relating these b currents. Analogous to our discussion of voltage variables, this means that from these equations, we may solve for each of $n - 1$ currents in terms of the other $b - (n-1) = b - n + 1$ currents. If the latter $b - n + 1$ currents are known, then automatically we also have the other $n - 1$ currents. What we are looking for then is a method for choosing $b - n + 1$ current variables such that knowing these, all other currents are determined.

One way is to pick a tree and *choose the $b - n + 1$ link currents* as an appropriate set of current variables. To see this we recall the discussion in Section 12.3 of passing hypothetical planes through one tree edge and a set of chords as in Figure 12.13, thus dividing the network into two (*a cut set*). This enables us to solve for the tree-edge current in terms of the chord currents. Since we can do this for all the $n - 1$ tree-branch currents, all currents are determined if we know the values of the chord currents. To mechanize the procedure more efficiently, it is advantageous to imagine

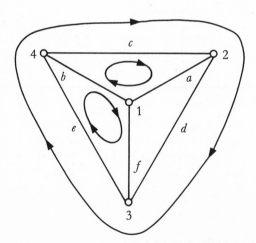

Figure 12.18 Loop-current variable assignment corresponding to the tree in Figure 12.10(b).

the link currents as causing *loop currents*. Thus, given a tree of a network, every time we put a link back (only one at a time) we generate exactly one loop. We imagine a current flowing through this loop. For instance, for the tree of Figure 12.10(b) we have the three loops in Figure 12.18. The three chord currents are equal to these loop currents and the tree currents may be obtained by inspection of the graph in Figure 12.18 with the loop currents superimposed.

The above rule, requiring that we find a tree, restore the chords one at a time, and locate an appropriate set of loops, is guaranteed to work for the most general conditions. No matter how complicated a network graph is, the resulting set of loop current variables will always be sufficient for solving the network problem.

Many network graphs however do not come under the heading of "very general" nor "very complicated." Although the chord-set procedure just described works all the time, it is usually much simpler to use special procedures for a special type of graphs. The procedure we will next describe is based on choosing loop-current variables around meshes. It works for *planar graphs*.

This method assigns $b - n + 1$ loop currents or *mesh currents* around the meshes of the network as shown in Figure 12.19 for the graph in Figure 12.17. By inspection of the graph in Figure 12.19, we see that every branch current is obtainable from knowledge of the mesh currents.

We have shown two methods of choosing $b - n + 1$ currents which determine all branch currents. We also recall that there are exactly $b - n + 1$ linearly independent KVL equations. So if we could write these KVL equations using only these $b - n + 1$ current variables, we would have $b - n + 1$

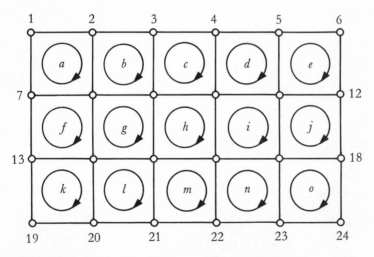

Figure 12.19 Mesh-current assignment for the graph in Figure 12.17.

linearly independent equations in $b - n + 1$ unknowns. Every branch voltage is related to the corresponding branch current by the branch constraint equation. We have already seen that every branch current is expressible in terms of link currents or mesh currents. Hence the branch voltages may be expressed in terms of the chosen $b - n + 1$ current variables. The details for obtaining these equations are described in the next chapter.

● EXERCISES

12.5-1   By inspection of Figure 12.18, determine the tree-edge currents for the tree in Figure 12.10(b) in terms of the loop currents. Verify this by the technique of passing planes through the graph as illustrated in Figure 12.13.

12.5-2   In Figure 12.19, which branch currents are equal to mesh currents?

12.5-3   Choose an appropriate set of loop current variables for the graph of Figure 12.16.

12.5-4   Can mesh current variables be assigned to the graph in Figure 12.16? Explain.

12.5-5   Choose an appropriate set of voltage variables for the graph in Figure 12.16, using node voltages.

12.5-6   Repeat Exercise 12.5-5 using tree-branch voltages.

Problems

12-1   Verify that the number of meshes equals the number of branches minus the number of nodes plus 1, for the network in the figure.

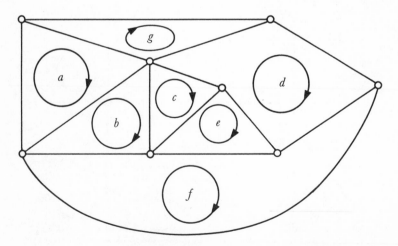

Figure Problem 12-1

12-2 (a) Draw a set of nonredundant mesh currents for the graph in Figure Exercise 12.2-4. (b) Draw a set of nonredundant mesh currents different from those in (a) for the same network. [*Hint:* Rearrange the geometrical location of the nodes to change the shape of the figure but not the topology of the graph. Then find the meshes.]

12-3 For the network in Figure 12.13, show that the sum of the branch currents intersecting the hypothetical plane is zero by applying KCL for the nodes in N_2 and adding the equations. Show that this result is true for any arbitrary network, as shown in Figure 12.12.

12-4 If a branch is added to a connected network N_1 without introducing any new nodes, what is the relationship between the number of current variable assignments in N_1 compared to the new network. Show that for the modified network, a suitable current variable assignment consists of a loop involving the added branch and the loops (based on chords) of N_1.

12-5 Suppose that there are two paths from node a to node b in a network. Is the sum of the branch voltages along one path from a to b equal to the sum of the branch voltages along the other path from a to b? Prove your answer.

12-6 Describe two methods of choosing current variables for a graph with s separate parts.

12-7 Describe two methods of choosing voltage variables for a graph with s separate parts.

12-8 Given a set of m linear equations in n unknowns, $m \le n$. If it is possible to renumber (rearrange) the equations in such a way that the second equation contains a variable not found in the first equation, then the first two equations are linearly independent. Likewise, if we can find a third equation which contains a variable not found in the first two, then the three equations are linearly independent. If all the equations are so arranged that the rth equation contains a variable not contained in the first $r - 1$ equations, for all r up to $m \le n$, then we say that the m equations are linearly independent. This argument is more general than the one we have often used in this chapter for proving several of the theorems. The earlier argument is that if *each* equation contains a variable not found in *any other* equation, then the equations are linearly independent. Apply the more general rule to show that the mesh equations for Figure 12.17 are linearly independent.

12-9 Read the argument in Problem 12-8 and use it to obtain a set of linearly independent KVL equations for the graph of Figure 12.17. Don't use mesh equations.

12-10 Read the argument in Problem 12-8. Using the rule mentioned there, show that the node equations for the graph of Figure 12.16 are linearly independent. Use node 5 as a reference.

12-11   Repeat Problem 12-10 using node 1 as reference.

12-12   Outline a procedure for determining all the branch voltages and branch currents in a connected linear time-invariant network using loop-current variables.

12-13   Outline a procedure for determining all the branch voltages and branch currents in a connected linear time-invariant network using node-voltage variables.

12-14   If in Figure 12.16 edge 34 is removed, is the resulting graph planar? How about removing 42 instead of 34?

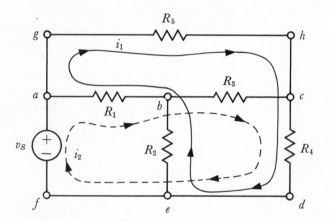

Figure Problem 12-15

12-15   Write KVL equations for the two loops of Figure Problem 12-15. Are these equations independent? What is the maximum number of linearly independent KVL equations that can be written for this network? For the two indicated loop variables, verify that KCL is satisfied at all nodes. Suppose that all resistances are constant and equal to 1 ohm and $v_s = 3$ volts, solve for i_1 and i_2 from your two equations. Verify whether KVL is satisfied in loops *abefa*, *bcdeb*, *aghcba*. Is there any loop for which KVL is satisfied? This problem demonstrates that although the equations are linearly independent and there are as many unknowns as equations, the equation solutions may not be network solutions. This is because the number of loop variables used is less than the maximum number of linearly independent loops. Thus the two loop variables in this problem do not completely determine the branch currents for this network.

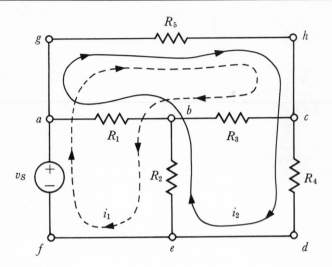

Figure Problem 12-16

12-16 Repeat Problem 12-15 for loops as shown in Figure Problem 12-16.

12-17 For the graph of Figure 12.16, show that the sum of the KCL equations applied at all vertices is zero, and thus the number of linearly independent node equations is less than five.

12-18 Generalize Problem 12-17 to a connected graph with n vertices. Show that the sum of the KCL equations applied at all vertices is zero, and hence the number of linearly independent node equations is less than n.

12-19 Add a loop-current variable to the set given in Figure Problem 12.15. Write an appropriate set of 3 linearly independent KVL equations.

12-20 Repeat Problem 12-19 for a different third loop-current variable.

12-21 Suppose a set of p equations is linearly independent. Take any subset $q(q < p)$ of the equations. Is the set of q equations linearly independent? Explain.

Loop, Node, and State Equations   **13**

In this chapter, we shall consider in more detail how we formulate network equations using the fundamentals developed in the last chapter. In all cases, we attempt to write as many linearly independent equations as there are unknowns. The general procedure for solving these equations will be given in the last chapter. However, it should be emphasized that although the techniques described here are applicable to general networks, the amount of algebra and arithmetic involved in solving a specific problem can usually be reduced drastically if one keeps in mind the powerful tools in Chapters 7–10 for linear networks. It is a common temptation on the part of a student to apply loop analysis or nodal analysis to every network problem encountered. The formulation of the equations is relatively simple, but the amount of actual computation involved is by no means trivial. A short reflection on how Thevenin's theorem can be utilized almost always pays off greatly. This is not to say that we can forget about general loop and node methods. They are useful in general theoretical studies, but they should not be blindly used for every network problem.

13.1   Formulation of linear time-invariant network equations on the node basis

In this section, our variables will be the node-to-datum voltages. We will apply KCL at $n-1$ nodes (assuming a connected graph) to arrive at a set of $n-1$ linearly independent equations in the $n-1$ voltage variables. We will explain the method by considering a number of examples first.

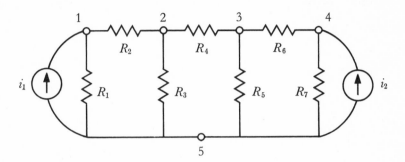

Figure 13.1   Linear time-invariant network for Example 13.1-1.

EXAMPLE 13.1-1.   Consider the linear time-invariant network shown in Figure 13.1. For this network, let us select node 5 as the datum node so that the voltage variables are v_{15}, v_{25}, v_{35}, and v_{45}. For simplification, we will drop the second number in the double-subscript notation. Applying KCL at node 1, and making use of the linear time-invariant branch characteristics, we have

$$\frac{v_1}{R_1}+\frac{v_1-v_2}{R_2}-i_1=0 \tag{13.1}$$

or

$$\left(\frac{1}{R_1}+\frac{1}{R_2}\right)v_1-\frac{1}{R_2}v_2+0+0=i_1. \tag{13.2}$$

For node 2, KCL yields

$$\frac{v_2-v_1}{R_2}+\frac{v_2}{R_3}+\frac{v_2-v_3}{R_4}=0 \tag{13.3}$$

or

$$-\frac{1}{R_2}v_1+\left(\frac{1}{R_2}+\frac{1}{R_3}+\frac{1}{R_4}\right)v_2-\frac{1}{R_4}v_3+0=0. \tag{13.4}$$

For node 3, the equation is

$$\frac{v_3 - v_2}{R_4} + \frac{v_3}{R_5} + \frac{v_3 - v_4}{R_6} = 0 \tag{13.5}$$

or

$$0 - \frac{1}{R_4} v_2 + \left(\frac{1}{R_4} + \frac{1}{R_5} + \frac{1}{R_6}\right) v_3 - \frac{1}{R_6} v_4 = 0. \tag{13.6}$$

Finally, applying KCL at node 4, we find that

$$\frac{(v_4 - v_3)}{R_6} + \frac{v_4}{R_7} - i_2 = 0 \tag{13.7}$$

or

$$0 + 0 - \frac{1}{R_6} v_3 + \left(\frac{1}{R_6} + \frac{1}{R_7}\right) v_4 = i_2. \tag{13.8}$$

The set of equations given by Equations 13.2, 13.4, 13.6, and 13.8 specifies sufficient and independent relationships to solve for the variables v_1, v_2, v_3, and v_4, so that the remaining problem is purely algebraic. We may eliminate the variables one at a time and end up with one equation in one unknown, or we may apply Cramer's rule† to obtain the solution in terms of determinants. We will postpone studying general methods of solution of simultaneous sets of network equations until Chapter 15. Just now, we are interested only in *formulating a correct set of network equations*. □

Consider the following array of numbers:

$$\mathcal{Y} = \begin{bmatrix} \left(\frac{1}{R_1} + \frac{1}{R_2}\right) & -\frac{1}{R_2} & 0 & 0 \\ -\frac{1}{R_2} & \left(\frac{1}{R_2} + \frac{1}{R_3} + \frac{1}{R_4}\right) & -\frac{1}{R_4} & 0 \\ 0 & -\frac{1}{R_4} & \left(\frac{1}{R_4} + \frac{1}{R_5} + \frac{1}{R_6}\right) & -\frac{1}{R_6} \\ 0 & 0 & -\frac{1}{R_6} & \left(\frac{1}{R_6} + \frac{1}{R_7}\right) \end{bmatrix}. \tag{13.9}$$

This array of numbers is called the *node-admittance matrix* for this network with node 5 as reference. Note that each entry in the array has the dimension of admittance. Similarly, the array of quantities on the right side of

† See Chapter 15.

Equations 13.2, 13.4, 13.6, and 13.8 may be symbolized by

$$\mathscr{I} = \begin{bmatrix} i_1 \\ 0 \\ 0 \\ i_2 \end{bmatrix}. \tag{13.10}$$

This array is called a column matrix. Denote the array of voltage variables by

$$\mathscr{V} = \begin{bmatrix} v_1 \\ v_2 \\ v_3 \\ v_4 \end{bmatrix}, \tag{13.11}$$

so that the four network equations are compactly expressed in the matrix form

$$\mathscr{Y}\mathscr{V} = \mathscr{I}. \tag{13.12}$$

The theory of matrices is well developed in mathematics and certain operations may be performed on Equation 13.12. Our sole intention in using matrices in this chapter is to simplify the writing of large arrays of coefficients. For the present purpose we may just as well call the array a *table of coefficients* or a *coefficient filing cabinet* instead of a matrix. The formulation of the set of node equations is to a large extent a matter of constructing a table which we call the *node admittance matrix*.

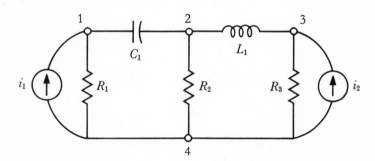

Figure 13.2   Linear time-invariant network for Example 13.1-2.

EXAMPLE 13.1-2.   Let us consider the linear time-invariant network in Figure 13.2 and select node 4 as the datum. Applying KCL at nodes 1, 2, and 3, and expressing each branch current in terms of the node voltages and the appropriate branch characteristics, we have

$$\frac{1}{R_1} v_1 + C_1 \frac{d}{dt}(v_1 - v_2) - i_1 = 0, \tag{13.13}$$

$$C_1 \frac{d}{dt}(v_2 - v_1) + \frac{1}{R_2} v_2 + \frac{1}{L_1} \int_0^t (v_2 - v_3)\, d\tau + i_{23}(0) = 0, \tag{13.14}$$

$$\frac{1}{L_1} \int_0^t (v_3 - v_2)\, d\tau + i_{32}(0) + \frac{1}{R_3} v_3 - i_2 = 0. \tag{13.15}$$

Using operational notation†

$$p = \frac{d}{dt} \tag{13.16}$$

and

$$\frac{1}{p} = \int_0^t d\tau, \tag{13.17}$$

we see that Equations (13.13), (13.14), and (13.15) become

$$\left(\frac{1}{R_1} + C_1 p\right) v_1 - C_1 p v_2 + 0 = i_1, \tag{13.18}$$

$$-C_1 p v_1 + \left(C_1 p + \frac{1}{R_2} + \frac{1}{L_1 p}\right) v_2 - \frac{1}{L_1 p} v_3 = -i_{23}(0), \tag{13.19}$$

$$0 - \frac{1}{L_1 p} v_2 + \left(\frac{1}{L_1 p} + \frac{1}{R_3}\right) v_3 = i_2 + i_{23}(0). \tag{13.20}$$

The array of coefficients in the node admittance matrix is

$$\mathscr{Y} = \begin{bmatrix} \left(\dfrac{1}{R_1} + C_1 p\right) & -C_1 p & 0 \\[2ex] -C_1 p & \left(C_1 p + \dfrac{1}{R_2} + \dfrac{1}{L_1 p}\right) & -\dfrac{1}{L_1 p} \\[2ex] 0 & -\dfrac{1}{L_1 p} & \left(\dfrac{1}{L_1 p} + \dfrac{1}{R_3}\right) \end{bmatrix}, \tag{13.21}$$

and the current matrix is

$$\mathscr{I} = \begin{bmatrix} i_1 \\ 0 \\ i_2 \end{bmatrix}. \tag{13.22}$$

† See any book on elementary differential equations.

If the signals are of the form e^{st}, and if we disregard complementary solutions, then the node-admittance matrix is

$$
\mathscr{Y} = \begin{bmatrix}
\left(\dfrac{1}{R_1} + C_1 s\right) & -C_1 s & 0 \\[2ex]
-C_1 s & \left(C_1 s + \dfrac{1}{R_2} + \dfrac{1}{L_1 s}\right) & -\dfrac{1}{L_1 s} \\[2ex]
0 & -\dfrac{1}{L_1 s} & \left(\dfrac{1}{L_1 s} + \dfrac{1}{R_3}\right)
\end{bmatrix}. \tag{13.23}
$$

If the sources are all sinusoidal and of the same frequency, and considering only the steady-state, then phasor network equations may be written and the resulting node-admittance matrix is

$$
\mathscr{Y} = \begin{bmatrix}
\left(\dfrac{1}{R_1} + j\omega C_1\right) & -j\omega C_1 & 0 \\[2ex]
-j\omega C_1 & \left(j\omega C_1 + \dfrac{1}{R_2} + \dfrac{1}{j\omega L_1}\right) & -\dfrac{1}{j\omega L_1} \\[2ex]
0 & -\dfrac{1}{j\omega L_1} & \left(\dfrac{1}{j\omega L_1} + \dfrac{1}{R_3}\right)
\end{bmatrix}, \tag{13.24}
$$

and the current source matrix is

$$
\mathscr{I} = \begin{bmatrix} I_1 \\ 0 \\ I_2 \end{bmatrix} \cdot \ \square \tag{13.25}
$$

In writing phasor equations for the sinusoidal steady-state components, we disregard the complementary solution as well as the initial conditions. This is also the case when we write equations for the particular solution when the input signals are of the form e^{st}.

EXAMPLE 13.1-3. Let us now consider a linear time-invariant network with a controlled source. Suppose that in the network of Figure 13.2, i_2 is a controlled source $i_2 = G v_{24}$ and $i_1(t) = I_1 e^{st}$. Choosing node 4 as reference, we have

$$
C_1 s (V_1 - V_2) + \frac{1}{R_1} V_1 = I_1, \tag{13.26}
$$

$$
C_1 s (V_2 - V_1) + \frac{1}{R_2} V_2 + \frac{1}{L_1 s} (V_2 - V_3) = 0, \tag{13.27}
$$

and

$$
\frac{1}{L_1 s} (V_3 - V_2) + \frac{V_3}{R_3} = G V_2. \tag{13.28}
$$

Simplifying the equations, we have

$$\left(C_1 s + \frac{1}{R_1}\right)V_1 - C_1 s V_2 + 0 = I_1,$$

$$-C_1 s V_1 + \left(C_1 s + \frac{1}{R_2} + \frac{1}{L_1 s}\right)V_2 - \frac{1}{L_1 s} V_3 = 0, \qquad (13.29)$$

$$0 - \left(\frac{1}{L_1 s} + G\right)V_2 + \left(\frac{1}{L_1 s} + \frac{1}{R_3}\right)V_3 = 0. \quad \square$$

The general idea in the nodal method for linear time-invariant networks is to write the network equations in the form

$$y_{11}V_1 + y_{12}V_2 + y_{13}V_3 + \cdots + y_{1m}V_m = I_1,$$
$$y_{21}V_1 + y_{22}V_2 + y_{23}V_3 + \cdots + y_{2m}V_m = I_2,$$
$$\cdot$$
$$\cdot \qquad\qquad\qquad (13.30)$$
$$\cdot$$
$$y_{m1}V_1 + y_{m2}V_2 + y_{m3}V_3 + \cdots + y_{mm}V_m = I_m,$$

for a network with $m + 1$ nodes (considering only a connected network). The basic procedure involved is to assign a reference node and to assign a node voltage variable to all the other $m = n - 1$ nodes. Then Kirchhoff's current law is applied at each of the $n - 1$ nodes. After some algebraic simplification, Equation 13.30 is obtained. For networks which contain no controlled sources as in Examples 13.1-1 and 13.1-2, there is some symmetry in the coefficients of the above formulation. Specifically, $y_{jk} = y_{kj}$ (check Examples 13.1-1 and 13.1-2). For networks with controlled sources, this may not be so (check Example 13.1-3). For the special case where no controlled sources are present, the y_{jk}'s may be obtained with hardly any

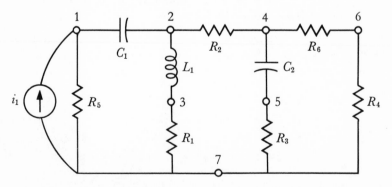

Figure 13.3 Linear time-invariant network for Example 13.1-4.

effort at all. The rules for linear time-invariant networks containing only R's, L's and C's are as follows:

(1) If $i = k$, then $y_{ik} = y_{kk}$ is obtained by adding all the admittances connected from node k to *all other* nodes.

(2) If $i \neq k$, then y_{ik} is the negative of the admittance connected directly between nodes i and k.

If we are writing the equations in differential-equation form, we use p instead of $j\omega$, where p is the differential operator. If we are writing the equation for e^{st}-type signals, then we use s to replace $j\omega$.

EXAMPLE 13.1-4. For the linear time-invariant network in Figure 13.3, we choose node 7 as the datum and our variables are v_1, v_2, v_3, v_4, v_5, v_6. By inspection of the network, we get

$$\mathcal{Y} = \begin{bmatrix} \left(\dfrac{1}{R_5}+C_1p\right) & -C_1p & 0 & 0 & 0 & 0 \\[2ex] -C_1p & \left(C_1p+\dfrac{1}{R_2}+\dfrac{1}{L_1p}\right) & -\dfrac{1}{L_1p} & -\dfrac{1}{R_2} & 0 & 0 \\[2ex] 0 & -\dfrac{1}{L_1p} & \left(\dfrac{1}{R_1}+\dfrac{1}{L_1p}\right) & 0 & 0 & 0 \\[2ex] 0 & -\dfrac{1}{R_2} & 0 & \left(\dfrac{1}{R_2}+\dfrac{1}{R_6}+C_2p\right) & -C_2p & -\dfrac{1}{R_6} \\[2ex] 0 & 0 & 0 & -C_2p & \left(C_2p+\dfrac{1}{R_3}\right) & 0 \\[2ex] 0 & 0 & 0 & -\dfrac{1}{R_6} & 0 & \left(\dfrac{1}{R_6}+\dfrac{1}{R_4}\right) \end{bmatrix}$$

$$\square \quad (13.31)$$

For the column matrix $\mathcal{I}$ the kth row i_k is the sum of the current sources with reference direction into node k minus the sum of the current sources with reference direction away from node k. For the network in Equation 13.31, the $\mathcal{I}$ matrix is

$$\mathcal{I} = \begin{bmatrix} i_1 \\ 0 \\ 0 \\ 0 \\ 0 \\ 0 \end{bmatrix}. \qquad (13.32)$$

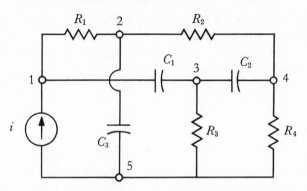

Figure 13.4 A twin-*T* network for Example 13.1-5.

EXAMPLE 13.1-5.   The linear time-invariant network shown in Figure 13.4 is known as a twin-*T*. Using node 5 as the reference node, the network differential equations are

$$\left(C_1\frac{d}{dt}+\frac{1}{R_1}\right)v_1-\frac{1}{R_1}v_2-C_1\frac{dv_3}{dt}+0=i_1,\qquad(13.33)$$

$$-\frac{1}{R_1}v_1+\left(\frac{1}{R_1}+\frac{1}{R_2}+C_3\frac{d}{dt}\right)v_2+0-\frac{1}{R_2}v_4=0,\qquad(13.34)$$

$$-C_1\frac{dv_1}{dt}+0+\left(C_1\frac{d}{dt}+C_2\frac{d}{dt}+\frac{1}{R_3}\right)v_3-C_2\frac{dv_4}{dt}=0,\qquad(13.35)$$

$$0-\frac{1}{R_2}v_2-C_2\frac{dv_3}{dt}+\left(\frac{1}{R_2}+\frac{1}{R_4}+C_2\frac{d}{dt}\right)v_4=0.\ \ \square\qquad(13.36)$$

● EXERCISES

13.1-1 Write the node equations in differential-equation form for the network in Figure 13.4, using node 3 as the reference.

13.1-2 Repeat Example 13.1-1, using node 4 as the reference.

13.1-3 Write the node equations in phasor form for the network in Figure 13.3, using node 3 as reference.

13.1-4 Repeat Exercise 13.1-3, using node 5 as reference.

13.1-5 Repeat Exercise 13.1-3, using node 2 as reference.

13.1-6 Write the node equations, assuming input signals of the form e^{st}, for the network in Figure 13.3, using node 4 as a reference.

13.1-7 Repeat Exercise 13.1-6, using node 6 as reference.

13.1-8 Repeat Exercise 13.1-6, using node 1 as reference.

13.1-9 Write the node equations in differential-equation form for the network in Figure 13.2, using node 2 as the reference.

13.1-10 Repeat the Exercise 13.1-9, using node 3 as reference.

13.1-11   Suppose in the network of Figure 13.1 that i_2 is a voltage-controlled current source $i_2 = Gv_{35}$, where G is a constant with dimension mhos. Using node 5 as reference, write the node equations. Is y symmetric?

13.1-12   For Figuse 13.3, add a current source i_2 connected from node 7 to node 5, with the reference arrow towards node 5. Suppose this i_2 is a controlled source $i_2 = Ki_{23}$. Write the node equations using node 7 as reference and $i_1(t) = I_1 e^{st}$.

13.2   Formulation of linear time-invariant network equations on the loop basis

The next topic in this chapter is the formulation of network equations using loop-current variables. As we have discussed in the previous chapter, $b - n + 1$ loop-current variables when properly chosen are sufficient to describe the behavior of a connected network. Furthermore, we can write $b - n + 1$ linearly independent KVL equations. This gives $b - n + 1$ equations in $b - n + 1$ unknowns if we express each branch voltage in terms of the loop-current variables and the appropriate branch characteristics. Again, we illustrate by examples.

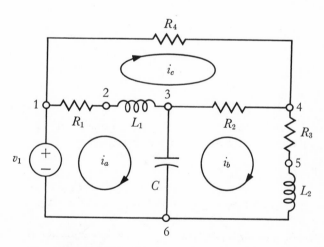

Figure 13.5 A network for Example 13.2-1.

EXAMPLE 13.2-1.   Consider the linear time-invariant network shown in Figure 13.5 with the three loop currents indicated. We apply KVL around these same three loops and make use of the branch constraints. First, let us apply KVL around the loop 1236. Thus we have

$$R_1(i_a - i_c) + L_1 \frac{d}{dt}(i_a - i_c) + \frac{1}{C} \int_0^t (i_a - i_b) \, d\tau + v_{36}(0) - v_1 = 0. \quad (13.37)$$

For the loop 3456, KVL yields

$$\frac{1}{C}\int_0^t (i_b - i_a)\, d\tau - v_{36}(0) + R_2(i_b - i_c) + R_3 i_b + L_2\frac{di_b}{dt} = 0, \quad (13.38)$$

and for the loop 1432, the equation is

$$R_4 i_c - R_2(i_b - i_c) + L_1\frac{d}{dt}(i_c - i_a) + R_1(i_c - i_a) = 0. \quad (13.39)$$

Collecting terms for i_a, i_b, and i_c, assuming e^{st} signals, and neglecting the initial conditions we get the set of equations

$$\left(L_1s + R_1 + \frac{1}{Cs}\right)I_a - \frac{1}{Cs}I_b - (L_1s + R_1)I_c = V_1,$$

$$-\frac{1}{Cs}I_a + \left(L_2s + R_2 + R_3 + \frac{1}{Cs}\right)I_b - R_2I_c = 0, \quad (13.40)$$

$$-(L_1s + R_1)I_a - R_2I_b + (R_1 + R_2 + R_4 + L_1s)I_c = 0.$$

The array of coefficients in the loop equations is called the *loop-impedance matrix* and for the example it is as follows:

$$\mathscr{Z} = \begin{bmatrix} \left(L_1s + R_1 + \dfrac{1}{Cs}\right) & -\dfrac{1}{Cs} & -(L_1s + R_1) \\[2ex] -\dfrac{1}{Cs} & \left(L_2s + R_2 + R_3 + \dfrac{1}{Cs}\right) & -R_2 \\[2ex] -(L_1s + R_1) & -R_2 & (R_1 + R_2 + R_4 + L_1s) \end{bmatrix} \cdot \quad (13.41)$$

Like the node admittance matrix, we may replace s by $j\omega$ if the sources are sinusoidal and the network is in the steady-state. □

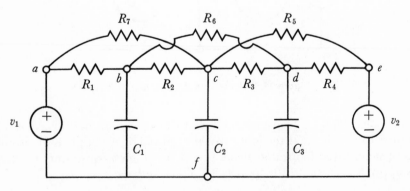

Figure 13.6   A network for Example 13.2-2.

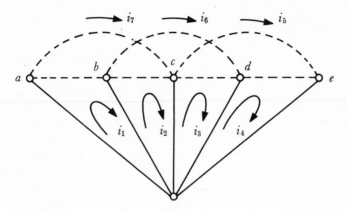

Figure 13.7 A tree for the graph of the network in Figure 13.6.

EXAMPLE 13.2-2. The problem in this example is to choose an appropriate set of loop-current variables for the linear time-invariant network in Figure 13.6, and to write the corresponding loop equations. We will use the chord-set method of choosing loops. The network or its corresponding graph has 12 branches, and 6 nodes, so we must use $12 - 6 + 1$ or 7 loop variables. A tree of the graph corresponding to the network is shown in Figure 13.7. The choice of loop variables is also shown. As discussed in the last chapter, these chord-set loops are generated by replacing the chords one at a time. The seven loops are $R_1C_1V_1$, $C_1R_2C_2$, $C_2R_3C_3$, $C_3R_4V_2$, $R_5V_2C_2$, $R_6C_3C_1$, and $R_7C_2V_1$. Applying KVL around these loops, and using the linear branch constraint equations, the following set of equations are obtained:

$$\left(R_1 + \frac{1}{C_1s}\right)I_1 - \frac{1}{C_1s}I_2 + 0 + \cdots + 0 + 0 - \frac{1}{C_1s}I_6 + 0 = V_1, \quad (13.42)$$

$$-\frac{1}{C_1s}I_1 + \left(\frac{1}{C_1s} + \frac{1}{C_2s} + R_2\right)I_2 - \frac{1}{C_2s}I_3 + 0 - \frac{1}{C_2s}I_5 + \frac{1}{C_1s}I_6 + \frac{1}{C_2s}I_7 = 0, \quad (13.43)$$

$$0 - \frac{1}{C_2s}I_2 + \left(\frac{1}{C_2s} + \frac{1}{C_3s} + R_3\right)I_3 - \frac{1}{C_3s}I_4 + \frac{1}{C_2s}I_5 + \frac{1}{C_3s}I_6 - \frac{1}{C_2s}I_7 = 0, \quad (13.44)$$

$$0 + 0 - \frac{1}{C_3s}I_3 + \left(\frac{1}{C_3s} + R_4\right)I_4 + 0 - \frac{1}{C_3s}I_6 + 0 = -V_2, \quad (13.45)$$

$$0 - \frac{1}{C_2s}I_2 + \frac{1}{C_2s}I_3 + 0 + \left(\frac{1}{C_2s} + R_5\right)I_5 + 0 - \frac{1}{C_2s}I_7 = -V_2, \quad (13.46)$$

$$-\frac{1}{C_1s}I_1 + \frac{1}{C_1s}I_2 + \frac{1}{C_3s}I_3 - \frac{1}{C_3s}I_4 + 0 + \left(\frac{1}{C_1s} + \frac{1}{C_3s} + R_6\right)I_6 + 0 = 0, \quad (13.47)$$

$$0 + \frac{1}{C_2 s} I_2 - \frac{1}{C_2 s} I_3 + 0 - \frac{1}{C_2 s} I_5 + 0 + \left(\frac{1}{C_2 s} + R_7\right) I_7 = V_1. \quad (13.48)$$

The purpose of this example is to demonstrate how to choose an appropriate set of loop-current variables and to write the corresponding loop equations. There is no implication that the loop basis is preferable to the node basis for this example. In fact, on the basis of number of unknowns and number of equations, this example is best treated by the node method. An examination of Figure 13.6 reveals that if node f is chosen as reference, then only three node voltages need to be determined, namely, v_b, v_c, and v_d. The node voltages v_a and v_e are known, since they are equal to the source voltages v_1 and v_2, respectively. The method of Section 13.1 may be used to write the three node equations for nodes b, c, and d.   □

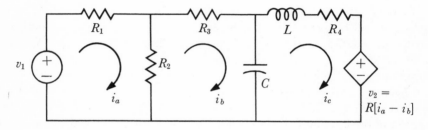

Figure 13.8 Network for Example 13.2-3.

EXAMPLE 13.2-3.   The linear time-invariant network in Figure 13.8 contains a controlled voltage source

$$v_2(t) = [i_a(t) - i_b(t)]R,$$

where R is a constant. Applying KVL and the usual branch constraint equations, and assuming $v_1(t) = V_1 e^{st}$, we have

$$(R_1 + R_2)I_a - R_2 I_b + 0 = V_1, \quad (13.49)$$

$$-R_2 I_a + \left(R_2 + R_3 + \frac{1}{Cs}\right) I_b - \frac{1}{Cs} I_c = 0, \quad (13.50)$$

and

$$-\frac{1}{Cs} I_b + \left(Ls + R_4 + \frac{1}{Cs}\right) I_c = -R(I_a - I_b)$$

or

$$R I_a - \left(R + \frac{1}{Cs}\right) I_b + \left(Ls + R_4 + \frac{1}{Cs}\right) I_c = 0. \quad □ \quad (13.51)$$

EXAMPLE 13.2-4.　Suppose that in the network of Figure 13.5, L_1 and L_2 are magnetically coupled with mutual inductance M. Let the polarity dots be at terminals 2 and 5. Assume $v_1(t) = V_1 e^{st}$.

Because of the change of i_b with time, there will a voltage induced in coil 1 with a + polarity on terminal 2. Hence for loop a we have to add a voltage $M(di_b/dt)$ and for loop c we add $-M(di_b/dt)$. Likewise for loop b we add $M(d/dt)(i_a - i_c)$. The other terms are the same as those in Equation 13.40 for no mutual inductance. The final equations are as follows:

$$\left(L_1 s + R_1 + \frac{1}{Cs}\right)I_a + \left(Ms - \frac{1}{Cs}\right)I_b - (L_1 s + R_1)I_c = V_1 ,$$

$$\left(Ms - \frac{1}{Cs}\right)I_a + \left(L_2 s + R_2 + R_3 + \frac{1}{Cs}\right)I_b - (R_2 + Ms)I_c = 0, \quad (13.52)$$

$$-(L_1 s + R_1)I_a - (R_2 + Ms)I_b + (R_1 + R_2 + R_4 + L_1 s)I_c = 0. \quad \square$$

In all of the above examples, our goal is to write KVL in the form

$$z_{11}I_1 + z_{12}I_2 + z_{13}I_3 + \cdots + z_{1m}I_m = V_1 ,$$
$$z_{21}I_1 + z_{22}I_2 + z_{23}I_3 + \cdots + z_{2m}I_m = V_2 ,$$
$$\cdot$$
$$\cdot \quad\quad (13.53)$$
$$\cdot$$
$$z_{m1}I_1 + z_{m2}I_2 + z_{m3}I_3 + \cdots + z_{mm}I_m = V_m .$$

The basic procedure involved is the writing of KVL equations around the same loops traversed by the assigned loop-current variables. As in the node method, z_{ik} is simply determined if the network contains only R, L, and C elements, and independent voltage sources. For this special case, $z_{ik} = z_{ki}$, and the impedance coefficients z_{ik} are obtained using the following rules:

(1) If $k = i(z_{ik} = z_{kk})$, z_{kk} may be calculated by adding up all the impedances in loop k.
(2) If $k \neq i$, z_{ik} is the negative of the impedance common to loops i and k, if i_i and i_k are directed through the element in opposite directions. If the current directions are the same through the elements, then z_{ik} is equal to the common impedance.

The entries in the $\mathscr{V}$ matrix are also obtained simply. The kth element V_K is equal to the sum of the source-voltage rises minus the sum of the source-voltage drops in the kth loop, following the reference orientation of the kth loop current.

● EXERCISES

13.2-1　If the reference direction of i_b in Figure 13.5 is reversed, write the loop equations in phasor form. Form the loop-impedance matrix.

13.2-2   Repeat Exercise 13.2-1 if i_c is reversed instead of i_b.

13.2-3   A tree for the network in Figure Exercise 13.2-3(a) is shown in Figure Exercise 13.2-3(b). Chords are shown dotted and arrows and letters are also indicated. Using the variables i_a, i_b, i_c, i_d, and i_e, write an appropriate set of loop equations.

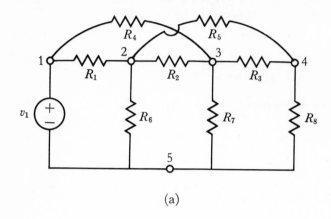

(a)

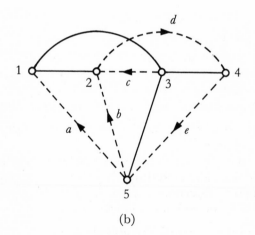

(b)

Figure Exercise 13.2-3

13.2-4   Repeat Exercise 13.2-3 for the chord set in Figure Exercise 13.2-4.

13.2-5   A tree for the network in Figure 13.6 is shown in Figure Exercise 13.2-5. The chords are shown dotted with arrows and numbers also are indicated. Using the variables i_0 to i_6, write an appropriate set of loop equations in differential-equation form.

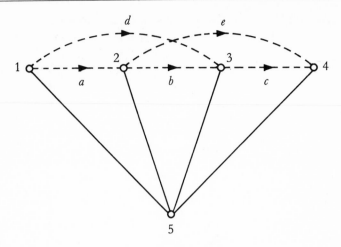

Figure Exercise 13.2-4

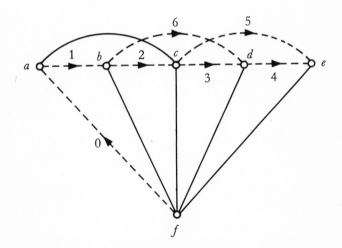

Figure Exercise 13.2-5

13.2-6   Suppose the source v_2 in the network of Figure 13.8 is a current-controlled voltage source $v_2 = Ri_b$, where R is a constant of dimension ohms, instead of the one indicated. Assuming that the signals are of the form e^{st}, find the loop-impedance matrix corresponding to the choice of loop variables as shown. Is the matrix symmetric?

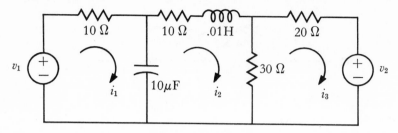

Figure Exercise 13.2-7

13.2-7   For the linear time-invariant network in Figure Exercise 13.2-7, we have

$$v_1(t) = 10 \sin 1000t, \quad \text{and} \quad v_2(t) = 5 \sin (1000t - 30°).$$

Using the loop variables indicated, show that the loop equations in phasor form are as follows:

$$(10 - j100)I_1 + j100I_2 + 0I_3 = 10,$$

$$j100I_1 + (40 - j90)I_2 - 30I_3 = 0,$$

$$0I_1 - 30I_2 + 50I_3 = -5e^{-j30°}.$$

13.2-8   Suppose that in the linear time-invariant network of Figure 13.5 we insert a controlled voltage source v_2 in series with R_4, such that $v_2 = R(i_a - i_b)$ with a + polarity towards node 4. Assume also that L_1 and L_2 are magnetically coupled with dots at terminals 3 and 5. Write loop equations for $v_1(t) = V_1 e^{st}$.

13.3   Linear time-invariant networks with mixed sources

In the two preceding sections, the formulation of node equations is carried out on the assumption that all the sources are current sources. Similarly, the loop equations are written on the assumption that all the sources are voltage sources. If both types of sources are present in a given network, source transformation (using Thevenin's or Norton's theorems) may be applied to convert the sources to one type. However, it is not necessary to transform all the sources into one type. Let us consider a few specific examples again.

EXAMPLE 13.3-1.   Consider the linear time-invariant network of Figure 13.9. We note that since there are five nodes, four node voltages are independent. Using node *e* as reference, the voltage variables are v_{ae}, v_{be}, v_{ce}, v_{de}. However, $v_{ae} = v_1$ is a known quantity, so that there are only three unknowns. Hence three independent equations should suffice. We may

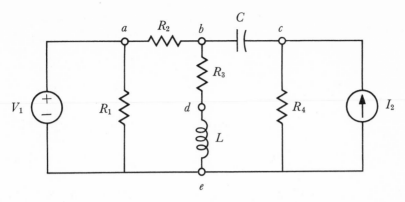

Figure 13.9 Network for Example 13.3-1.

apply KCL at nodes b, c, and d, and in phasor form we obtain

$$\left(\frac{1}{R_2}+\frac{1}{R_3}+j\omega C\right)V_{be}-j\omega CV_{ce}-\frac{1}{R_3}V_{de}-\frac{1}{R_2}V_1=0, \qquad (13.54)$$

$$-j\omega CV_{be}+\left(j\omega C+\frac{1}{R_4}\right)V_{ce}+0=I_2, \qquad (13.55)$$

$$-\frac{1}{R_3}V_{be}+0+\left(\frac{1}{R_3}+\frac{1}{j\omega L}\right)V_{de}=0. \qquad (13.56)$$

Since V_1 is known, we may transpose V_1/R_2 in Equation 13.54 to the right, and the equations will be in the same form as in Section 13.1. If voltage sources appear in series with elements, there is no difficulty since they can be transformed into current sources in parallel with the impedances. □

EXAMPLE 13.3-2. Consider the network in Figure 13.10 which is the same as the one in Figure 13.9 except that a voltage source is inserted in

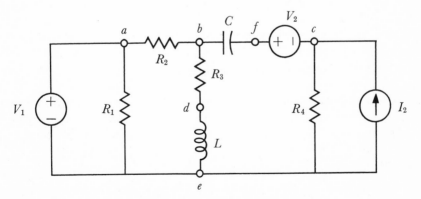

Figure 13.10 Network for Example 13.3-2.

branch bc. First we transform the branch bc into a capacitor in parallel with a current source. Then using node e as reference, KCL applied at nodes b, c, and d yields

$$\left(\frac{1}{R_2}+\frac{1}{R_3}+j\omega C\right)V_{be}-j\omega CV_{ce}-\frac{1}{R_3}V_{de}=\frac{1}{R_2}V_1+j\omega CV_2, \quad (13.57)$$

$$-j\omega CV_{be}+\left(\frac{1}{R_4}+j\omega C\right)V_{ce}+0=I_2-j\omega CV_2, \quad (13.58)$$

$$-\frac{1}{R_3}V_{be}+0+\left(\frac{1}{R_3}+\frac{1}{j\omega L}\right)V_{de}=0. \quad (13.59)$$

Once V_{be}, V_{ce}, and V_{de} are found, then V_{fe} is obtained simply as $V_{fe}=V_{ce}+V_2$. ☐

Similarly, in the application of KVL to obtain loop equations, source transformation may be used to convert all the sources into voltage sources. However, the current sources which are not directly in parallel with any impedance are not directly transformable. In this case, it is best to leave these sources alone.

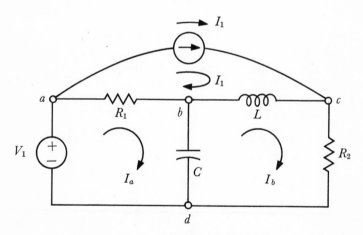

Figure 13.11   Network for Example 13.3-3.

EXAMPLE 13.3-3.   Consider the network in Figure 13.11. Suppose we wish to write loop equations. We note that I_1 cannot be transformed directly. By inspection there are three meshes or windows, but since I_1 is known, only I_a and I_b are unknown. Hence we need to write only two independent equations. Applying KVL to loops a and b, we have

$$\left(R_1+\frac{1}{j\omega C}\right)I_a-\frac{1}{j\omega C}I_b-R_1I_1=V_1, \quad (13.60)$$

$$-\frac{1}{j\omega C}I_a + \left(j\omega L + R_2 + \frac{1}{j\omega C}\right)I_b - j\omega L I_1 = 0. \qquad (13.61)$$

Since I_1 is known, the last terms on the left-hand side of these equations may be transposed to the right to reduce them to standard form.   □

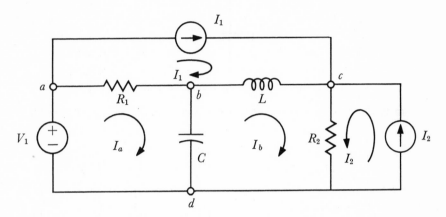

Figure 13.12   Network for Example 13.3-4.

EXAMPLE 13.3-4.   The network in Figure 13.12 is the same as the one in Figure 13.11 except that a current source I_2 is added in parallel with R_2. Again, since I_1 and I_2 are known, we need to write only two loop equations. They are as follows:

$$\left(R_1 + \frac{1}{j\omega C}\right)I_a - \frac{1}{j\omega C}I_b = V_1 + R_1 I_1, \qquad (13.62)$$

$$-\frac{1}{j\omega C}I_a + \left(j\omega L + R_2 + \frac{1}{j\omega C}\right)I_b = j\omega L I_1 - R_2 I_2. \qquad (13.63)$$

The $R_1 I_1$ and $R_2 I_2$ terms have already been transposed to the right in the above equations, and I_a and I_b may be determined from the two simultaneous equations. Alternatively, we may apply a source transformation on I_2 first and obtain the network in Figure 13.13. Writing two loop equations for loop currents I_a and I_b, we again obtain Equations 13.62 and 13.63. Suppose that after we have obtained I_a and I_b for Figure 13.13 we wish to determine the current through R_2 in Figure 13.12. A point of caution here is that the current through R_2 of Figure 13.12 is not the same as the current through R$_2$ of Figure 13.13. This is because our transformed portion of the network is equivalent to the original portion of the network only insofar as external behavior is concerned. Thus, in Figures 13.14(a) and (b), the V_{12}'s are equal and the I_b's are equal. However, the current

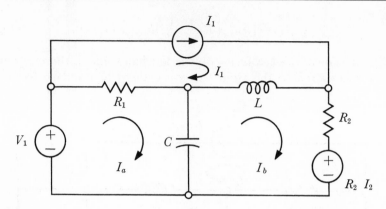

Figure 13.13   Network in Figure 13.12 with I_2 and R_2 transformed into R_2I_2 and R_2.

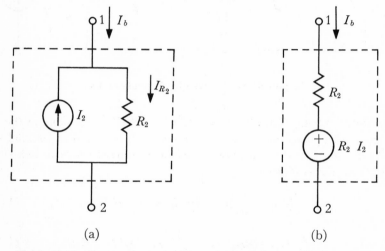

(a)   (b)

Figure 13.14   The transformed portion of the network in Example 13.3-4.

through R_2 in Figure 13.14(b) is I_b, but the current through R_2 in Figure 13.14(a) is

$$I_{R_2} = I_b + I_2 . \tag{13.64}$$

Likewise, from Figure 13.14(a), the voltage V_{12} is

$$V_{12} = R_2(I_b + I_2) \tag{13.65}$$

and not simply R_2I_b. Equation 13.65 is also obtained by examining Figure 13.14(b), which shows the voltage V_{12} to be

$$V_{12} = R_2I_b + R_2I_2 , \tag{13.66}$$

which is the same as Equation 13.65. Similar caution should be observed when dealing with voltage to current source transformation as in Example 13.3-2. $\square$

The following rules summarize the important steps in analyzing networks with mixed sources.

(A) If a formulation on the loop basis is desired:

    (1) Choose a set of mesh current variables or chord-set variables so that the current sources become some of the mesh variables or chord-set variables.

    (2) Apply KVL to the loops which do not correspond to the current sources. The number of KVL equations that are required is $(b - n + 1) - n_i$, where $b - n + 1$ is the usual number of meshes or chords and n_i is the number of current sources.

    (3) If some of the current sources are transformed into voltage sources before applying 1, care should be taken in computing currents or voltages for elements which are involved in the transformation (see Example 13.3-4).

(B) If a formulation on the node basis is desired:

    (1) Choose a set of voltage variables (such as node voltages or tree-branch voltages) so that the voltage sources become some of the voltage variables.

    (2) The number of KVL equations that are required is $n - 1 - n_v$, where $n - 1$ is the usual number of independent voltage variables for a connected network, and n_v is the number of voltage sources.

    (3) If some of the voltage sources are transformed into current sources, care should be taken in computing currents or voltages for elements involved in the transformation.

EXAMPLE 13.3-5. As a final example, we consider the linear time-invariant network of Figure 13.15 with two voltage sources and a current source. Suppose we wish to write node equations. Since there are four nodes, three voltages are required to characterize the network. Since two voltage sources are present, only one voltage remains to be computed. Figure 13.15(b) shows a tree for the network. If we choose tree-branch voltages as variables, we notice that v_{ad} and v_{bc} correspond to the two voltage sources. So we pick v_{bd} as the unknown voltage variable.

Writing KCL at node b, we have

$$\frac{V_{bd}}{R_2} + I_{ba} + I_{bc} = 0. \tag{13.67}$$

But we see that

$$I_{ba} = \frac{V_{bd} - V_1}{R_1} \tag{13.68}$$

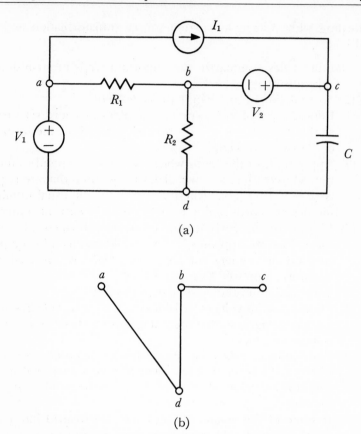

(a)

(b)

Figure 13.15   Network of Example 13.3-5.

and

$$I_{bc} = -I_1 + I_{cd} = -I_1 + j\omega C V_{cd} = -I_1 + j\omega C (V_{bd} + V_2). \quad (13.69)$$

Hence we have

$$\frac{V_{bd}}{R_2} + \frac{V_{bd} - V_1}{R_1} - I_1 - j\omega C (V_{bd} + V_2) = 0$$

or

$$\left(\frac{1}{R_1} + \frac{1}{R_2} + j\omega C\right) V_{bd} = \frac{V_1}{R_1} + I_1 - j\omega C V_2. \quad (13.70)$$

● **EXERCISES**

13.3-1   Suppose that in Example 13.3-2 with the network transformed, and the variables V_{be}, V_{ce}, and V_{de} determined from Equations

13.57, 13.58, and 13.59, we wish to determine the current through C in the *original* network. Find an expression for this current. Is this the same as the current through C in the transformed network?

13.3-2   Are the currents through R_1, R_2, and R_3, and R_4 in the original network in Example 13.3-2 the same as the corresponding currents in the transformed network? Formulate a rule for determining whether or not the current in a particular branch of a network is the same as the corresponding current in the transformed network.

13.3-3   For the network in Figure 13.11, how many node equations are necessary to determine all the node-pair voltages? Write an appropriate set of node equations.

13.3-4   Repeat Exercise 13.3-3 for the network in Figure 13.12.

13.3-5   How many loop equations are necessary for determining the currents in the network of Figure 13.9? Write an appropriate set of loop equations.

13.4   State-variable method

In the nodal method, we use voltage variables in writing Kirchhoff's current equations. In the loop method, we use current variables in writing Kirchhoff's voltage equations. It is possible, of course, to choose a set of variables some of which are voltages and some of which are currents and to use both KVL and KCL. From the previous chapter, we recall that we could write $2b$ linearly independent equations in b voltage variables and b current variables, where b is the number of branches in the network. In the method we will describe, the total number of variables is equal to the total number of linearly independent initial conditions. These initial conditions are usually in the form of capacitor voltages and inductor currents at the initial instant.

If capacitor voltages and inductor currents are chosen as the variables and KVL and KCL applied to a linear time-invariant network, then the system of equations can be reduced to the standard state-variable form

$$\frac{dx_1}{dt} = a_{11}x_1(t) + a_{12}x_2(t) + \cdots + a_{1n}x_n(t) + f_1(t),$$

$$\frac{dx_2}{dt} = a_{21}x_1(t) + a_{22}x_2(t) + \cdots + a_{2n}x_n(t) + f_2(t),$$

$$\cdot$$
$$\cdot \qquad\qquad\qquad\qquad\qquad\qquad\qquad\qquad (13.71)$$
$$\cdot$$

$$\frac{dx_n}{dt} = a_{n1}x_1(t) + a_{n2}x_2(t) + \cdots + a_{nn}x_n(t) + f_n(t).$$

Some of the $x(t)$'s are capacitor voltages and some are inductor currents. The functions $f_1(t), f_2(t), \ldots, f_n(t)$ depend directly on the input signals, and the coefficients a_{ik} are constants if the network is linear and time-invariant.

The reader may wonder at this point what could possibly be the advantage of writing equations in the standard state-variable form of Equation 13.71. It will turn out that these equations are in a convenient form for solution using either a digital computer or an analog computer. It will also turn out that this form does not present any obvious advantage for the solution of equations by routine manipulation of variables in order to obtain numerical values. But in terms of general manipulations with Equations 13.71 in matrix form, there will turn out to be conceptual advantages.

The concept of *state* is one that is not obvious upon first reading. It is shown in advanced treatises on the subject that if all voltages of capacitors and currents of inductors in a given network are known, then all other voltages and currents in the entire network are determined. Thus capacitor voltages and inductor currents fix the conditions in the network or the state of the network. It is thus proper to refer to these variables as state variables.

These concepts become clear only by working specific problems. We next illustrate how equations in the general form of Equations 13.71 may be obtained.

EXAMPLE 13.4-1.   In the simple series RLC network of Figure 11.5 (see p. 271) we know that two initial conditions are needed so that there are two state variables. The usual initial conditions are capacitor voltage and inductor current, which may be used as state variables. Let us choose v_c to be x_1 and i_L (which is also equal to the loop current i in Figure 11.5) to be x_2. Applying KVL around the loop and using the variables x_1 and x_2, we obtain

$$v + Rx_2 + L\frac{dx_2}{dt} + x_1 = 0. \tag{13.72}$$

Putting Equation 13.72 in standard form, we have

$$\frac{dx_2}{dt} = -\frac{1}{L}x_1 - \frac{R}{L}x_2 - \frac{1}{L}v. \tag{13.73}$$

Next we apply KCL to the junction between L and C to obtain

$$C\frac{dx_1}{dt} = x_2, \tag{13.74}$$

or

$$\frac{dx_1}{dt} = \frac{1}{C}x_2. \tag{13.75}$$

The standard state-variable equations for this network are

$$\frac{dx_1}{dt} = \frac{1}{C}x_2$$

$$\tag{13.76}$$

$$\frac{dx_2}{dt} = -\frac{1}{L}x_1 - \frac{R}{L}x_2 - \frac{1}{L}v.$$

In terms of the notation in Equation 13.71, $a_{11} = 0$, $a_{12} = 1/C$, $f_1 = 0$, $a_{21} = -1/L$, $a_{22} = -R/L$, and $f_2 = -(1/L)v$.   □

EXAMPLE 13.4-2. For the network in Figure 11.9 (see p. 278), let us assign a reference direction of top to bottom for the current i_L in the inductor. The voltage across the capacitor is v as shown. Choose i_L to be x_1 and v to be x_2, the two state variables for the network. Applying KVL around the RLC loop we obtain

$$-x_2 + L\frac{dx_1}{dt} + Rx_1 = 0. \tag{13.77}$$

Application of KCL to the top node yields

$$-i + C\frac{dx_2}{dt} + x_1 = 0. \tag{13.78}$$

Equations 13.77 and 13.78 are easily reduced to the standard form

$$\frac{dx_1}{dt} = -\frac{R}{L}x_1 + \frac{1}{L}x_2$$

$$\tag{13.79}$$

$$\frac{dx_2}{dt} = -\frac{1}{C}x_1 + \frac{1}{C}i$$

In terms of the notation in Equation 13.71, we have $a_{11} = -R/L$, $a_{12} = 1/L$, $f_1 = 0$, $a_{21} = -1/C$, $a_{22} = 0$, and $f_2 = 0$.   □

EXAMPLE 13.4-3. In the network of Figure 13.2, the inductor current and the capacitor voltage may be used as state variables. Let us choose x_1 to be the capacitor voltage v_{12} and x_2 the inductor current i_{23}. We apply KCL at node 1 to obtain

$$C_1\frac{dx_1}{dt} + \frac{v_{14}}{R_1} = i_1. \tag{13.80}$$

Let us express v_{14} in terms of x_1 and x_2. Since

$$v_{14} = v_{12} + v_{24} = x_1 + R_2 i_{24} = x_1 + R_2(i_{12} + i_{32})$$

$$= x_1 + R_2\left(C_1 \frac{dx_1}{dt} - x_2\right), \tag{13.81}$$

Equation 13.80 becomes

$$C_1 \frac{dx_1}{dt} + \frac{1}{R_1}\left[x_1 + R_2 C_1 \frac{dx_1}{dt} - R_2 x_2\right] = i_1$$

or

$$\frac{dx_1}{dt} = \frac{-1}{C_1(R_1 + R_2)} x_1 + \frac{R_2}{C_1(R_1 + R_2)} x_2 + \frac{R_1}{C_1(R_1 + R_2)} i_1. \tag{13.82}$$

From the last equation, we may make identifications as

$$a_{11} = \frac{-1}{C_1(R_1 + R_2)}$$

$$a_{12} = \frac{R_2}{C_1(R_1 + R_2)} \tag{13.83}$$

$$f_1 = \frac{R_1}{C_1(R_1 + R_2)} i_1.$$

We now apply KVL around loop 1234 which includes $L_1 \dfrac{di_{23}}{dt} = L_1 \dfrac{dx_2}{dt}$. We have

$$x_1 + L_1 \frac{dx_2}{dt} + v_{34} + v_{41} = 0. \tag{13.84}$$

Expressing v_{41} and v_{34} in terms of x_1 and x_2,

$$v_{41} = i_{R_1} R_1 = R_1\left(C_1 \frac{dx_1}{dt} - i_1\right) \tag{13.85}$$

and

$$v_{34} = R_3 i_{R_3} = R_3(x_2 + i_2), \tag{13.86}$$

where I_{R_1} is the current through R_1 from 4 to 1, and I_{R_3} is the current through R_3 from 3 to 4. Hence, Equation 13.84 becomes

$$x_1 + L_1 \frac{dx_2}{dt} + R_3(x_2 + i_2) + R_1\left(C_1 \frac{dx_1}{dt} - i_1\right) = 0. \tag{13.87}$$

Replacing dx_1/dt by the expression in Equation 13.82, we finally have

$$\frac{dx_2}{dt} = \frac{R_2}{L_1(R_1+R_2)}x_1 + \frac{1}{L_1}\left(R_3 + \frac{R_1R_2}{R_1+R_2}\right)x_2 - \frac{R_1R_2}{L_1(R_1+R_2)}i_1 + \frac{R_3}{L_1}i_2. \qquad (13.88)$$

Thus a_{21}, a_{22}, and f_2 are

$$a_{21} = \frac{R_2}{L_1(R_1+R_2)}$$

$$a_{22} = \frac{1}{L_1}\left(R_3 + \frac{R_1R_2}{R_1+R_2}\right) \qquad (13.89)$$

$$f_2 = -\frac{R_1R_2}{L_1(R_1+R_2)}i_1 + \frac{R_3}{L_1}i_2. \qquad \square$$

The four coefficients a_{11}, a_{12}, a_{21}, and a_{22} in the above example depend only on the network parameters and not on the input. That is, regardless of what i_1 and i_2 are, they remain the same. If we exploit linearity, these coefficients may be obtained much more directly and simply. Assuming zero input temporarily, the desired equations are

$$\frac{dx_1}{dt} = a_{11}x_1 + a_{12}x_2, \qquad (13.90)$$

$$\frac{dx_2}{dt} = a_{21}x_1 + a_{22}x_2. \qquad (13.91)$$

In Equations 13.90 and 13.91 we see that the left-hand side expressions are linear combinations of x_1 and x_2. We also see that if $x_2 = 0$ at $t = 0$ in Equation 13.90, a_{11} is the ratio of dx_1/dt and x_1 both evaluated at $t = 0$. Likewise, if $x_1 = 0$ at $t = 0$, a_{12} is the ratio of dx_1/dt and x_2 both evaluated at $t = 0$. The same applies to a_{21} and a_{22}. So to obtain a_{11}, we set $x_2 = 0$ and $x_1 = 1$ at $t = 0$, and a_{11} is automatically the resulting dx_1/dt at $t = 0$.

EXAMPLE 13.4-4.   Going back to our network in Example 13.4-3 (i_1 and i_2 are set to zero), we set $x_2 = 0$ (open L_1), and set $x_1 = v_{12} = 1$. This makes $v_{14} + v_{42} = 1$, and a current of $1/(R_1 + R_2)$ flows through R_1 from 1 to 4. Therefore, $i_{12} = i_{41} = -i_{14} = C_1\,dx_1/dt$ at $t = 0$. Hence we have

$$\frac{dx_1}{dt} = -\frac{1}{(R_1+R_2)C_1} = a_{11}, \qquad (13.92)$$

which checks with Equation 13.83. Likewise, to calculate a_{12} we set $x_1 = 0$, $x_2 = 1$ and compute $dx_1/dt = a_{12}$, all at $t = 0$. From the network, the one-ampere current through L_1 splits into two, one part in R_1 and the other in R_2. The current i_{R_1} is

$$i_{R_1} = \frac{R_2}{R_1+R_2} \cdot 1.$$

Since $i_{R_1} = i_{12} = C_1 \dfrac{dx_1}{dt}$, we have

$$\frac{dx_1}{dt} = \frac{R_2}{C_1(R_1 + R_2)}, \tag{13.93}$$

which agrees with Equation 13.75 again.

The use of linearity (superposition) as in this example is applicable to a general case. That is, to compute a_{ik}, we set all inputs to zero, set all x_j's to zero except x_k which is set equal to 1, and solve for dx_i/dt, all conditions being at $t = 0$. The answer is a_{ik}. The solution is obtained almost directly from the network diagram.   □

In some networks, not all of the capacitor voltages are independent. For example, if two capacitors are in parallel, their voltages are constrained to be equal so that both voltages may not be independently specified. Likewise, if a network contains a loop of m capacitors, only $m - 1$ of the voltages can be arbitrary since KVL must be satisfied. One voltage is the negative of the sum of the other capacitor voltages in the loop. To check whether such loops are present, we draw a subgraph of the original network (with sources removed) replacing all R's, L's, and current sources with open circuits and voltage sources with short circuits. The subgraph should not contain loops. If it does, then remove enough capacitor branches to break all loops. The remaining capacitor voltages may be chosen as variables.

Similarly not all inductor currents may have arbitrary values. If two inductors are in series, their currents are equal. Likewise, if the network contains a node to which are connected only inductor branches, one of the inductor currents is the negative of the sum of all other inductor currents at the junctions, since KCL must be satisfied. If such junctions are present, we draw a subgraph of the network with the sources removed (short v's and open i's) and all R's and C's replaced by short circuits. Pick any tree for the subgraph of inductors. The set of chords for the chosen tree may be chosen as variables. The above subsets of capacitor voltages and inductor currents taken together constitute a set of *state variables* for the network. The number of variables required is equal to the number of required initial conditions.

The state-variable method is very important in network and system analysis. There are several reasons for this. For time-varying and for non-linear networks, it is very difficult to reduce the system of loop or node equations (or other equivalent equilibrium equations) to a single differential equation in one unknown. Secondly, there is an extensive amount of mathematical literature for systems of first-order differential equations such as that in Equation 13.71 for the nonlinear case. Thirdly, the equations in Equation 13.71 are in a very convenient form for both analog and digital computer simulation or computation.

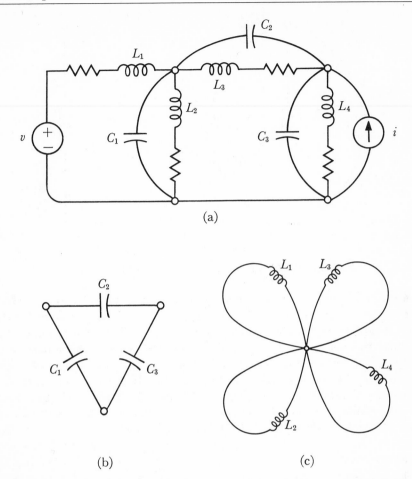

(a)

(b)   (c)

Figure 13.16 Network for Example 13.4-5. From (b), note that any two of the three capacitor voltages are linearly independent. From (c), the only possible tree is a node.

EXAMPLE 13.4-5.   Let us next illustrate the procedure for picking state variables in case there are redundant inductor currents or capacitor voltages. For the network in Figure 13.16(a), we short v, open i, and open all L's and R's to obtain the subgraph of C's in Figure 13.16(b). Removing any one of the C's breaks the loop. Hence any two of the capacitor voltages may be chosen as state variables. For the subgraph of L's, we short v, open i, and short all R's and C's to obtain Figure 13.16(c). The only possible tree is a node. Hence all inductor currents are links so that the currents in L_1, L_2, L_3, and L_4 may be chosen as state variables. This network has a total of six state variables. $\square$

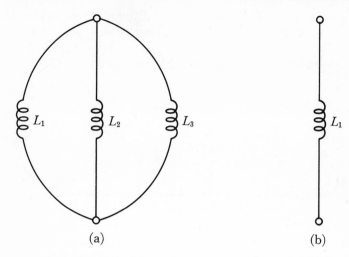

Figure 13.17   Inductor subgraph for Example 13.4-6.

EXAMPLE 13.4-6.   Suppose that the network in Figure 13.16(a) is modified by removing C_1 and C_2. It is desired to choose state variables for the modified network. First we notice that there is no all-capacitor loop so that v_{C_3} may be chosen as a state variable. Next we examine the subgraph of inductors. This is accomplished by shorting all v's, R's, and C's and opening all i's. The result is shown in Figure 13.17(a). A tree for the network in Figure 13.17(a) is shown in Figure 13.17(b). Hence the two link currents corresponding to L_2 and L_3 may be chosen as state variables, and the total number of state variables for this problem is three.   □

● EXERCISES

13.4-1   Compute a_{21} and a_{22} for Example 13.4-1 using superposition and check your answer with Equation 13.89.

13.4-2   How many state variables are there for the network in Figure 13.3?

13.4-3   How many state variables are there for the network in Figure 13.5?

13.4-4   How many state variables are there for the network in Figure 13.8?

13.4-5   Suppose for the network of Figure 13.4, we choose $x_1 = v_{13}$, $x_2 = v_{34}$, and $x_3 = v_{25}$ as state variables. Use superposition to compute a_{11}, a_{21}, and a_{31}.

13.4-6   Repeat Exercise 13.4-5 for a_{12}, a_{22}, and a_{32}.

13.4-7   Repeat Exercise 13.4-5 for a_{13}, a_{23}, and a_{33}.

13.5   Linear time-varying and nonlinear branch constraints

If the branch characteristics are not linear and time-invariant, the network equations are not so easy to reduce. It is always possible to write $2b$

equations in $2b$ variables, where b is the number of branches. These $2b$ equations consist of b branch constraint equations relating the v's and i's, $b - n + p$ KVL equations relating the v's, and $n - p$ KCL equations relating to i's, where p is the number of separate disconnected parts of the network. However, for large values of b, it is desirable to be able to write fewer equations in fewer unknowns. For the linear time-invariant network, for example, it is always possible to choose $n - p$ node voltages as unknowns and apply KCL to $n - p$ nodes. By automatically incorporating the branch constraints, the KCL equations may be written using only the unknown node voltages, the network parameters, and the sources. After the $n - p$ equations are solved for the $n - p$ unknowns, the other voltages may be obtained as a consequence of KVL, and the currents are also obtained from the branch constraint equations. Similarly, $b - n + p$ loop-current or link-current variables may be used as unknowns in $b - n + p$ equations obtained by applying KVL. Once these $b - n + p$ loop variables are obtained, the branch currents are obtained via KCL, and the branch voltages are also obtained using the branch constraint equations.

As a third alternative, we may choose the maximum number of linearly independent capacitor voltages and the maximum number of linearly independent inductor currents as state variables. The total number of state variables equals the maximum number of linearly independent initial conditions. Once the state variables are obtained, the branch voltages and branch currents may be easily obtained via KVL, KCL, and the branch constraints.

For linear time-varying networks, it is always possible to formulate node equations, loop equations, and state equations similar to the time-invariant case. However, only the differential equation form is generally meaningful. For this case the procedure is to choose either $b - n + p$ loop currents, $n - p$ node voltages, or state variables (capacitor charges and inductor fluxes are more convenient than capacitor voltages and inductor currents), and apply KVL, KCL, or both, with the branch constraints automatically incorporated.

EXAMPLE 13.5-1.   Consider the network structure of Figure 13.2 and assume that the elements are linear but time-varying. Let us write node equations. Since the network is connected and since there are four nodes, we need three node voltages. Let v_1, v_2, and v_3 be the node voltages with node 4 as reference. Then we apply KCL to nodes 1, 2, and 3. Thus we have

$$\frac{d}{dt}\{C_1(t)[v_1(t) - v_2(t)]\} + \frac{v_1(t)}{R_1(t)} = i_1(t), \qquad (13.94)$$

$$\frac{d}{dt}\{C_1(t)[v_2(t) - v_1(t)]\} + \frac{v_2(t)}{R_2(t)} + \frac{1}{L_1(t)}\int_{-\infty}^{t}[v_2(\tau) - v_3(\tau)]\,d\tau, \qquad (13.95)$$

and

$$\frac{1}{L_1(t)} \int_{-\infty}^{t} [v_3(\tau) - v_2(\tau)] \, d\tau + \frac{v_3(t)}{R_3(t)} = i_2(t). \qquad (13.96)$$

Note that current through a capacitor is $d(Cv)/dt$ and voltage across an inductor is $d(Li)/dt$. Equations 13.94, 13.95, and 13.96 are three integro-differential equations in the three unknowns, v_1, v_2, and v_3. □

For nonlinear networks, it is possible to write node equations using node voltage variables, provided the resistors, capacitors, and inductors are voltage-controlled (flux-controlled). For loop equations, the elements must be current-controlled.

EXAMPLE 13.5-2.   Consider the network of Figure 13.5. Suppose that the elements are all nonlinear and current-controlled with the following branch characteristics: $v_{12} = f_{R_1}(i_{12})$, $v_{23} = d\psi_{L_1}(i_{23})/dt$, $v_{34} = f_{R_2}(i_{34})$, $v_{14} = f_{R_4}(i_{14})$, $v_{45} = f_{R_3}(i_{45})$, $v_{56} = d\psi_{L_2}(i_{56})/dt$, and $v_{36} = f_C(q_{36})$, where f_{R_1}, ψ_{L_1}, $f_{R_2}, f_{R_4}, f_{R_3}$, ψ_{L_2}, and f_C are given nonlinear functions and q_{36} is the integral of i_{36}. Applying KVL to the three loops, expressing the branch currents in terms of the loop currents, and making use of the branch constraint equations, we obtain

$$f_{R_1}(i_a - i_c) + \frac{d}{dt}\psi_{L_1}(i_a - i_c) + f_C\left[\int (i_a - i_b) \, dt\right] = v_1, \qquad (13.97)$$

$$-f_C\left[\int (i_a - i_b) \, dt\right] + f_{R_2}(i_b - i_c) + f_{R_3}(i_b) + \frac{d}{dt}\psi_{L_2}(i_b) = 0, \qquad (13.98)$$

and

$$f_{R_4}(i_c) - f_{R_2}(i_b - i_c) - \frac{d}{dt}\psi_{L_1}(i_a - i_c) - f_{R_1}(i_a - i_c) = 0. \qquad (13.99)$$

Equations 13.97, 13.98, and 13.99 are three nonlinear integro-differential equations in the three variables, i_a, i_b, and i_c. □

The question of the existence of solutions for the system of simultaneous equations is a separate matter. Nothing has been said about the existence of solutions thus far. The branch constraint equations are necessarily idealizations of the physical network characteristics, and even though the branch idealizations are accurate, they are not exact. The fact that the actual network has a solution does not guarantee that the ideal network has a solution. Obviously, the answer to the question of existence depends on the nature of the nonlinear functions. Conditions for existence of solutions of nonlinear differential equations are known but their treatment is beyond the scope of this introductory book.

For the state-variable formulation, it is more convenient to use capacitor charges and inductor fluxes. To make this choice efficiently, choose a tree which contains the maximum number of capacitors and a minimum number of inductors. If the tree chosen has a minimum number of inductors, then the corresponding chord or link set contains a maximum number of inductors. Such a tree is called a *normal tree*. If all the capacitors are contained in the normal tree and if all inductors are in links, then the total number of energy-storage elements is the number of state variables. Tree-branch characteristics must be current- (or charge) controlled and link-branch characteristics must be voltage- (or flux) controlled. If in addition to the above conditions, if the resistor links form loops with capacitor tree branches and voltage sources only, and if resistor tree branches form cut sets with inductor links and current sources only, then the state equations are easily obtained.†

EXAMPLE 13.5-3.   Consider the network structure in Figure 13.11 and assume that all the branch characteristics are nonlinear. We pick a tree $V_1 C R_2$. Since there is only one capacitor and one inductor, the inductor is obviously a link so that there are two state variables. Assume that C is charge-controlled and R_2 is current-controlled. Then R_1 is assumed to be voltage-controlled and L is flux-controlled. Denote the nonlinear branch characteristics by the following equations: $i_{ab} = f_{R_1}(v_{ab})$, $v_{cd} = f_{R_2}(i_{cd})$, $v_{bd} = f_C(q_{bd})$, and $i_{bc} = f_L(\psi_{bc})$, where $q_{bd} = \int i_{bd}\, dt$ and $\psi_{bc} = \int v_{bc}\, dt$. Let $q_{bd} = q$ and $\psi_{bc} = \psi$ be the state variables. Then, applying KCL at node b, we have

$$\frac{dq}{dt} = i_{ab} - i_{bc}. \tag{13.100}$$

But we see that

$$i_{ab} = f_{R_1}(v_{ab}) = f_{R_1}(v_1 - v_{bd}) = f_{R_1}[v_1 - f_C(q)]. \tag{13.101}$$

Then Equation (13.100) may be written as

$$\frac{dq}{dt} = f_{R_1}[v_1 - f_C(q)] - f_L(\psi), \tag{13.102}$$

which is one of the state equations. Applying KVL around loop b, we obtain

$$v_{bc} = \frac{d}{dt}\psi = v_{bd} - v_{cd} = f_C(q) - f_{R_2}(i_{cd}). \tag{13.103}$$

---

† For more details on the state-variable approach to network analysis, see E. S. Kuh and R. A. Rohrer, "The State Variable Approach to Network Analysis," *Proc. IEEE, 53* (July, 1965), 672-686.

But from KCL at node C, we have

$$i_{cd} = i_1 + i_{bc} = i_1 + f_L(\psi), \tag{13.104}$$

so Equation 13.103 may be written as

$$\frac{d}{dt}\psi = f_C(q) - f_{R_2}[i_1 + f_L(\psi)], \tag{13.105}$$

which is the second state equation. Note that dq/dt is expressed as some nonlinear function of q and ψ, and $d\psi/dt$ is also expressed as some nonlinear function of q and ψ, so that we have a set of two nonlinear first-order differential equations in two unknowns.   □

The set of first-order differential equations in the state variables where the left-hand side is the set of first-order derivatives and the right-hand side is the set of functions is usually called the standard form of the state equations. The existence of the standard form for more general situations depends on the specific nature of the nonlinear functions. However, for the class of networks just described, the standard form always exists.

● EXERCISES

13.5-1   Assume that the network in Figure 13.2 is linear and time-varying. Write appropriate loop equations.

13.5-2   Assume that the network in Figure 13.5 is linear and time-varying. Write appropriate loop equations.

13.5-3   Write node equations for the network in Exercise 13.5-2.

13.5-4   Suppose that for the network in Figure 13.5, the branch characteristics are nonlinear and given by $v_{12} = (i_{12})^2$, $\psi_{23} = (i_{23})^2$, $v_{34} = (i_{34})^2$, $v_{14} = (i_{14})^2$, $v_{45} = (i_{45})^2$, $\psi_{56} = (i_{56})^2$, and $v_{36} = (q_{36})^2$. Write the loop equations.

13.5-5   For the network structure in Figure 13.12, suppose that $v_{bd} = (q_{bd})^2$, $i_{bc} = (\psi_{bc})^2$, and R_1 and R_2 are constants. Write state equations, using q_{bd} and ψ_{bc} as state variables.

Problems

13-1   For the linear time-invariant network of the figure, write the node equations in matrix form

$$\mathcal{Y}\begin{bmatrix} v_1 \\ v_2 \\ v_3 \\ v_4 \end{bmatrix} = \mathcal{I},$$

where the variables are node-to-datum voltages, using node b as the reference and with $v_1 = v_{cb}$, $v_2 = v_{db}$, $v_3 = v_{ab}$, and $v_4 = v_{cb}$. Use the differential operator p in your formulation.

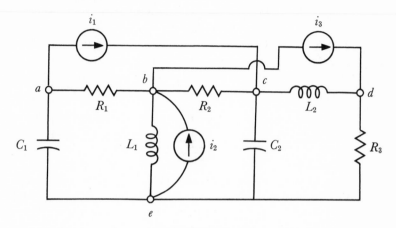

Figure Problem 13-1

13-2   For the linear time-invariant network of the figure, use node 7 as the datum and make the voltage identification $v_{j7} = v_j$ for $j = 1, \ldots,$ 6. Write the node equations for this network in a matrix form similar to that of Problem 13-1 with six voltage variables.

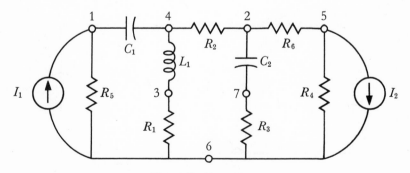

Figure Problem 13-2

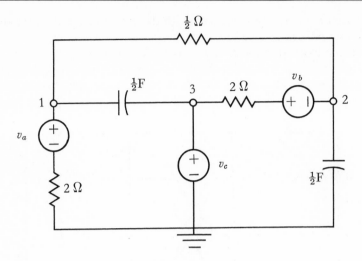

Figure Problem 13-3

13-3   For the linear time-invariant network given, determine the differ-
       ential equation for $v_1(t)$, the voltage of node 1 with respect to the
       datum in terms of the voltage sources v_a, v_b, and v_c. Write the
       equation with the coefficient of the highest-ordered derivative of
       $v_1(t)$ normalized to unity.

13-4   Repeat Problem 13-3 with $v_2(t)$ replacing $v_1(t)$. The voltage $v_2(t)$
       is that of node 2 with respect to the datum.

13-5   Determine the voltage at each node with respect to the datum for

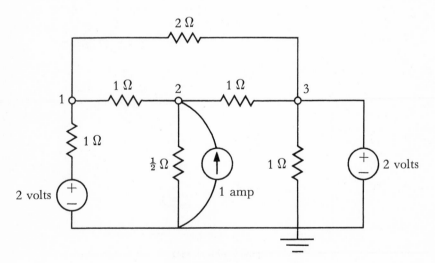

Figure Problem 13-5

the linear time-invariant network of the figure. The sources are time-invariant.

13-6 For the linear time-invariant network given, determine the node-to-datum voltages in terms of $i_1(t)$ and $v_2(t)$.

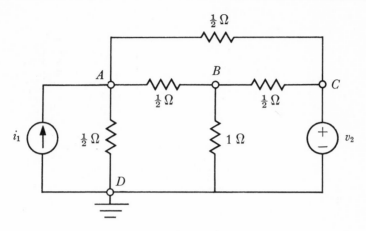

Figure Problem 13-6

13-7 The network of the figure is operating in the steady-state. Find the rms value of the voltage at node B with respect to the datum.

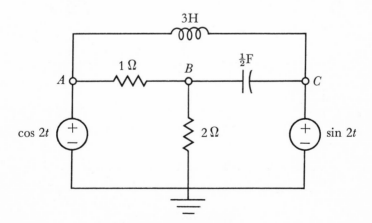

Figure Problem 13-7

13-8   Both sinusoidal sources in the given network operate at the frequency $\omega = 1$ radian/sec, and both are in phase with the reference. The values indicated are rms values of voltage. Find the voltage at node B with respect to the datum node.

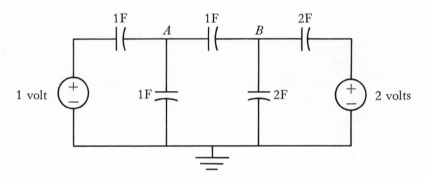

Figure Problem 13-8

13-9   For the conditions of Problem 13-8, determine the voltage at node B with respect to node A.

13-10   The network shown in the figure is operating in the sinusoidal steady-state. If $v_1(t) = \cos t$, and $v_2(t) = \sin t$, find the voltage at node B with respect to that at node A.

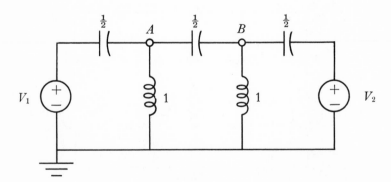

Figure Problem 13-10

13-11   The network of the figure is in the steady-state and the source is sinusoidal, described by the equation, $v(t) = 2 \sin (t + 90°)$ volts. If $L_1 = L_2 = 1$ henry, $M = \frac{1}{4}$ henry, and $C = 1$ farad, find the voltage at node A with respect to the datum.

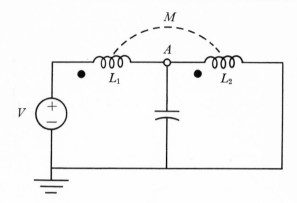

Figure Problem 13-11

13-12   In the given network the capacitors are charged to Q_0 each at time $t = 0^-$. What will be the time variation of the voltage at the two nodes with respect to the datum for $t > 0$? Use numerical values where possible.

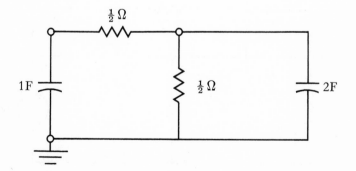

Figure Problem 13-12

13-13   For the network of the figure, determine the voltage at node *B* with respect to the datum.

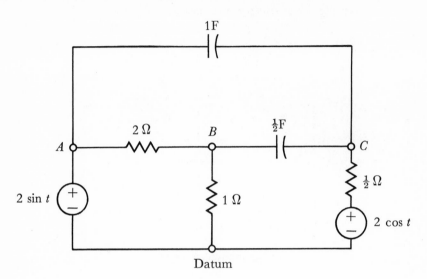

Figure Problem 13-13

13-14   Repeat Problem 13-13, solving for the voltage at node *C* with respect to the datum.

13-15   The figure shows a network containing two voltage sources each turned on at $t = 0$. For the element values given, find the time

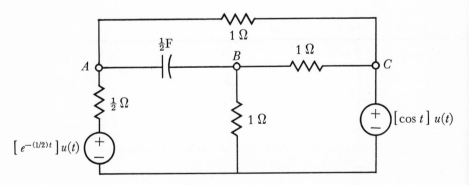

Figure Problem 13-15

variation of the voltage at node B with respect to the datum. Assume that the capacitor is uncharged prior to $t = 0$.

13-16 Repeat Problem 13-15 for the voltage of node A with respect to the datum.

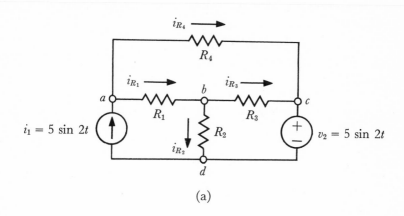

(a)

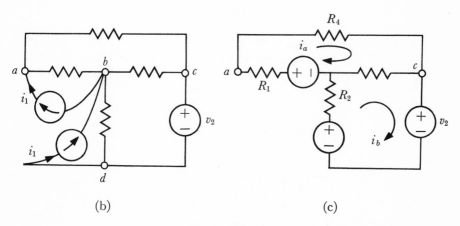

(b)   (c)

Figure Problem 13-17

13-17 The current source of a linear time-invariant network in the (a) figure is shifted as in (b) and transformed as in (c). The solutions for i_a and i_b for the network of (c) are $i_a(t) = i_b(t) = 2.5 \sin 2t$. Find $i_{R_1}(t)$, $i_{R_2}(t)$, $i_{R_3}(t)$, and $i_{R_4}(t)$ in the network of (a).

13-18   A tree for the linear time-invariant network in (a) of the figure is
shown in (b) by solid lines. The corresponding chord set is shown
by dashed lines. Choosing the directions indicated on the chords
for the three current variables, I_1, I_2, and I_3, write three equations
which are sufficient for solving for the currents. Assume that $v_S(t)$
is a sinusoidal source and that the system is operating in the steady-
state.

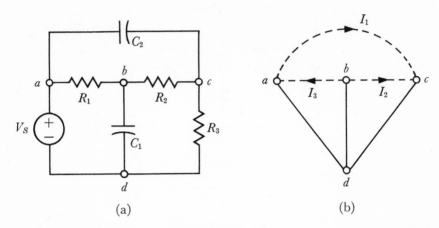

Figure Problem 13-18

13-19   The figure shows the graph of a network with orientations indicated by arrow directions. For this graph, find solutions to the
following problems. (a) Which of the following are trees of the

1, 2, . . . = branches
a, b, c, d = loops (meshes)

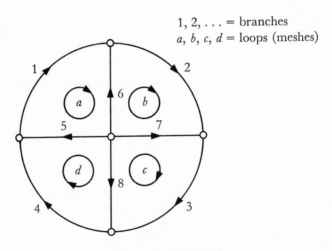

Figure Problem 13-19

graph: 1234, 1572, 1673, 5678, 5724, 1683, 1237, 1238, and 1235; (b) Write a matrix equation expressing the branch currents in terms of the loop currents; (c) Let branch 1 contain a one-volt sinusoidal source in series with a one-ohm resistor. All other branches contain only a one-ohm resistor. Write a matrix equation of the form

$$\mathcal{R}\mathcal{I}_b = \mathcal{V},$$

where $\mathcal{I}_b$ is the branch-current matrix.

13-20 In the network of the figure, all resistor values are in ohms and all sources are sinusoidal, having an rms voltage or current as given. Write a matrix equation from which all unknown voltages in the network can be determined, in the form

$$\mathcal{Y}\mathcal{V} = \mathcal{I},$$

where $\mathcal{V}$ is the node-to-datum voltage matrix.

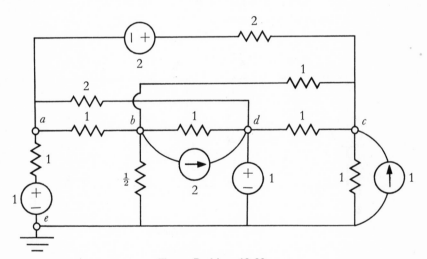

Figure Problem 13-20

13-21 For the network of Problem 13-20, write a matrix equation, from which all unknown currents in the network can be determined, in the form

$$\mathcal{L}\mathcal{I}_l = \mathcal{V},$$

where $\mathcal{I}_l$ is the loop-current matrix. Also write a matrix equation which relates all branch currents to the loop currents you have used in working this problem.

13-22 Suppose that for the linear time-invariant network of Figure 13.5 L_1 and L_2 are magnetically coupled with dots at nodes 3 and 6. A controlled current source i is connected from 6 to 4 with the reference arrow pointing towards 4. If $i = K(i_a - i_c)$ and $v_1(t) = V_1 e^{st}$, write the loop equations using I_a, I_b, and I_c as variables. Is the impedance matrix symmetric?

13-23 Write loop equations for the network in Figure 13.2.

13-24 Draw the network of Figure 13.4 in planar form, choose mesh variables, and write a corresponding set of loop equations.

13-25 For the network of Figure 13.3, replace R_4 by L_2, assign polarity dots on terminals 3 and 6, and write loop equations.

13-26 For the network of Figure 13.3, replace R_1 by L_2, assign polarity marks at terminals 2 and 7, and write loop equations. Is your $\mathscr{Z}$ matrix symmetric?

13-27 Show that the effect of mutual inductance can be represented by controlled sources by comparing the loop equations in Figure Problem 13.27(a) and Figure Problem 13.27(b). The elements are linear and time-invariant.

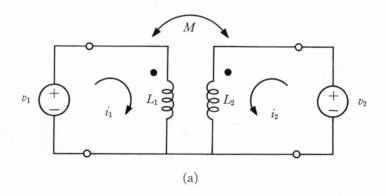

(a)

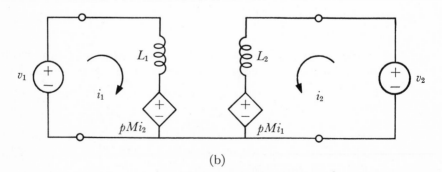

(b)

Figure Problem 13-27

13-28 Suppose the polarity dot for L_2 in Figure Problem 13.27(a) is at the bottom terminal. What is its equivalent circuit using controlled sources?

13-29 Using the inductor current and capacitor voltage as state variables x_1 and x_2, respectively, write two first-order differential equations of the form as in Equation 13.71 for the linear time-invariant network in the figure.

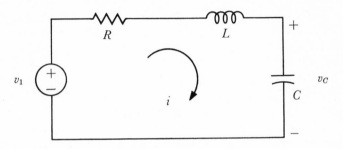

Figure Problem 13-29

13-30 Draw a block diagram based on the equations of Problem 13-29, using two integrators, adders, and amplifiers.

13-31 Investigate whether for the network of Figure Problem 13-29, the voltages across the *LC* combination and *RL* combination can be used as state variables. That is, determine whether the equations can be reduced as in Equation 13.71, using the voltage across *RL* and the voltage across *LC* as variables.

13-32 The three inductors in the linear time-invariant network of the figure are all mutually coupled. The polarity marks are given by three different sets of symbols for the three pairings of coils. Assuming $v = Ve^{st}$, write the loop equations, using i_a and i_b as loop variables.

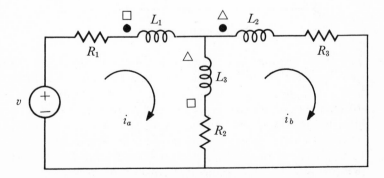

Figure Problem 13-32

13-33   Write the loop equation for the network for $v = Ve^{j\omega t}$, assuming the network to be linear and time-invariant.

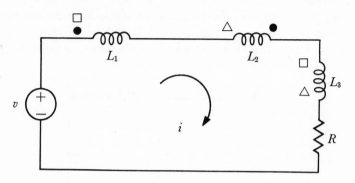

Figure Problem 13-33

13-34   For the linear time-invariant network of the figure, find the driving-point impedance at terminals 1-1' in terms of Z_1, Z_2, and a, the transformation ratio of the ideal transformer.

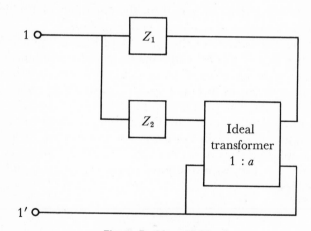

Figure Problem 13-34

13-35   The linear time-invariant network shown in the figure contains two 1:1 ideal transformers, one capacitor and two inductors. (a) Find the impedance at terminals 1-1' with terminals 2-2' open. (b) Find the impedance at terminals 2-2' with 1-1' open.

13-36   Find the driving-point impedance of the network of the figure. Assume that the system is operating in the sinusoidal steady-state.

13-37   In the network of the figure, $v_2(t) = \sin 2t$ and the network is in the steady-state. Determine $v_1(t)$, using numerical values where given.

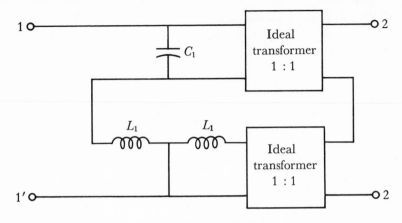

Figure Problem 13-35

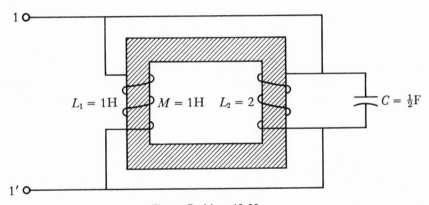

Figure Problem 13-36

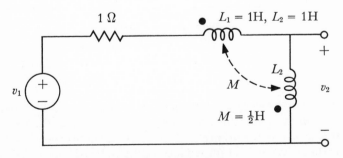

Figure Problem 13-37

13-38   In the linear time-invariant network of the figure, determine an expression for $v_a(t)$ if $v_1(t) = V \sin \omega t$ and the system is in the steady-state.

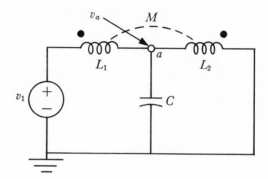

Figure Problem 13-38

13-39   In the network of the figure, it is given that $L_1 = L_2 = 1$ henry, $L_3 = 2$ henrys, $M_{12} = \frac{1}{2}$ henry, $M_{23} = 1$ henry, and $M_{31} = 1$ henry. If $v_1(t) = 2 \sin t$, solve for the two loop currents, $i_1(t)$ and $i_2(t)$.

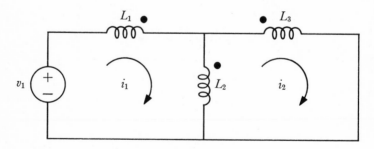

Figure Problem 13-39

13-40   In the network of the figure, all self-inductance values are 1 henry and all mutual inductance values are $\frac{1}{2}$ henry. If the network is in the steady-state and $v(t) = 2 \sin t$, find an expression for $i(t)$. What is the driving-point impedance of the network at $\omega = 1$ radian/sec?

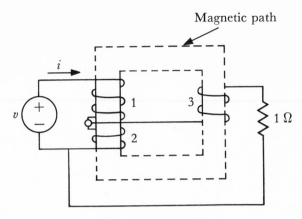

Figure Problem 13-40

13-41 Redraw the network shown in the figure without the magnetic core and with appropriate polarity marks on the coils (like that shown in Figure Problem 13-32). Assuming that all inductors are linear and time-invariant, write an appropriate set of loop equations in phasor form.

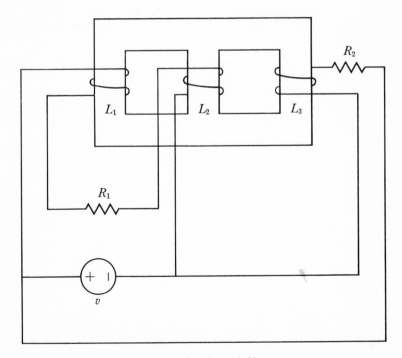

Figure Problem 13-41

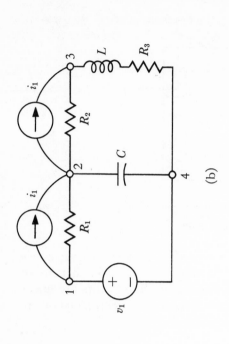

(b)

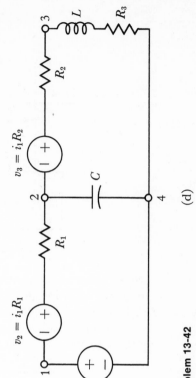

(d)

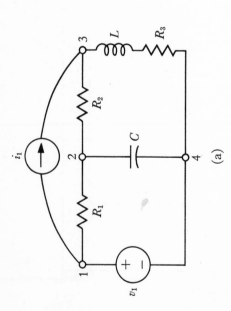

(a)

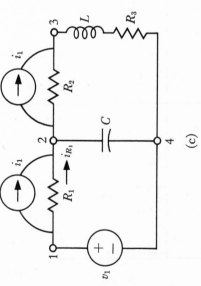

(c)

Figure Problem 13-42

13-42 The current source i_1 in the linear time-invariant network of (a) is shifted as shown in (b). Show that the node equations are not affected and hence the node voltages should remain the same. The current sources are further transformed as in (d). Show that the loop equations for (a) and (d) of the figure are the same.

13-43 Show that the node equations for the linear time-invariant networks are identical.

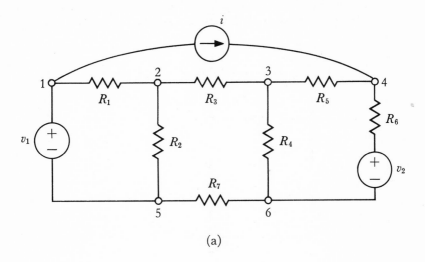

(a)

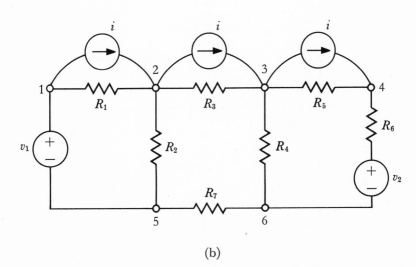

(b)

Figure Problem 13-43

13-44   Examine how the voltage sources are shifted out of the branches
of the linear time-invariant network. Thus v_1 in branch 14 is
pushed out of node 1. As many replicas of v_1 emerge as there are
branches connected to node 1 aside from branch 14. The polarity
positions are preserved (no twisting allowed as v_1 goes through the
node). The result is Figure Problem 13-44 (b). Similarly, if v_1 is
pushed through node 4 and replicas of v_1 are manufactured as it
emerges from node 4, Figure Problem 13-44 (c) results. Show that
the loop equations for all these networks are identical.

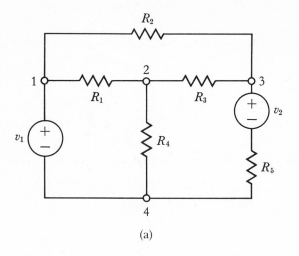

(a)

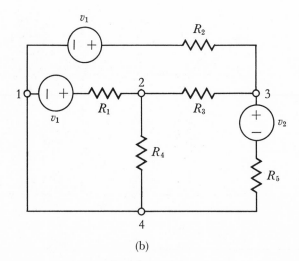

(b)

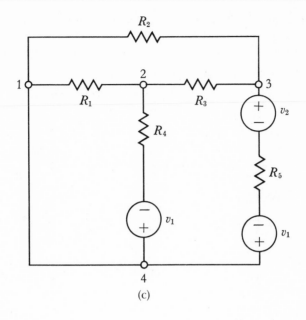

(c)

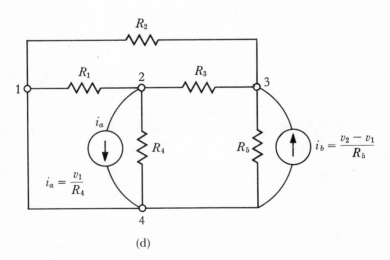

(d)

Figure Problem 13-44

13-45   Write loop equations for the linear time-invariant network of the figure. Assume sinusoidal steady-state.

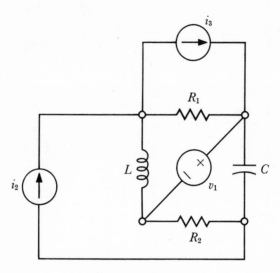

Figure Problem 13-45

13-46   Write node equations for the linear time-invariant network in Figure Problem 13-45.

13-47   Write node equations for the network in the figure. Assume that the sources are of the form $v_1 = V_1 e^{st}$, $i_2 = I_2 e^{st}$, $v_3 = V_3 e^{st}$.

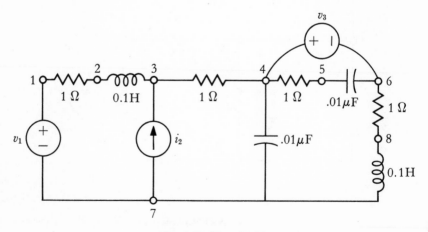

Figure Problem 13-47

13-48 Write loop equations for the network in Figure Problem 13.47 with sources as specified in Problem 13.47.

13-49 How many state variables are there for the network in Figure Problem 13-33? How about for the network in Figure Problem 13-32? Write the state-variable equations for the latter.

13-50 Assume that the elements in the network of Figure Problem 13-1 are linear time-varying and write an appropriate set of node equations.

13-51 Write an appropriate set of loop equations for the linear time-varying network of Problem 13-50.

13-52 Suppose that in a nonlinear network, every resistor is either in parallel with a capacitor or in series with an inductor, and suppose further that the number of state variables is equal to the number of energy-storage elements. All capacitors are charge-controlled and all inductors are flux-controlled. Resistors in series with inductors are current-controlled and resistors in parallel with capacitors are voltage-controlled. Verify that state equations in normal form can always be written.

13-53 Consider a linear time-invariant network with both voltage and current sources. Suppose it is desired to write a set of node equations. Justify and briefly discuss the following pointers. (a) If a voltage source is connected from a node k to the reference node, KCL need not be applied at node k. (b). If a voltage source is connected from node k to node m, then v_k and v_m are simply related. Moreover, if the node equations applied at nodes k and m are added together, the equation that is obtained is the cut-set equation that separates nodes k and m from the rest of the network. For such situations, KCL need not be applied to nodes k and m singly, but instead KCL may be applied to the cut set separating nodes k and m from the rest of the network.

Terminals and Ports 14

14.1 Classes of networks: breadboards and black boxes

In our discussions in past chapters, we have most often assumed that
we had access to all elements and all nodes in the network under study.
In other discussions, we have dealt with networks to which access was possible only at the network ports. Electrical engineers deal with both classes of
networks. In the early stages of design, it is common to "breadboard" the
network—meaning to temporarily arrange the components such that easy
access may be had to any node or any component for measurement or
adjustment. When the preliminary design is complete, the network is
transferred to a chassis or perhaps it is encased in plastic. The network
then becomes a "black box" in the sense that we can no longer measure
voltages or currents except through the connections to the outside world,
the terminals or the ports. The black box of which we speak may be created
by encasing it in metal or plastic, as we have mentioned, or it may be created
by spatial separation as in the case of the transmission line, or it may be the
result of the network being distributed (an integrated network, for example) so that discrete elements cannot be identified.

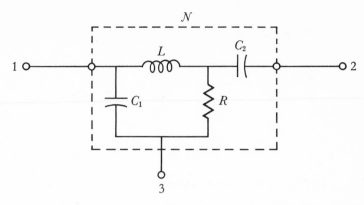

Figure 14.1 An example of a three-terminal network.

Clearly, the black-box network is as important in electrical engineering as is the breadboard-type network; we must know how to deal with either situation. Breadboard-type networks are analyzed by the application of the Kirchhoff laws, as studied in Chapter 13. For the black-box type of network, it is convenient to work in terms of one of the sets of port parameters which describe the network.

We find it useful to talk about networks in terms of individual terminals and associated pairs of terminals which constitute the ports. In Figure 14.1, a network is shown with the boundaries of the black box shown by the dashed lines. The terminals are formed by soldering on lead wires; in this example, there are three such wires to form a three-terminal network. This idea may be generalized as shown in Figure 14.2 by identifying n such

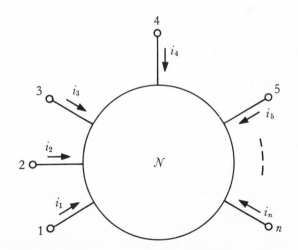

Figure 14.2 A network N in which n terminals are identified. Note the reference direction for the n currents.

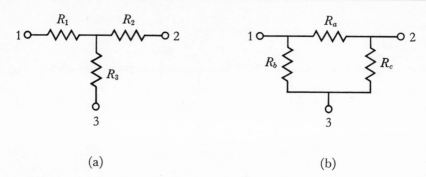

Figure 14.3 Two common three-terminal networks: (a) the resistive *T* section, and (b) the resistive π section.

terminals and so forming an *n*-terminal network. These terminals may be used in pairs to connect energy sources. The terminals may be used in various combinations of two for the measurement of voltages. Or there may be other parts of the network connected to these terminals. In this sense, the *n*-terminal network may be embedded in another network.

Examples of networks that are frequently embedded in more complex networks are the three-terminal networks shown in Figure 14.3. That of (a) of the figure is known as a *T-network*; that of (b) as a π-*network*. If the elements of these networks are all of the same kind, then one network may always replace the other in the sense that one may be substituted for

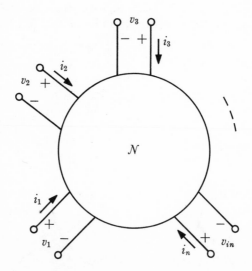

Figure 14.4 An *n*-terminal pair or *n*-port network with the assigned reference directions for the *n* currents and *n* voltages.

the other without disturbing voltages and currents of the network within which the *T*- or π-network is embedded.

The *n*-port network of Figure 14.4 is similar in appearance to the *n*-terminal network of Figure 14.2. The important difference is that the terminals are identified in associated pairs; we will not be interested in terminal-to-terminal voltages other than port voltages. Sources of energy will be connected to one or more of the ports. These ports of energy entry

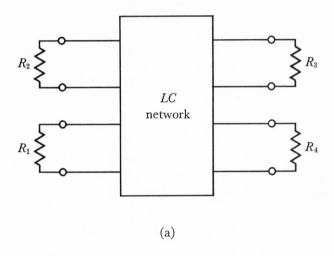

(a)

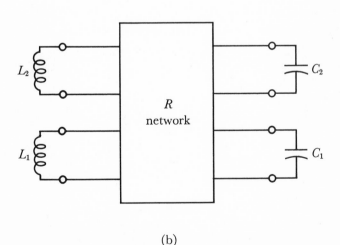

(b)

Figure 14.5   (a) A lossless 4-port network embedded in a resistive network. (b) A resistive 4-port network embedded in a lossless network.

will be distinguished from ports of energy exit which are connected to the loads. A port may not involve energy transfer but may be provided for the recording of a voltage of interest.

Applications of the port concept are shown in Figure 14.5. In some cases, we are interested in separating the lossless L and C elements from the R elements in accomplishing design. Thus in (a) of the figure, all ports of the lossless network are terminated in resistors, while the opposite situation takes place in (b) of the figure. This type of display may be used simply to give prominence to a given part of a network.

While we find the generality of the n-port descriptions useful in advanced applications, most problems of the electrical engineer may be formulated in terms of the familiar 1-port network, the 2-port network of Figure 14.6, or, at most, the 3-port network of Figure 14.7. The 3-port network finds application in the analysis of tunnel-diode amplifiers or oscillators.

Reference directions for the two kinds of network representations are illustrated by the figures. In the n-terminal network, the current reference direction is taken to be directed into the network. In the n-port network, the reference direction for the current is into the network at the positive terminal (and, of course, out for the negative terminal).

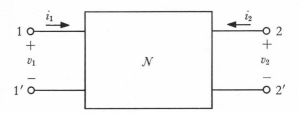

Figure 14.6 Standard representation of the 2-port network, including voltage and current reference directions for the two ports.

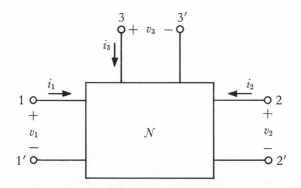

Figure 14.7 A 3-port network with reference directions.

● **EXERCISES**

14.1-1   (a) Rearrange the network shown in Figure Exercise 14.1-1 in the form shown in Figure 14.5(a), showing the connections in the *LC* network in detail.
(b) Rearrange the network of Figure Exercise 14.1-1 in the form of Figure 14.5(b), showing the connections in the *R* network in detail.

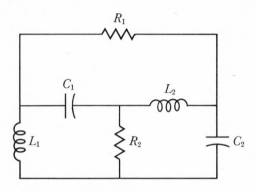

Figure Exercise 14.1-1

14.1-2   Repeat parts (a) and (b) of Exercise 14.1-1 for the network shown in Figure Exercise 14.1-2.

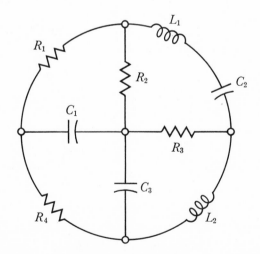

Figure Exercise 14.1-2

14.1-3   For the two networks of Figure 14.3, determine R_1, R_2 and R_3 as functions of R_a, R_b, and R_c in order that the two networks be equivalent for embedding within a more complex network.

14.2   Two-port parameters

In this discussion, we will consider only the time-invariant linear 2-port network, containing no independent sources, with the assurance that the 2-port approach can be generalized for the 3-port, 4-port, or the n-port case. We recall from Section 10.2 that a 1-port network is characterized by a single network function, the driving-point impedance, or the reciprocal of this quantity which is the driving-point admittance. For the 2-port network, there are four variables, as shown in Figure 14.6, and thus more possible functions for describing the network.

As in Chapter 10, we will use $I(s)$ and $V(s)$ as the network variables for exponential signals of the form Ke^{st}. The four variables in Figure 14.6 are the quantities, V_1 and I_1 at port 1, and the quantities, V_2 and I_2 at port 2. Our objective is to express any two of these variables in terms of the remaining two; clearly there are a number of possibilities.

Consider first a linear time-invariant system for which there are two input signals, X_1 and X_2, and for which two responses, Y_1 and Y_2, are to be found. We assume that the system is linear so that the principle of superposition applies. Assuming that the system is in the steady-state with exponential signals, and that the system was initially in the zero state, we may write

$$Y_1 = Q_{11}X_1 + Q_{12}X_2 , \tag{14.1}$$

$$Y_2 = Q_{21}X_1 + Q_{22}X_2 . \tag{14.2}$$

The quantities Q_{11}, Q_{12}, Q_{21}, and Q_{22} are network functions, of course, with their nature depending on the dimensions of the Y's and X's.

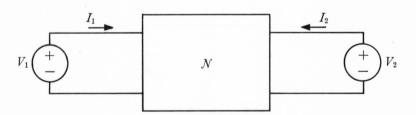

Figure 14.8   A 2-port network N.

For the 2-port network of Figure 14.8, the inputs are V_1 and V_2, and the responses are I_1 and I_2. Then the general equations of Equations 14.1

and 14.2 specialize to

$$I_1 = y_{11}V_1 + y_{12}V_2, \tag{14.3}$$

$$I_2 = y_{21}V_1 + y_{22}V_2. \tag{14.4}$$

Here we have used y_{jk} in place of Q_{jk} because the dimensions of these network functions are clearly admittances.

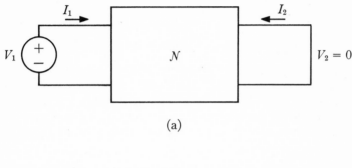

(a)

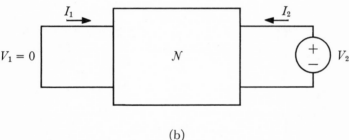

(b)

Figure 14.9 The network of Figure 14.8, with one port shorted such that the short-circuit admittance functions are defined.

The y-functions of Equation 14.3 and 14.4 have a meaningful interpretation in terms of the 2-port network with one of the two ports shorted as shown in Figure 14.9. The shorting of port 2 in (a) of the figure causes $V_2 = 0$ and makes possible the following definitions from Equations 14.3 and 14.4:

$$y_{11} = \frac{I_1}{V_1}\bigg|_{V_2 = 0} \tag{14.5}$$

and

$$y_{21} = \frac{I_2}{V_1}\bigg|_{V_2 = 0}. \tag{14.6}$$

In other words, y_{11} is the driving-point admittance at port 1 with port 2 shorted, and y_{21} is the transfer admittance relating port-2 current to port-1 voltage with port 2 shorted.

Similarly, the shorting of port 1 in Figure 14.9(b) results in the simplification of Equations 14.3 and 14.4, and we find that

$$y_{22} = \frac{I_2}{V_2}\bigg|_{V_1 = 0} \tag{14.7}$$

and

$$y_{12} = \frac{I_1}{V_2}\bigg|_{V_1 = 0}. \tag{14.8}$$

Thus we see that y_{22} is the driving-point admittance at port 2 with port 1 shorted, and y_{12} is the transfer admittance relating port-1 current and port-2 voltage with port 1 shorted. Because of these interpretations and the dimension of the y-functions, they are known as the *short-circuit admittance functions*. They play an important role in the description of black-box networks.

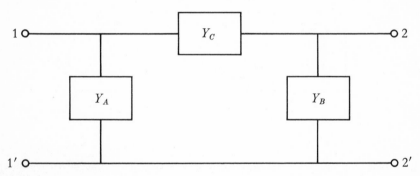

Figure 14.10   A general π-network in which the three arm admittances are Y_A, Y_B, and Y_C. This network is used in Example 14.2-1.

EXAMPLE 14.2-1.   The π-network of Figure 14.10 is an example of a network for which the y-functions can be found by inspection. Thus we see that

$$y_{11} = Y_A + Y_C \tag{14.9}$$

and

$$y_{22} = Y_B + Y_C. \tag{14.10}$$

Shorting port 1, we have $I_1 = -Y_C V_2$, and shorting port 2 gives $I_2 = -Y_C V_1$, the minus sign arising because of the reference directions chosen for the currents. Then we have

$$y_{12} = y_{21} = -Y_C. \tag{14.11}$$

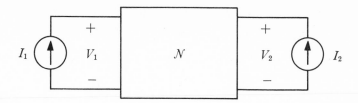

Figure 14.11 The standard 2-port network in which current sources provide the excitation. This network is used in deriving the open-circuit impedance functions.

If the arm admittances of the network of Figure 14.10 satisfy the condition $Y_A = Y_B$, then we see that

$$y_{11} = y_{22}, \tag{14.12}$$

and the network is said to be *symmetrical*. As we shall see in the next section, the condition

$$y_{12} = y_{21} \tag{14.13}$$

implies that the network is *reciprocal*. □

For the 2-port network of Figure 14.11, the inputs are now I_1 and I_2 and the responses are V_1 and V_2. For this case, Equations 14.1 and 14.2 become

$$V_1 = z_{11}I_1 + z_{12}I_2 \tag{14.14}$$

and

$$V_2 = z_{21}I_1 + z_{22}I_2. \tag{14.15}$$

We have selected z_{ij} notation for the network functions because the dimensions are impedance. The functions are also called *open-circuit* functions for reasons that parallel those given for the y-functions. This time we open-circuit the ports as shown in Figure 14.12. When either $I_1 = 0$ or $I_2 = 0$,

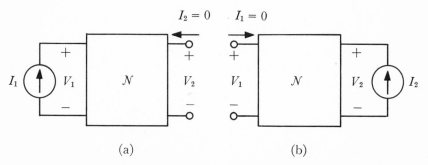

(a)   (b)

Figure 14.12 The 2-port network of Figure 14.11, modified such that the open-circuit impedance functions are defined.

Equations 14.14 and 14.15 may be manipulated such that

$$z_{11} = \frac{V_1}{I_1}\bigg|_{I_2 = 0}, \tag{14.16}$$

$$z_{21} = \frac{V_2}{I_1}\bigg|_{I_2 = 0}, \tag{14.17}$$

$$z_{12} = \frac{V_1}{I_2}\bigg|_{I_1 = 0}, \tag{14.18}$$

and

$$z_{22} = \frac{V_2}{I_2}\bigg|_{I_1 = 0}. \tag{14.19}$$

Thus we see that z_{11} is the driving-point impedance at port 1 with port 2 open, and z_{22} is the driving-point impedance of port 2 with port 1 open. Further, z_{12} and z_{21} are transfer impedances computed under open-circuit conditions. The four functions constitute the *open-circuit impedance functions* which describe a 2-port network.

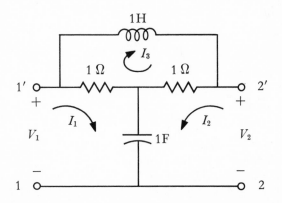

Figure 14.13   A bridged-*T*-network which is analyzed in Example 14.2-2.

EXAMPLE 14.2-2.   For some networks such as the *T*-network or a ladder network, the defining equations, Equations 14.16 through 14.19, together with their interpretation as shown in Figure 14.12, may be used for routine determination of the *z*-functions. In some cases, it may be necessary to write the network equations. For the network of Figure 14.13, from KVL we may write

$$\left(1 + \frac{1}{s}\right)I_1 + \frac{1}{s}I_2 - I_3 = V_1, \tag{14.20}$$

$$\frac{1}{s}I_1 + \left(1 + \frac{1}{s}\right)I_2 + \qquad I_3 = V_2, \tag{14.21}$$

$$-I_1 + \qquad I_2 + (2 + s)I_3 = 0. \tag{14.22}$$

Eliminating I_3 from the first two equations, we obtain

$$V_1 = \left(\frac{s^2 + 3s + 1}{s^2 + 2s}\right)I_1 + \left(\frac{2s + 2}{s^2 + 2s}\right)I_2, \tag{14.23}$$

$$V_2 = \left(\frac{2s + 2}{s^2 + 2s}\right)I_1 + \left(\frac{s^2 + 3s + 1}{s^2 + 2s}\right)I_2. \tag{14.24}$$

Thus we have

$$z_{11} = z_{22} = \frac{s^2 + 3s + 1}{s^2 + 2s} \tag{14.25}$$

and

$$z_{12} = z_{21} = \frac{2s + 2}{s^2 + 2s}. \tag{14.26}$$

The network is both symmetrical and reciprocal. □

Since Equations 14.3 and 14.4 and Equations 14.14 and 14.15 describe the same 2-port network, it is clear that the z-functions can be expressed in terms of the y-functions and vice versa. If we start with Equations 14.3 and 14.4 and solve for V_1 and V_2, we obtain

$$V_1 = \frac{y_{22}}{\Delta_y}I_1 + \frac{-y_{12}}{\Delta_y}I_2 \tag{14.27}$$

and

$$V_2 = \frac{-y_{21}}{\Delta_y}I_1 + \frac{y_{11}}{\Delta_y}I_2, \tag{14.28}$$

where

$$\Delta_y = y_{11}y_{22} - y_{12}y_{21}. \tag{14.29}$$

Similarly, starting with Equations 14.14 and 14.15 and solving for I_1 and I_2 yields

$$I_1 = \frac{z_{22}}{\Delta_z}V_1 + \frac{-z_{12}}{\Delta_z}V_2 \tag{14.30}$$

and

$$I_2 = \frac{-z_{21}}{\Delta_z}V_1 + \frac{z_{11}}{\Delta_z}V_2, \tag{14.31}$$

where

$$\Delta_z = z_{11}z_{22} - z_{12}z_{21}. \tag{14.32}$$

The relationships we have found between the y- and z-functions are summarized compactly in Table 14.1, together with other relationships important to studies of this section.

Table 14.1   Relationships of 2-port parameters; $\Delta_x = x_{11}x_{22} - x_{12}x_{21}$.

	z		y		h		g	
z	z_{11}	z_{12}	$\dfrac{y_{22}}{\Delta_y}$	$\dfrac{-y_{12}}{\Delta_y}$	$\dfrac{\Delta_h}{h_{22}}$	$\dfrac{h_{12}}{h_{22}}$	$\dfrac{1}{g_{11}}$	$\dfrac{-g_{12}}{g_{11}}$
	z_{21}	z_{22}	$\dfrac{-y_{21}}{\Delta_y}$	$\dfrac{y_{11}}{\Delta_y}$	$\dfrac{-h_{21}}{h_{22}}$	$\dfrac{1}{h_{22}}$	$\dfrac{g_{21}}{g_{11}}$	$\dfrac{\Delta_g}{g_{11}}$
y	$\dfrac{z_{22}}{\Delta_z}$	$\dfrac{-z_{12}}{\Delta_z}$	y_{11}	y_{12}	$\dfrac{1}{h_{11}}$	$\dfrac{-h_{12}}{h_{11}}$	$\dfrac{\Delta_g}{g_{22}}$	$\dfrac{g_{12}}{g_{22}}$
	$\dfrac{-z_{21}}{\Delta_z}$	$\dfrac{z_{11}}{\Delta_z}$	y_{21}	y_{22}	$\dfrac{h_{21}}{h_{11}}$	$\dfrac{\Delta_h}{h_{11}}$	$\dfrac{-g_{21}}{g_{22}}$	$\dfrac{1}{g_{22}}$
h	$\dfrac{\Delta_z}{z_{22}}$	$\dfrac{z_{12}}{z_{22}}$	$\dfrac{1}{y_{11}}$	$\dfrac{-y_{12}}{y_{11}}$	h_{11}	h_{12}	$\dfrac{g_{22}}{\Delta_g}$	$\dfrac{-g_{12}}{\Delta_g}$
	$\dfrac{-z_{21}}{z_{22}}$	$\dfrac{1}{z_{22}}$	$\dfrac{y_{21}}{y_{11}}$	$\dfrac{\Delta_y}{y_{11}}$	h_{21}	h_{22}	$\dfrac{-g_{21}}{\Delta_g}$	$\dfrac{g_{11}}{\Delta_g}$
g	$\dfrac{1}{z_{11}}$	$\dfrac{-z_{12}}{z_{11}}$	$\dfrac{\Delta_y}{y_{22}}$	$\dfrac{y_{12}}{y_{22}}$	$\dfrac{h_{22}}{\Delta_h}$	$\dfrac{-h_{12}}{\Delta_h}$	g_{11}	g_{12}
	$\dfrac{z_{21}}{z_{11}}$	$\dfrac{\Delta_z}{z_{11}}$	$\dfrac{-y_{21}}{y_{22}}$	$\dfrac{1}{y_{22}}$	$\dfrac{-h_{21}}{\Delta_h}$	$\dfrac{h_{11}}{\Delta_h}$	g_{21}	g_{22}

Another set of parameters are defined by the equations

$$V_1 = h_{11}I_1 + h_{12}V_2 \tag{14.33}$$

and

$$I_2 = h_{21}I_1 + h_{22}V_2 \tag{14.34}$$

and are known as the *hybrid parameters*. These are particularly important in the representation of transistor networks where it is inconvenient to measure all of the y or z parameters. Following the pattern of our previous studies, we note that

$$h_{11} = \frac{V_1}{I_1}\bigg|_{V_2 = 0} ,$$
(14.35)

$$h_{21} = \frac{I_2}{I_1}\bigg|_{V_2 = 0} ,$$
(14.36)

$$h_{12} = \frac{V_1}{V_2}\bigg|_{I_1 = 0} ,$$
(14.37)

and

$$h_{22} = \frac{I_2}{V_2}\bigg|_{I_1 = 0} .$$
(14.38)

We may now see the justification for calling the parameters hybrid. Note that they are dimensionally inhomogeneous, being in order an impedance, current ratio, voltage ratio, and an admittance. Note also that h_{11} and h_{21} are short-circuit parameters, while h_{12} and h_{22} are open-circuit parameters. In fact, a simple relationship exists for h_{11} and h_{22} in terms of other parameters:

$$h_{11} = \frac{1}{y_{11}} \quad \text{and} \quad h_{22} = \frac{1}{z_{22}}.$$
(14.39)

Still another set of parameters are defined by the equations

$$I_1 = g_{11}V_1 + g_{12}I_2$$
(14.40)

and

$$V_2 = g_{21}V_1 + g_{22}I_2$$
(14.41)

and are known as the g or inverse hybrid parameters. The relationship of the h and g parameters to each other and to the y and z parameters is given in Table 14.1.

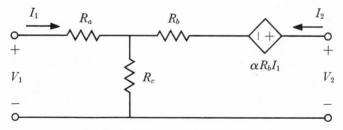

Figure 14.14 A network with a controlled source which is analyzed in Example 14.2-3 for the hybrid h parameters.

Example 14.2-3. The network shown in Figure 14.14 contains one current-controlled voltage source. Making use of Equations 14.35 to 14.38, we find that

$$h_{11} = \frac{R_a R_b + R_a R_c + R_b R_c (1 - \alpha)}{R_b + R_c}, \qquad (14.42)$$

$$h_{12} = \frac{R_c}{R_b + R_c}, \qquad (14.43)$$

$$h_{21} = -\frac{(\alpha R_b + R_c)}{R_b + R_c}, \qquad (14.44)$$

and

$$h_{22} = \frac{1}{R_b + R_c}. \qquad \square \quad (14.45)$$

● **EXERCISES**

14.2-1   For each of the three networks shown in Figure Exercise 14.2-1, determine the y, z, h, and g parameters.

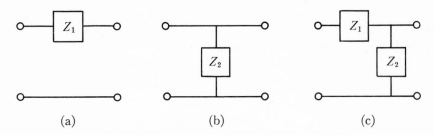

Figure Exercise 14.2-1

14.2-2   Repeat Exercise 14.2-1 for the two resistive networks of Figure Exercise 14.2-2.

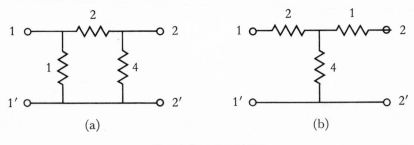

Figure Exercise 14.2-2

14.2-3   For the *RC* network shown in Figure Exercise 14.2-3, show that

$$y_{11} = \frac{(s+1)(s+3)}{(s+2)(s+4)} \quad\text{and}\quad -y_{21} = \frac{k_{21}(s+1)}{(s+2)(s+4)}$$

and determine the numerical value of k_{21}.

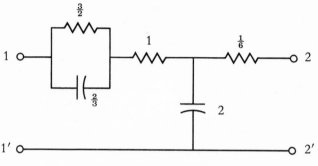

Figure Exercise 14.2-3

14.2-4   Figure Exercise 14.2-4 shows a 2-port network embedded in another resistive network. The network is described by the short-circuit parameters $y_{11} = y_{22} = 2$ mho, $y_{21} = 2$ mho, and $y_{12} = 1$ mho. If $I_0 = 1$ ampere, determine V_1 and V_2.

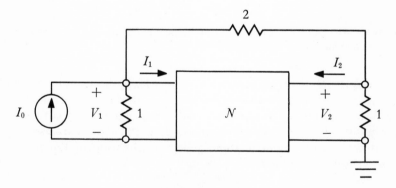

Figure Exercise 14.2-4

14.2-5   Consider the network of Figure 14.14 which is analyzed in Example 14.2-3. (a) Does $h_{11} \neq h_{22}$ imply that the network is non-symmetrical? Why? (b) Does $h_{21} \neq h_{12}$ imply that the network is nonreciprocal? Why?

14.3 Two-port reciprocity

The principle of reciprocity applies to many physical systems. In antenna theory, for example, it is well known that all of the receiving properties of an antenna can be deduced from the known transmitting properties of the same antenna.† Thus the directional radiation pattern for a transmitting antenna is determined by measuring its pattern as a receiving antenna. The reciprocity principle has interesting and important consequences when applied to the 2-port network, as we shall see in this section.

Our derivation relating to 2-port reciprocity stems from Tellegen's theorem which was studied in Section 6.5. Although the theorem was given there in terms of instantaneous quantities, it relies upon KVL and KCL and so applies to phasor quantities representing voltage and current as well as for $V(s)$ and $I(s)$ for exponential signals since we are considering only linear time-invariant networks.

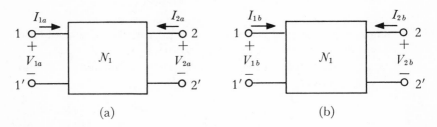

(a)   (b)

Figure 14.15 The same network, N_1, shown twice, for voltages and currents which are assumed to be different for the two cases.

Consider the Network N_1, two views of which are shown in Figure 14.15. While the networks of (a) and (b) are identical, the signals for the two networks are assumed to be different with the voltages and currents distinguished by an additional subscript a or b. If the signals are assumed to be sinusoidal or exponential, then Tellegen's theorem of Equation 6.36 may be written in the form

$$V_1 I_1 + V_2 I_2 = \sum_{\substack{k \text{ internal} \\ \text{elements}}} V_k I_k. \tag{14.46}$$

The first two terms in this equation have positive signs because the voltages at the ports have opposite reference conventions than those within the

† E. C. Jordan, *Electromagnetic Waves and Radiating Systems* (Englewood Cliffs, N.J.: Prentice-Hall, Inc., 1950), 326 ff.

network. Now the amazing thing we discovered in Chapter 6 was that it was necessary only that all V's in Equation 14.46 satisfy KVL and that all I's satisfy KCL. We exploit this fact by using voltages from one of the networks of Figure 14.15 and currents from the other, in Equation 14.46. This appears to be a most unusual thing to do, but wait until you see the results! Using the voltages of the network of (a) in Figure 14.15 and the currents from (b), we have the following form of Equation 14.46:

$$V_{1a}I_{1b} + V_{2a}I_{2b} = \sum_k V_{ka}I_{kb} . \tag{14.47}$$

If instead we use the currents of the network of (a) in Figure 14.15 and the voltages from (b), then Equation 14.46 has a different form which is

$$V_{1b}I_{1a} + V_{2b}I_{2a} = \sum_k V_{kb}I_{ka} . \tag{14.48}$$

At this point, we assume that the network contains no independent sources, and that each branch is described by

$$V_{ka} = Z_k I_{ka} \tag{14.49}$$

and

$$V_{kb} = Z_k I_{kb} . \tag{14.50}$$

Using these relationships, we may modify the summation of Equation 14.47 as follows:

$$\sum_k V_{ka}I_{kb} = \sum_k (Z_k I_{ka})I_{kb} = \sum_k (Z_k I_{kb})I_{ka} = \sum_k V_{kb}I_{ka} , \tag{14.51}$$

which is identical with the summation of Equation 14.48. Hence, we have the important result

$$V_{1a}I_{1b} + V_{2a}I_{2b} = V_{1b}I_{1a} + V_{2b}I_{2a} . \tag{14.52}$$

Any 2-port network for which this identity holds is said to be a *reciprocal* 2-port. The reciprocity formula of Equation 14.52 has been derived, assuming that the 2-port is linear and time-invariant, and that there are no independent sources inside the network. Furthermore, it has been assumed that the internal branches are 1-ports, such that Equations 14.49 and 14.50 hold. Note that our branches can be 1-port subnetworks that may contain elements like gyrators, controlled sources, coupled coils, negative converters, and ideal transformers, in addition to resistors, inductors, and capacitors, as long as Equations 14.49 and 14.50 hold. For a slightly more general situation, see Problem 14-14.

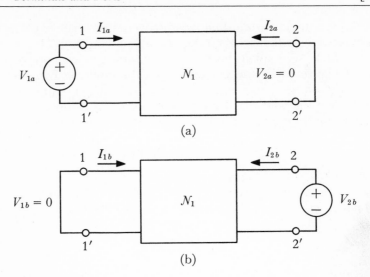

Figure 14.16 The networks of Figure 14.15, with one port of each network shorted. Analysis of these two networks leads to the conclusion that $y_{21} = y_{12}$ under the assumptions of the derivation.

As the first application of the result of Equation 14.52, consider the networks of Figure 14.16 with one port of each network shorted such that $V_{1b} = 0$ and $V_{2a} = 0$. For this condition, Equation 14.52 reduces to

$$V_{1a}I_{1b} = V_{2b}I_{2a}. \tag{14.53}$$

Rearranging this equation, we have

$$\left.\frac{I_{2a}}{V_{1a}}\right|V_{2a} = 0 = \left.\frac{I_{1b}}{V_{2b}}\right|V_{1b} = 0. \tag{14.54}$$

Now the first term is recognized as the short-circuit admittance of N_1, y_{21}, while the second is the short-circuit admittance of N_1, y_{12}. From this result, we see that reciprocity in a 2-port network implies

$$y_{21} = y_{12} \tag{14.55}$$

as stated in the last section.

From Equation 14.54, we also see what might be regarded as the "classical" statement of the reciprocity theorem: In any linear passive network, if a voltage V applied between any two terminals causes a current I in any branch as measured by an ammeter, then the same V and I will be obtained if the positions of the generator and ammeter are interchanged.

As a second application, we let $I_{2a} = 0$ and $I_{1b} = 0$ by the mechanism of opening the ports as shown in Figure 14.17. Under these conditions, Equa-

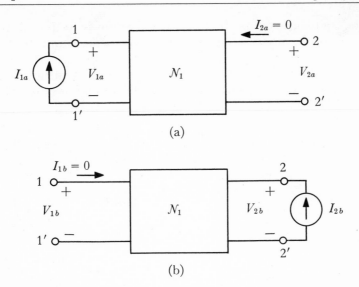

Figure 14.17 The networks of Figure 14.15, with one port of each network open. These networks are used in the derivation of Equation 14.57 or 14.58.

tion 14.52 becomes

$$V_{2a}I_{2b} = V_{1b}I_{1a}.$$ (14.56)

This equation may be arranged as

$$\frac{V_{2a}}{I_{1a}}\bigg|_{I_{2a}=0} = \frac{V_{1b}}{I_{2b}}\bigg|_{I_{1b}=0}.$$ (14.57)

Comparing these equations with those defining the z parameters, we see that reciprocity implies that

$$z_{21} = z_{12},$$ (14.58)

again a condition stated in the last section.

The analysis associated with the networks in Figure 14.17 makes it possible to compare a property of a reciprocal 2-port network with the transmitting and receiving antennas mentioned at the beginning of the section. Suppose that we connect a source at port 1 in Figure 14.17(a) and then record the output at port 2. The fact that the ratios of Equation 14.57 are equal tells us that for the same network we could connect our source at port 2, as shown in Figure 14.17(b), and then record the output at port 2. If the Network N_1 is a reciprocal network, the outputs for the two cases will be exactly the same. In the same way, the network of (a) may be considered the analog of a receiving antenna while that of (b) is the analog of the transmitting antenna. If the antenna system is reciprocal, the characteristics of the transmitting system will be identical with those for the receiving system.

An interesting third application of the reciprocity principle is made by letting $I_{2a}=0$ and $V_{1b}=0$ corresponding to the connections shown in Figure 14.18. Then Equation 14.52 reduces to

$$V_{1a}I_{1b} + V_{2a}I_{2b} = 0, \tag{14.59}$$

which may be written in the following form

$$\left.\frac{V_{2a}}{V_{1a}}\right|_{I_{2a}=0} = \left.\frac{-I_{1b}}{I_{2b}}\right|_{V_{1b}=0}. \tag{14.60}$$

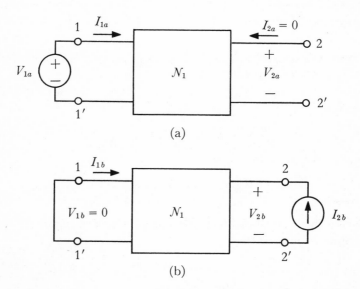

(a)

(b)

Figure 14.18 The modified networks derived from those of Figure 14.15 from which Equation 14.60 is found.

This result shows that the voltage ratio for one connection of the network, that of (a), is equal to the negative of the inverse current ratio for the connection of the network shown in (b). We see that a Network N_1 driven by a voltage source at port 1 has an open-circuit voltage response at port 2, which is the same as the negative of the short-circuit current response at port 1, if the Network N_1 is driven by a current source at port 2, provided that the excitations are numerically equal.

● EXERCISES

14.3-1 Investigate the consequences of $I_{1a} = 0$ and $V_{2b} = 0$ in Equation 14.52 interpreted in terms of the networks of Figure 14.15. Compare your conclusions with those reached from Equation 14.60.

14.3-2 Starting with the equations

$$V_1 = z_{11}I_1 + z_{12}I_2 \quad \text{and} \quad V_2 = z_{21}I_1 + z_{22}I_2$$

derive Equation 14.60 for the networks of Figure 14.18 under the condition that $z_{12} = z_{21}$.

14.3-3 We have seen that $y_{12} = y_{21}$ and $z_{12} = z_{21}$ for reciprocal networks. What is the corresponding condition for a reciprocal network in terms of the h parameters?

14.3-4 The network of Figure Exercise 14.3-4 contains a current-controlled current source. For what range of values of α will the 2-port network be reciprocal?

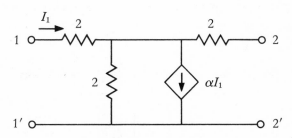

Figure Exercise 14.3-4

14.3-5 We have shown in this section that all RLC 2-ports (with linear time-invariant elements) are reciprocal. What can we say about 2-port networks containing negative R's?

14.3-6 Give an example of a reciprocal 2-port which contains a controlled source. Your network should remain reciprocal, regardless of the values of the parameters in the controlled source.

Problems

14-1 The network shown in Figure Problem 14-1 contains coupled inductors L_1 and L_2 of mutual inductance M. (a) For this network, find the z parameters. (b) From the results of (a), show that if $R_1 = R_2$ and $L_1 = L_2$, then $z_{11} = z_{22}$.

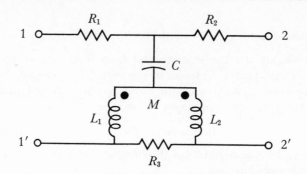

Figure Problem 14-1

14-2   Given a 2-port network composed of passive linear elements for
        which $z_{12} = z_{21}$ (and $y_{12} = y_{21}$). (a) Show that the T-network shown
        in Figure Problem 14-2 is an equivalent network with respect to
        measurements made at either port (but no other place). (b) Show
        that the π-network of Figure Problem 14-2 is equivalent to the
        2-port network for measurements made at either port.

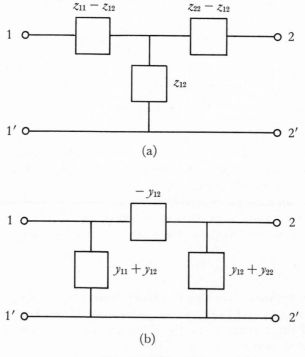

Figure Problem 14-2

14-3   Given the 2-port network of Figure Problem 14-3, in which port 2 is terminated in Z_L. (a) Find the driving-point impedance at port 1 in terms of the z-functions and Z_L. (b) Repeat part (a) but in terms of the y-functions and $Y_L = 1/Z_L$.

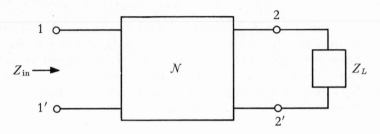

Figure Problem 14-3

14-4   For the capacitive network shown in Figure Problem 14-4(a), determine the T-section equivalent network shown in (b) of the figure which is the equivalent 2-port network for an excitation.

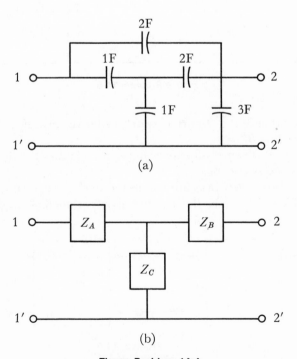

Figure Problem 14-4

14-5   For the series of problems that follow, we will consider another set
of parameters for characterizing 2-port networks known as the
transmission parameters. These parameters serve to relate parameters at one port to those parameters for the other port. We have

$$V_1 = AV_2 - BI_2 \qquad \text{and} \qquad I_1 = CV_2 - DI_2.$$

(a) Define the A, B, C, and D parameters in terms of short-circuit
or open-circuit measurements made on the 2-port network as in
Equations 14.5 to 14.8. (b) Express each of the transmission parameters in terms of the z-functions; the y-functions.

14-6   Find the transmission parameters for the network shown in Figure
Problem 14-6 if $\alpha = 2$ and $\beta = 2$.

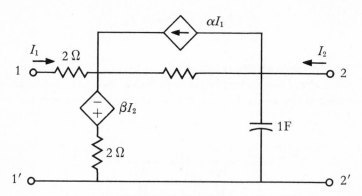

Figure Problem 14-6

14-7   Show that for a 2-port network to be reciprocal, it is necessary
that $AD - BC = 1$.

14-8   Repeat Problem 14-3 expressing Z_{in} in terms of the A, B, C, and D
parameters and Z_L.

14-9   Two 2-port networks are connected in cascade as shown in Figure
Problem 14-9. Let the transmission parameters of the two net-

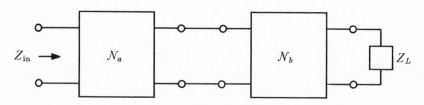

Figure Problem 14-9

works be distinguished by subscripts a and b. Determine the driving-point impedance Z_{in} in terms of the eight transmission parameters and Z_L.

14-10 Given the network of Figure Problem 14-10 with $R_x = 2$ ohms. (a) Determine the value of g (if one exists) for which the 2-port is reciprocal. (b) Determine the value of g (if one exists) for which the 2-port is electrically symmetrical.

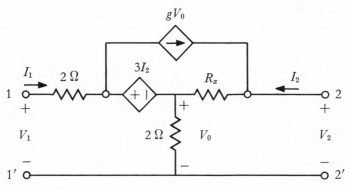

Figure Problem 14-10

14-11 Repeat Problem 14-10 with $R_x = 1$ ohm.

14-12 Consider the network of Figure Problem 14-6. Does there exist a combination of values of α and β for which the 2-port network is reciprocal? Express in the form of an equation if possible.

14-13 We are given a resistive 2-port network for which an equivalent T- or π-section is desired for further analysis under different load conditions. We are permitted only driving-point measurements at port 1 and port 2, although a small boy is available for shorting either port if desired. How many and what kinds of measurements must be made to determine the equivalent T- or π-section?

14-14 In our discussion of 2-port reciprocity, we have assumed that the 2-port network is linear, time-invariant, with no independent sources inside, and that it is an interconnection of 1-ports. Consider the 4-port network shown in Figure Problem 14-14 in which Network N contains only 1-ports satisfying Equations 14.49 and 14.50. Using Tellegen's theorem of Chapter 6, show that this network exhibits 2-port reciprocity with respect to ports 1 and 2. Generalize this result to show that a 2-port network with any number of coupled inductors is reciprocal.

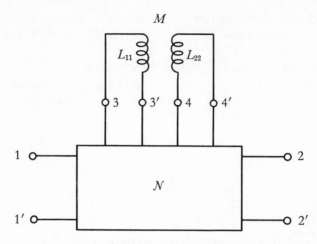

Figure Problem 14-14

14-15   A textbook published in 1948 states the reciprocity theorem in the following manner:

If at any particular frequency the only generator of a linear, bilateral network, located in the ith branch, and an impedance in the kth branch equal to the internal impedance of the generator are interchanged, the current of the kth branch before the interchange is the same as the current in the ith branch after the interchange.

Using the approach of this chapter, prove (or disprove) this theorem.

14-16   Repeat Problem 14-14, with the coupled inductors replaced by an ideal transformer.

14-17   Instead of Equations 14.49 and 14.50, assume that

$$V_k = \sum_d Z_{kj} I_j$$

and $Z_{kj} = Z_{jk}$ for all k and j. Derive the reciprocity formula of Equation 14.52.

Determination of Solutions for

Linear Time-Invariant Networks **15**

15.1 Gauss's elimination method

From an engineering standpoint, writing a set of equilibrium equations which completely characterizes an arbitrary network is only part of an over-all goal. Obtaining numerical solutions to specific sets of equations is usually at least as important. In this section, we review a well-known method, Gauss's elimination method, for solving one of the simplest sets of equations, a set of linear algebraic equations. A linear time-invariant resistive network, for instance, has loop or node equations which are linear algebraic equations with real constant coefficients. A linear time-invariant network with sinusoidal sources (of the same frequency) in the steady-state has steady-state solutions which are obtainable through the use of phasors. The phasor variables (say loop currents or node voltages) satisfy a set of linear algebraic equations with complex constant coefficients.

The Gauss algorithm is a systematic way for organizing the elimination of variables. Clearly, both sides of any equation may be multiplied by the same constant without disturbing the equality. Also, the validity of an equation is not changed by adding another equation to it. The general goal in the Gauss elimination procedure is to end up with a set of equations such that one equation contains only one unknown, say x_n, another equation contains only two unknowns, x_n and x_{n-1}, a third equation contains only three unknowns, x_n, x_{n-1}, and x_{n-2}, and so on. Clearly, the solution for x_n may be readily obtained. With x_n computed, x_{n-1} may be readily obtained from the second equation. The algorithm is continued until all solutions are obtained. Before describing the general procedure, let us consider a simple specific case.

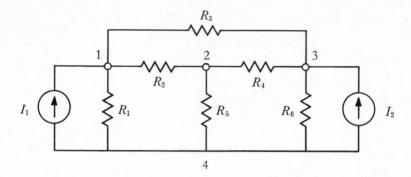

Figure 15.1 Network for Example 15.1-1.

EXAMPLE 15.1-1. Suppose that the resistor values for the network in Figure 15.1 are $\frac{1}{2}$ ohm each, and suppose $I_1 = 1$ ampere and $I_2 = 2$ amperes. Using node 4 as the reference, the node equations are as follows:

$$6v_1 - 2v_2 - 2v_3 = 1, \qquad \text{(a)}$$

$$-2v_1 + 6v_2 - 2v_3 = 0, \qquad \text{(b)} \qquad\qquad (15.1)$$

$$-2v_1 - 2v_2 + 6v_3 = 2. \qquad \text{(c)}$$

We may divide Equation (a) by 3 and add the result to Equation (b), with the result that we have

$$0 + \left(\frac{16}{3}\right)v_2 - \left(\frac{8}{3}\right)v_3 = \frac{1}{3}. \qquad \text{(b')}$$

Similarly we may divide Equation (a) by 3 and add the result to (c), with the result that we have

$$0 - \left(\frac{8}{3}\right)v_2 + \left(\frac{16}{3}\right)v_3 = \frac{7}{3}. \qquad \text{(c')}$$

Equations (a), (b), and (c) are now equivalent to Equations (a), (b'), and (c'). Note that v_1 was eliminated from Equations (b) and (c), yielding (b') and (c'). Now we eliminate v_2 from (c'). This is accomplished by adding $\frac{1}{2}$ of (b') to (c'). Thus we have

$$0 \cdot v_1 + 0 \cdot v_2 + 4v_3 = \frac{15}{6}. \qquad \text{(c'')}$$

By judicious elimination of variables, the set of equations in 15.1 generated Equations (b') and (c''). Note that from (c''), v_3 can be obtained as $\frac{5}{8}$. Then (b') readily gives the value of v_2 as

$$v_2 = \frac{3}{16}\left[\frac{1}{3} + \left(\frac{8}{3}\right)\left(\frac{5}{8}\right)\right] = \frac{3}{8}.$$

Finally, from (a) we have

$$v_1 = \tfrac{1}{6}[2(\tfrac{3}{8}) + 2(\tfrac{5}{8}) + 1] = \tfrac{1}{2}$$

The set of equations (a), (b'), and (c'') is said to be in triangular form as follows:

$$6v_1 - 2v_2 - 2v_3 = 1,$$

$$0 + \frac{16}{3}v_2 - \frac{8}{3}v_3 = \frac{1}{3}, \qquad (15.2)$$

$$0 + 0 + 4v_3 = \frac{15}{6}.$$

Notice the triangular array of zeros. $\square$

We now discuss the general case. Suppose we have a set of n linear algebraic equations in n unknowns, $x_1, x_2, \ldots, x_n$. We assume that the set of equations has a unique solution. Among the n equations, at least one will contain a term in x_1, otherwise there is no unique solution. Denote this equation by

$$a_{11}x_1 + a_{12}x_2 + a_{13}x_3 + \cdots + a_{1n}x_n = b_1, \qquad (15.3)$$

where $a_{11} \neq 0$. The other equations are of the form

$$a_{i1}x_1 + a_{i2}x_2 + \cdots + a_{in}x_n = b_i,$$

where $i = 2, 3, \ldots, n$. If Equation 15.3 is multiplied by $-(a_{i1}/a_{11})$ and the result added to the equation whose coefficient for x_1 is a_{i1}, then the result is

$$0 + \left(a_{i2} - \frac{a_{12}a_{i1}}{a_{11}}\right)x_2 + \cdots + \left(a_{in} - \frac{a_{1n}a_{i1}}{a_{11}}\right)x_n = b_i - \frac{a_{i1}}{a_{11}}b_1,$$

thus eliminating x_1. This is done for all the $n-1$ equations of $i = 2, \ldots, n$. At this stage, we have one equation in n unknowns, and $n-1$ equations in the $n-1$ unknowns, $x_2, x_3, \ldots, x_n$. From the set of $n-1$ equations, there is at least one equation with a term in x_2; otherwise there is no unique solution. Let this equation be

$$a_{22}^{(1)}x_2 + a_{23}^{(1)}x_3 + \cdots + a_{2n}^{(1)}x_n = b_2^{(1)}, \tag{15.4}$$

where $a_{22}^{(1)} \neq 0$. The other equations are of the form

$$a_{i2}^{(1)}x_2 + a_{i3}^{(1)}x_3 + \cdots + a_{in}^{(1)}x_n = b_i^{(1)},$$

for $i = 3, \ldots, n$. Now we eliminate x_2 from the $n - 2$ equations, $i = 3, \ldots, n$, using the same algorithm for eliminating x_1. That is, multiply Equation 15.4 by $-a_{i2}^{(1)}/a_{22}^{(1)}$ and add the resulting equation to the equation whose coefficient for x_2 is $a_{i2}^{(1)}$, for $i = 3, 4, \ldots, n$. After this is done $n - 2$ times, we have one equation in n unknowns, Equation 15.3, one equation in $n - 1$ unknowns, $x_2, x_3, \ldots, x_n$, which is labeled Equation 15.4, and $n - 2$ equations in the $n - 2$ unknowns, $x_3, x_4, \ldots, x_n$. The algorithm is continued until we obtain a triangular form of the system of equations of the following form:

$$a_{11}x_1 + a_{12}x_2 + a_{13}x_3 + \cdots + a_{1n}x_n = b_1,$$

$$0 + a_{22}^{(1)}x_2 + a_{23}^{(1)}x_3 + \cdots + a_{2n}^{(1)}x_n = b_2^{(1)},$$

$$0 + 0 + a_{33}^{(2)}x_3 + a_{34}^{(2)}x_4 + \cdots + a_{3n}^{(2)}x_n = b_3^{(2)},$$

$$0 + 0 + 0 + a_{44}^{(3)}x_4 + \cdots + a_{4n}^{(3)}x_n = b_4^{(3)}, \tag{15.5}$$

$$\cdot$$
$$\cdot$$
$$\cdot$$

$$0 + 0 + 0 + \cdots + a_{nn}^{(n-1)}x_n = b_n^{(n-1)}.$$

This triangularization method and variants of it are widely used for machine computation. As a rule, this procedure is very economical in terms of arithmetical calculations. The determinant method to be discussed later is *not* advisable for actual computations where there are more than three unknowns.

EXAMPLE 15.1-2.   Consider the following set of four equations:

$$x_1 - 2x_2 + 2.5x_3 + 3x_4 = 16.5, \tag{15.6}$$

$$-8x_1 + 20x_2 + 14x_3 - 16x_4 = 10, \tag{15.7}$$

$$5x_1 + 7x_2 + 2x_3 - 10x_4 = -15, \tag{15.8}$$

$$6x_1 - 8x_2 - 10x_3 + 12x_4 = 8. \tag{15.9}$$

Multiplying Equation 15.6 by 8 and adding this to Equation 15.7, we obtain

$$0 + 4x_2 + 34x_3 + 8x_4 = 142. \tag{15.7a}$$

Similarly, multiplying Equation 15.6 by 5 and subtracting this from Equation 15.8, we obtain

$$0 + 17x_2 - 10.5x_3 - 25x_4 = -97.5. \tag{15.8a}$$

Multiplying Equation 15.6 by 6 and subtracting the result from Equation 15.9 gives us

$$0 + 4x_2 - 25x_3 - 6x_4 = -91. \tag{15.9a}$$

Our system of equations is now 15.6, 15.7a, 15.8a, and 15.9a, where x_1 appears in Equation 15.6 only. Next we eliminate x_2 from Equations 15.8a and 15.9a. This is obtained by adding $-17/4$ of Equation 15.7a and subtracting Equation 15.7a from Equations 15.8a and 15.9a, respectively. Thus we have

$$0 + 0 - 155x_3 - 59x_4 = -701, \tag{15.8b}$$

$$0 + 0 - 59x_3 - 14x_4 = -233. \tag{15.9b}$$

Finally, we eliminate x_3 from Equation 15.9b by adding $-59/155$ of Equation 15.8b to Equation 15.9b to obtain

$$0 + 0 + 0 + 8.45x_4 = 34. \tag{15.9c}$$

The triangularized set of equations is then

$$
\begin{aligned}
x_1 - 2x_2 + 2.5x_3 + 3x_4 &= 16.5, \\
0 + 4x_3 + 34x_3 + 8x_4 &= 142, \\
0 + 0 - 155x_3 - 59x_4 &= -701, \\
0 + 0 + 0 + 8.45x_4 &= 34.
\end{aligned}
\tag{15.10}
$$

The solution is

$$x_4 = \frac{34}{8.45} = 4.03, \qquad x_3 = \frac{-701 + 59(4.03)}{-155} = 2.99,$$

$$x_2 = \frac{142 - 8(4.03) - 34(2.99)}{4} = 2.04,$$

$$x_1 = \frac{16.5 - 3(4.03) - 2.5(2.99) + 2(2.04)}{1} = 0.995.$$

The same algorithm applies to equations with complex constant coefficients and complex valued solutions, although the arithmetic is approximately doubled as compared to that for a corresponding set of equations with real coefficients but the same number of variables.   □

● **EXERCISES**

15.1-1   (a) Suppose that in the set of Equations (a), (b), and (c) of Example 15.1-1, we multiply (a) by $\frac{1}{2}$ to get a new equation (a'), multiply (b) by -10 to get a new equation (b'), and divide (c) by -5 to get (c'), what can you say of the solution of the new system of Equations (a'), (b'), and (c') as compared to the solution for (a), (b), and (c)?

(b) Given equations (a), (b), and (c) of Example 15.1-1, form new equations (a') = (a) + (b), (b') = (a) − (b), and (c') = (b) − (c). What is the relationship between the solution of (a), (b), and (c) as compared to the solution of (a'), (b'), and (c').

15.1-2   For the network of Figure 15.1, suppose that $R_1 = R_2 = R_3 = R_4 = R_5 = R_6 = 1$ ohm, $I_1 = 1$ amp, and $I_2 = 2$ amps. Using node 4 as reference, solve for v_1, v_2, and v_3, using Gauss's elimination procedure. Compare this network to the network of Example 15.1-1. Compare the two solutions.

15.1-3   (a) For the network of Figure 15.1, suppose that $R_1 = 1$, $R_2 = \frac{1}{2}$, $R_3 = \frac{1}{3}$, $R_4 = \frac{1}{4}$, $R_5 = \frac{1}{5}$, and $R_6 = \frac{1}{6}$ ohm. Let $I_1 = 1$ amp and $I_2 = 2$ amp. Solve for v_1, v_2, and v_3, using node 4 as reference.

(b) Suppose that instead of $I_1 = 1$ amp and $I_2 = 2$ amp in part (a), we have $I_1 = \sin 1000t$ amp and $I_2 = 2 \sin 1000t$ amp. Determine the solution.

(c) Suppose that instead of the current sources in part (b) we have $I_1 = \sin 500t$ amp and $I_2 = 2 \sin 3000t$ amp. Determine v_1, v_2, and v_3.

15.1-4   In Example 15.1-1, note that we also get a triangular set of equations by considering Equations (b), (c'), and (c''). Solve for v_1, v_2, and v_3 from this new set of equations and compare with the answer in Example 15.1-1. From the given equations (a), (b), (c), (b'), (c'), and (c'') of Example 15.1-1, how many other triangular sets of equations are there? Should they all yield the same solutions?

15.1-5   Suppose that for the network of Figure 15.1, R_2 is replaced by a capacitor C_2. Let all the other resistors have a value of $\frac{1}{2}$ ohm and let I_1 and I_2 be sinusoidal currents of the same frequency. Thus we have $I_1 = \sin \omega t$ amp, $I_2 = 2 \sin (\omega t + 30°)$ amp, and $\omega C_2 = 2$ mhos. Use the Gauss elimination procedure for computing v_1, v_2, and v_3.

15.2   Cramer's rule

Instead of the Gauss elimination procedure or any of its variants, the solutions to linear algebraic equations may be obtained as ratios of determinants. However, if the number of equations is more than four, the arithmetic involved in evaluating the determinants is much more than that in the Gauss procedure. In theoretical work where specific numerical solutions are not the primary goal, determinants are often useful tools. For instance, it may be desirable to express the solutions in terms of literal coefficients a_{ij} rather than in terms of specific values of the coefficients. This form might be sought because the sensitivity of a solution to changes in a_{ij} might be under investigation, and thus it is desirable to obtain the functional dependence of the solution on a_{ij}. For such studies, the exploitation of properties of determinants yields useful results. In this section, we shall state without proof some results from determinant theory.

A determinant is a function of a square array of elements (which are either real or complex numbers) or a matrix usually written in the form

$$\det A = \begin{vmatrix} a_{11} & a_{12} & \cdots & a_{1n} \\ a_{21} & a_{22} & \cdots & a_{2n} \\ \vdots & & & \\ a_{n1} & a_{n2} & \cdots & a_{nn} \end{vmatrix}, \tag{15.11}$$

where a_{ij}'s are the elements of the array or matrix A. Notice that in the double subscript the first symbol denotes the row location and the second denotes the column location. Thus a_{ij} is an element in the ith row and jth column. The determinant, $\det A$, has the following defining properties:

(a) The value of $\det A$ is not changed if the elements of any row (or any column) are added to the respective elements of another row (or column).

(b) The value of $\det A$ is multiplied by K if all the elements of any row (or column) of A are multiplied by K.

(c) The value of a determinant is unity if the elements on the principal diagonal (elements a_{ij}, where $i = j$) are unity and all other elements are zero. (An element is said to be on the principal diagonal if its row and column locations are identical. Thus if it is on the third row it must also be on the third column in order for the element to be on the principal diagonal.) A degeneracy occurs when the matrix has only one element. In this case when the element is unity, the determinant is unity.

From the above defining properties, it can be shown that for a two-by-two matrix, the determinant is

$$\det A = \begin{vmatrix} a_{11} & a_{12} \\ a_{21} & a_{22} \end{vmatrix} = a_{11}a_{22} - a_{12}a_{21}. \tag{15.12}$$

Also, for the degenerate one-by-one matrix, we have

$$\det a_{11} = a_{11}. \tag{15.13}$$

The *minor* M_{ij} of a matrix A is defined as the determinant of a matrix which is obtained by deleting the ith row and jth column from A. The cofactor A_{ij} of the element a_{ij} of a matrix A is defined as $A_{ij} = (-1)^{i+j}M_{ij}$.

We state without proof the *Laplace expansion* of a determinant as follows:

$$\det A = \sum_{k=1}^{n} a_{ik}A_{ik}, \quad \text{for} \quad i = 1, 2, \ldots, n, \quad (15.14)$$

and

$$\det A = \sum_{k=1}^{n} a_{kj}A_{kj}, \quad \text{for} \quad j = 1, 2, \ldots, n. \quad (15.15)$$

Equation 15.14 gives the expansion along the ith row where i may be any integer between 1 and n, inclusive, and Equation 15.15 gives the Laplace expansion along the jth column where j is an integer, $1 \le j \le n$. We also state without proof that

$$\sum_{k=1}^{n} a_{ik}A_{rk} = 0, \quad i \ne r, \quad (15.16)$$

and

$$\sum_{k=1}^{n} a_{kj}A_{kr} = 0, \quad j \ne r. \quad (15.17)$$

The expression in Equation 15.16 is like a Laplace expansion along the ith row, except that cofactors for the rth row are used. Similarly, the expression in Equation 15.17 is like a Laplace expansion along the jth column, except that cofactors for the rth column are used. All of the above statements can be proved using the defining properties of determinants.

Now consider the following set of equations:

$$a_{11}x_1 + a_{12}x_2 + \cdots + a_{1n}x_n = b_1,$$

$$a_{21}x_1 + a_{22}x_2 + \cdots + a_{2n}x_n = b_2,$$

$$\cdot$$
$$\cdot \quad\quad\quad\quad\quad\quad\quad\quad\quad\quad\quad\quad (15.18)$$
$$\cdot$$

$$a_{n1}x_1 + a_{n2}x_2 + \cdots + a_{nn}x_n = b_n.$$

Suppose that we multiply the first equation by A_{1k}, the second equation by $A_{2k}, \ldots$, and the nth equation by A_{nk} and then add all the resulting equations. We obtain

$$\sum_{i=1}^{n} A_{ik} \sum_{j=1}^{n} a_{ij}x_j = \sum_{i=1}^{n} A_{ik}b_i. \quad (15.19)$$

Interchanging the order of summation, we have

$$\sum_{j=1}^{n} x_j \sum_{i=1}^{n} a_{ij}A_{ik} = \sum_{i=1}^{n} A_{ik}b_i. \quad (15.20)$$

But from Equations 15.15 and 15.17 we have

$$\sum_{i=1}^{n} a_{ij}A_{ik} = \begin{cases} \det A, & j = k, \\ 0, & j \neq k. \end{cases} \tag{15.21}$$

Hence, provided $\det A \neq 0$, Equation 15.20 reduces to

$$x_k = \frac{\sum_{i=1}^{n} A_{ik}b_i}{\det A}, \qquad k = 1, 2, \ldots, n. \tag{15.22}$$

Note that

$$\sum_{i=1}^{n} A_{ik}b_i = \begin{vmatrix} a_{11} & a_{12} & \cdots & a_{1k-1} & b_1 & a_{1k+1} & \cdots & a_{1n} \\ a_{21} & a_{22} & \cdots & a_{2k-1} & b_2 & a_{2k+1} & \cdots & a_{2n} \\ \cdot & & & & & & & \\ \cdot & & & & & & & \\ \cdot & & & & & & & \\ a_{n1} & a_{n2} & \cdots & a_{nk-1} & b_n & a_{nk+1} & \cdots & a_{nn} \end{vmatrix} \tag{15.23}$$

by expanding along the kth column. Let D_k denote the determinant in Equation 15.23 which is the determinant of an array obtained by replacing the kth column of A by the column of b_i's. Denote $\det A$ by D. Then Equation 15.22 may be written as

$$x_k = \frac{D_k}{D}, \qquad k = 1, 2, \ldots, n. \tag{15.24}$$

Equation 15.24 is *Cramer's rule* for solving linear equations. If $D = 0$ and if the b_i's are not all zero, the system has no solution.

The Laplace expansion may be applied to the minors of a determinant, and the process may be repeated until an nth-order determinent is expressed in terms of second-order determinants. Although, in principle, this process is simple, this involves $n!$ multiplications and if n is large, the required arithmetic is astronomical. Nevertheless, for theoretical developments, Cramer's rule may be useful. For example, from the Laplace expansion it is clear that D is a linear function of any of the elements a_{ij}. By expanding along the jth column, none of the cofactors involves a_{ij}, and the only term that depends on a_{ij} is $a_{ij}A_{ij}$. Hence D is linear in a_{ij}. Similarly, D_K is linear in any a_{ij}. Hence the solution x_k from Cramer's rule in Equation 15.24 is bilinear in a_{ij} (that is, a ratio of linear functions in a_{ij}). This important theoretical result is obtained without having to evaluate specific determinants.

EXAMPLE 15.2-1.   Consider the following system of equations:

$$a_{11}x_1 + a_{12}x_2 + a_{13}x_3 = b_1, \tag{15.25}$$

$$a_{21}x_1 + a_{22}x_2 + a_{23}x_3 = b_2, \tag{15.26}$$

$$a_{31}x_1 + a_{32}x_2 + a_{33}x_3 = b_3\,, \tag{15.27}$$

To solve for x_1, assuming $\det A \neq 0$, we have

$$x_1 = \frac{\begin{vmatrix} b_1 & a_{12} & a_{13} \\ b_2 & a_{22} & a_{23} \\ b_3 & a_{32} & a_{33} \end{vmatrix}}{\begin{vmatrix} a_{11} & a_{12} & a_{13} \\ a_{21} & a_{22} & a_{23} \\ a_{31} & a_{32} & a_{33} \end{vmatrix}}. \tag{15.28}$$

The determinant $\det A$ may be expanded along the first column to obtain

$$\det A = a_{11}A_{11} + a_{21}A_{21} + a_{31}A_{31}$$

$$= a_{11}\begin{vmatrix} a_{22} & a_{23} \\ a_{32} & a_{33} \end{vmatrix} - a_{21}\begin{vmatrix} a_{12} & a_{13} \\ a_{32} & a_{33} \end{vmatrix} + a_{31}\begin{vmatrix} a_{12} & a_{13} \\ a_{22} & a_{23} \end{vmatrix} \tag{15.29}$$

$$= a_{11}(a_{22}a_{33} - a_{23}a_{32}) - a_{21}(a_{12}a_{33} - a_{13}a_{32})$$

$$+ a_{31}(a_{12}a_{23} - a_{13}a_{22}).$$

The numerator of Equation 15.28 may be expanded along the first column to yield

$$x_1 = [b_1(a_{22}a_{33} - a_{23}a_{32}) - b_2(a_{12}a_{33} - a_{13}a_{32})$$

$$+ b_3(a_{12}a_{23} - a_{13}a_{22})]/\det A. \tag{15.30}$$

Note that all of the elements appear linearly in $\det A$.

● EXERCISES

15.2-1   Expand the determinant in Example 15.2-1 along the second column and compare with Equation 15.29. Repeat for an expansion along the third column.

15.2-2   (a) Expand the determinant in Example 15.2-1 along the first row and compare with Equation 15.29. (b) Repeat for an expansion along the second row. (c) Repeat for an expansion along the third row.

15.2-3   (a) Solve for x_2 in Example 15.2-1.
(b) Solve for x_3 in Example 15.2-1.

15.2-4   Starting from a second-order determinant, use the defining properties of determinants to transform the array of coefficients so that off-diagonal elements are zero. By factoring out certain quantities, reduce the determinant to

$$\begin{vmatrix} a_{11} & a_{12} \\ a_{21} & a_{22} \end{vmatrix} = K \begin{vmatrix} 1 & 0 \\ 0 & 1 \end{vmatrix} = K,$$

and verify that $K = a_{11}a_{22} - a_{12}a_{21}$ as given by Equation 15.12.

15.2-5 Count the number of multiplications, divisions, and additions involved in applying Cramer's rule for solving for x_1 and x_2 from a system of two equations. Do the same counting for Gauss's elimination procedure and compare.

15.3 Simultaneous differential equations

The methods of the preceding sections may be applied to the solution of systems of linear differential equations. We confine our attention to the simple but common situation when the coefficients are constants. The first step is to use operational notation by replacing d/dt by the differential operator p. The coefficient matrix A will now contain elements which are polynomials in p. Thus, in Equation 15.18, the coefficients a_{ij} may be regarded as polynomials in p. The quantities b_i may be constants or functions of time. In applying Cramer's rule, we note that $\det A$ is now a polynomial in p and, likewise, the various cofactors are now polynomials in p. Instead of Equation 15.22, we have

$$\det A[x_k] = \sum_{i=1}^{n} A_{ik}[b_i], \qquad (15.31)$$

which is an ordinary linear differential equation with constant coefficients.

EXAMPLE 15.3-1. Suppose we are given

$$\frac{dx_1}{dt} + 3x_1 - x_2 = u_1, \qquad (15.32)$$

$$-x_1 + \frac{2dx_2}{dt} + 2x_2 = 3u_2. \qquad (15.33)$$

We wish to obtain a single differential equation containing the dependent variable x_1 but not x_2. Using Cramer's rule, we have

$$\begin{vmatrix} p+3 & -1 \\ -1 & 2p+2 \end{vmatrix} x_1 = \begin{vmatrix} u_1 & -1 \\ 3u_2 & 2p+2 \end{vmatrix},$$

$$[(p+3)(2p+2) - 1]x_1 = (2p+2)u_1 + 3u_2, \qquad (15.34)$$

$$\frac{2d^2x_1}{dt^2} + \frac{8dx_1}{dt} + 5x_1 = \frac{2du_1}{dt} + 2u_1 + 3u_2.$$

Similarly, for x_2 we have

$$(2p^2 + 8p + 5)x_2 = \begin{vmatrix} p + 3 & u_1 \\ -1 & 3u_2 \end{vmatrix} = (p + 3)3u_2 + u_1. \qquad (15.35)$$

The techniques of Chapters 7 and 8 may be applied to the solutions of Equations 15.34 and 15.35 for specified input functions $u_1(t)$ and $u_2(t)$. The order of the system is given by the degree of the polynomial in p of $\det A$. In this example, $\det A$ is second degree in p so the system is second-order. This means that we require two linearly independent initial conditions to determine the solution uniquely. The complementary solution for Equation 15.34 involves two constants. Likewise, the complementary solution for Equation 15.35 involves two constants. However, these four constants are linearly dependent since there are only two linearly independent initial conditions.   □

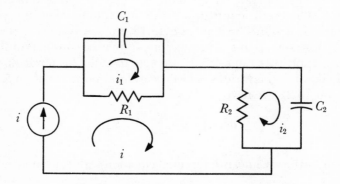

Figure 15.2 Network for Example 15.3-2.

EXAMPLE 15.3-2.   For the network of Figure 15.2, if we assume that the elements are constant, applying KVL to loop 1 and 2 yields

$$\frac{1}{C_1} \int i_1 \, dt + R_1 i_1 - R_1 i = 0 \qquad (15.36)$$

and

$$\frac{1}{C_2} \int i_2 \, dt + R_2 i_2 - R_2 i = 0. \qquad (15.37)$$

In terms of charges q_1 and q_2, we have

$$\left(R_1 p + \frac{1}{C_1}\right)q_1 + 0 = R_1 i, \qquad (15.38)$$

$$0 + \left(R_2 p + \frac{1}{C_2}\right)q_2 = R_2 i. \tag{15.39}$$

For this example, since the A matrix is diagonal, the equations are not coupled so that the equations may be solved separately. However, if we insist on applying Cramer's rule, we have

$$\left(R_1 p + \frac{1}{C_1}\right)\left(R_2 p + \frac{1}{C_2}\right)q_1 = \left(R_2 p + \frac{1}{C_2}\right)R_1 i \tag{15.40}$$

and

$$\left(R_1 p + \frac{1}{C_1}\right)\left(R_2 p + \frac{1}{C_2}\right)q_2 = \left(R_1 p + \frac{1}{C_1}\right)R_2 i. \tag{15.41}$$

Clearly, no matter what R_1, R_2, C_1, and C_2 are, $(R_2 p + 1/C_2)$ is a common factor in Equation 15.40 so that it may be reduced to Equation 15.38. Similarly, $(R_1 p + 1/C_1)$ is a common factor in Equation 15.41 so that after cancellation we obtain Equation 15.39. Although it is not necessary to cancel the common factors, unnecessary computation is avoided if cancellable factors are cancelled!

Suppose that for this example, we wish to solve for the zero-input response $(i = 0)$ for $q_1(0) = Q_1$ and $q_2(0) = Q_2$. Then, from Equation 15.38 we have

$$q_1 = Q_1 e^{-t/R_1 C_1}, \qquad t \geq 0, \tag{15.42}$$

and from Equation 15.39 we have

$$q_2 = Q_2 e^{-t/R_2 C_2}, \qquad t \geq 0. \tag{15.43}$$

But suppose that we did not notice the cancellation of factors in Equations 15.40 and 15.41. Then our tentative solutions would be

$$q_1 = K_1 e^{-t/R_1 C_1} + K_2 e^{-t/R_2 C_2} \tag{15.44}$$

and

$$q_2 = K_3 e^{-t/R_1 C_1} + K_4 e^{-t/R_2 C_2}. \tag{15.45}$$

From the initial-condition specification, we have

$$Q_1 = K_1 + K_2, \tag{15.46}$$

$$Q_2 = K_3 + K_4. \tag{15.47}$$

But from Equation 15.36, with $i \equiv 0$, and setting t equal to zero, we have

$$\frac{1}{C_1} q_1(0) + R_1 q_1'(0) = 0$$

or

$$q_1'(0) = -\frac{1}{R_1 C_1} Q_1. \tag{15.48}$$

Likewise, from Equation 15.37, with $i \equiv 0$ and $t = 0$, we have

$$\frac{1}{C_2} q_2(0) + R_2 q_2'(0) = 0$$

or

$$q_2'(0) = -\frac{1}{R_2 C_2} Q_2. \tag{15.49}$$

Differentiating $q_1(t)$ in Equation 15.44 and setting $t = 0$, we have

$$\frac{-K_1}{R_1 C_1} - \frac{K_2}{R_2 C_2} = q_1'(0) = \frac{-1}{R_1 C_1} Q_1. \tag{15.50}$$

Similarly, differentiating $q_2(t)$ in Equation 15.45 and setting $t = 0$, we have

$$\frac{-K_3}{R_1 C_1} - \frac{K_4}{R_2 C_2} = q_2'(0) = \frac{-1}{R_2 C_2} Q_2. \tag{15.51}$$

From Equations 15.46, 15.47, 15.50, and 15.51 we obtain

$$K_1 = Q_1, \qquad K_2 = 0, \qquad K_3 = 0, \qquad K_4 = Q_2,$$

which checks with our earlier solution. As expected, we have more computation although the answer comes out the same. In general, it is desirable to reduce each equation to minimum order by cancelling the common factors. ☐

● EXERCISES

15.3-1   (a) $(2p + 3)x_1 - px_2 - 2x_3 = 2u_1$
(b) $-px_1 + (3p + 5)x_2 - (p + 1)x_3 = u_2$
(c) $-2x_1 - (p + 1)x_2 + (p + 2)x_3 = 4u_3$

Obtain a single differential equation in x_1 whose solution satisfies the given system of differential equations. How many linearly independent initial conditions are needed?

15.3-2   Repeat Exercise 15.3-1 for x_2.

15.3-3   Repeat Exercise 15.3-1 for x_3.

15.3-4   Triangularize the system of equations in Exercise 15.3-1. *Suggestion:* (1) Label (c) as Equation 1 and eliminate x_1 from (a) and (b). (2) Eliminate x_2 from one of the remaining equations. This elimination step may require several multiplications and additions. Avoid unnecessary increase in the order of the differential equations. Compute the product of the main diagonal elements of the triangularized system and compare with the determinant of the original array of coefficients in Exercise 15.3-1.

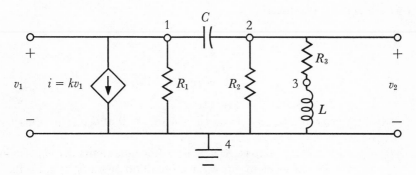

Figure Exercise 15.3-5

15.3-5 (a) For the linear time-invariant network of Figure Exercise 15.3-5 where v_1 is the source and v_2 is the output, write node equations in differential-equation form from which v_2 and v_3 may be determined.

(b) Determine a differential equation involving v_2 but not v_3 whose solution satisfies the node equations.

(c) Assume that $R_1 = R_2 = R_3 = 100$ ohms, $L = 10^{-3}$ henry, $C = 10^{-8}$ farad, $k = .01$, $v_{12}(0+) = 1$ volt, $i_{34}(0+) = 10^{-3}$ ampere, and $v_1 \equiv 0$. Solve for $v_2(t)$.

Problems

15-1 Determine x_1, x_2, x_3 and x_4 which satisfy the equations

$$x_1 - 2x_2 + 2.5x_3 + 3x_4 = 8,$$
$$-8x_1 + 20x_2 + 14x_3 - 16x_4 = 5,$$
$$5x_1 + 7x_2 + 2x_3 - 10x_4 = 4,$$
$$6x_1 - 8x_2 - 10x_3 + 12x_4 = 6.$$

15-2 Rewrite the equations of Problem 15-1 by solving for x_1 from the first equation, x_2 from the second equation, x_3 from the third equation, and x_4 from the fourth equation, in terms of the other variables. Assume that x_1, x_2, x_3, and x_4 are dc signals that may be measured from an analog computer set-up involving amplifiers, adders, and voltage sources. Using your rewritten equations as a guide, draw a suitable block diagram and label the points where you would measure x_1, x_2, x_3, and x_4.

15-3 Compute the determinant of the A matrix of Problem 15-1, using a Laplace expansion along the first column.

15-4 For the system of equations in Problem 15-1, write x_2 as a ratio of determinants.

15-5 Consider the matrix

$$\begin{bmatrix} 20 & 14 & -16 \\ 7 & 2 & -10 \\ -8 & -10 & 12 \end{bmatrix}.$$

(a) Compute A_{11}, A_{21}, and A_{31}.

(b) Verify that $a_{12}A_{11} + a_{22}A_{21} + a_{32}A_{31} = 0$ and $a_{12}A_{11} + a_{23}A_{21} + a_{33}A_{31} = 0$.

15-6 Given a square matrix $A(n \times n)$ whose elements are a_{ij}, form a matrix B whose elements b_{ij} are obtained from $b_{ij} = a_{ji}$. That is, the ith-row jth-column element of B is equal to the jth row ith column of A. Show that $\det A = \det B$. Here B is said to be the transpose of A. [*Hint:* Use Laplace expansion.]

15-7 For the linear time-invariant network of Figure Problem 15-7 where $R_1 = R_2 = L_1 = L_2 = C = 1$ (normalized values) and $i_1(0^-) = 0$, $i_2(0^-) = 0$, $v_c(0^-) = 1$, $v_1 \equiv 0$, solve for $i_1(t)$ and $i_2(t)$ for $t \geq 0$.

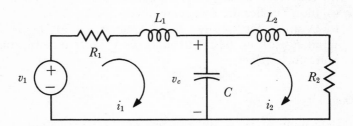

Figure Problem 15-7

15-8 Repeat Problem 15-7 for v_1 equal to a unit step function $u(t)$ instead of zero.

15-9 The sources in the linear time-invariant network of Figure Problem 15-9 are all sinusoidal and they have the same frequency. It is desired to examine the steady-state behavior of the network. At the frequency of the sources, the impedances are as follows: $Z_1 = Z_2 = Z_3 = -j1$, $Z_5 = Z_6 = 1 + j1$, and $Z_7 = j1$. The sources are $i_a(t) = 2 \sin \omega t$, $i_b(t) = 2 \sin \omega t$, $e_4(t) = \sin \omega t$, and $e_7(t) = \sin \omega t$. Write an appropriate set of node equations for solving for the steady-state components of $v_{ae}(t)$, $v_{be}(t)$, $v_{ce}(t)$, and $v_{de}(t)$.

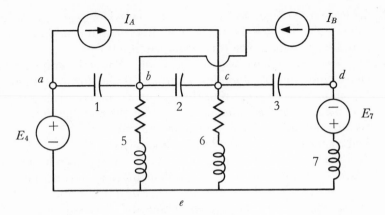

Figure Problem 15-9

15-10 Write an appropriate set of loop currents for the network in Problem 15-9 for solving for the steady-state components of the branch currents $i_{ae}(t)$, $i_{be}(t)$, $i_{ce}(t)$, and $i_{de}(t)$.

15-11 In the three-phase power system of Figure Problem 15-11, the impedances at 377 radians/sec (60 Hertz) are as follows: $Z_{01} = Z_{02} = Z_{03} = 0.1 + j1$, $Z_{11'} = Z_{22'} = Z_{33'} = 0.5 + j0.8$, $Z_{1'n} = 5 + j0$, $Z_{2'n} = 0 + j5$, and $Z_{3'n} = 0 - j5$. Also e_a, e_b, e_c form a balanced set of voltages where the phase sequence is acb, that is, e_c lags e_a by 120°, and e_b lags e_c by 120°. The voltage $e_a = 141.4 \sin(377t + 30°)$. Calculate the steady-state components of the line currents.

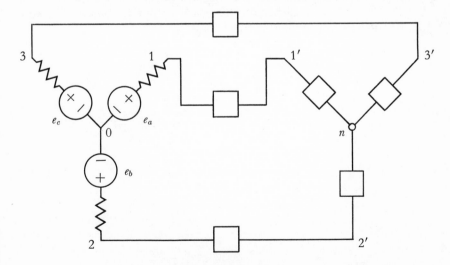

Figure Problem 15-11

15-12   (a) Repeat Problem 15-11 if the load impedances are balanced as follows: $Z_{1'n} = Z_{2'n} = Z_{3'n} = 5 + j0$. (b) Repeat (a) if in addition nodes n and 0 are joined by a wire of impedance $0.1 + j1$.

15-13   Suppose that we have a set of linear equations with complex coefficients and possibly complex solutions of the form as shown in Equation 15.18, except that the a's and b's are complex numbers, and the x's may be complex. By writing the complex numbers in rectangular form, derive an expanded set of linear equations with real coefficients involving $2n$ real unknowns.

15-14   Suppose the current source in Figure 15.2 is replaced by a voltage source. Assume that the network elements have normalized values of $R_1 = 1$, $C_1 = 1$, $R_2 = 2$, $C_2 = 3$. Let $q_1(0^-) = 1$ and $q_2(0^-) = 3$. (a) Assuming $v \equiv 0$, solve for $i_1(t)$ and $i_2(t)$. (b) Assuming $v = r(t)$, a unit ramp function, solve for $i_1(t)$ and $i_2(t)$.

15-15   Using $q_1(t)$ and $q_2(t)$ as state variables, write an appropriate set of state equations for the network of Figure 15.2. Draw an elementary analog-computer diagram for solving the network problem.

15-16   Repeat Problem 15-15 replacing the source $i(t)$ by a voltage source $v(t)$.

15-17   (a) For the three-phase network in Problem 15-12(a), compute the average power delivered to the three-phase load.
(b) Compute the average power delivered to the three-phase load for the three-phase network in Problem 15-12(b).

15-18   For the network in Problem 15-11 (a) Compute the average power delivered to the individual phase loads $Z_{1'n}$, $Z_{2'n}$, and $Z_{3'n}$. (b) Compute the total power into the three-phase load using the result of Problem 10-45 (see p. 266). Check your answer against the sum of the load phase powers in part (a).

Bibliography

SIGNAL ANALYSIS (ELEMENTARY)

ASELTINE, JOHN A. *Transform Method in Linear System Analysis*. McGraw-Hill Book Co., Inc., New York, 1958.

CRAIG, EDWARD J. *Laplace and Fourier Transforms for Electrical Engineers*. Holt, Rinehart and Winston, Inc., New York, 1964.

JAVID, M., and E. BRENNER. *Analysis, Transmission, and Filtering of Signals*. McGraw-Hill Book Co., Inc., New York, 1963.

KUO, FRANKLIN F. *Network Analysis and Synthesis*, 2nd ed. John Wiley and Sons, Inc., New York, 1966.

LATHI, B. P. *Signals, Systems and Communications*. John Wiley and Sons, Inc., New York, 1965.

MARSHALL, JAMES L. *Introduction to Signal Theory*. International Textbook Co., Scranton, Pa., 1965.

MASON, S. J., and H. J. ZIMMERMANN. *Electronic Circuits, Signals, and Systems*. John Wiley and Sons, Inc., New York, 1960.

PIERCE, JOHN R. *Symbols, Signals, and Noise*. Harper and Row, New York, 1961. (A popular presentation of a complex subject.)

SCHWARTZ, M. *Information Transmission, Modulation, and Noise.* McGraw-Hill Book Co., Inc., New York, 1959.

STEWART, J. L. *Fundamentals of Signal Theory.* McGraw-Hill Book Co., Inc., New York, 1960.

SIGNAL ANALYSIS (ADVANCED)

GOLDMAN, S. *Frequency Analysis, Modulation and Noise.* McGraw-Hill Book Co., Inc., New York, 1948.

GUILLEMIN, E. A. *Theory of Linear Physical Systems.* John Wiley and Sons, Inc., New York, 1963.

LIGHTHILL, M. J. *Introduction to Fourier Analysis and Generalized Functions.* Cambridge University Press, New York, 1958.

PAPOULIS, A. *The Fourier Integral and Its Applications.* McGraw-Hill Book Co., Inc., New York, 1962.

ROWE, H. E. *Signals and Noise in Communications Systems.* D. Van Nostrand Co., Inc., Princeton, N. J., 1965.

CIRCUIT ANALYSIS (ELEMENTARY)

ATEBEKOV, G. I. *Linear Network Theory.* Pergamon Press, New York, 1965. (This is a translation from the Russian of a book first published in 1960.)

BALABANIAN, NORMAN. *Fundamentals of Circuit Theory.* Allyn and Bacon, Inc., Boston, 1961.

BOOKER, HENRY G. *An Approach to Electrical Science.* McGraw-Hill Book Co., Inc., New York, 1959.

BOSE, AMAR G., and KENNETH N. STEVENS. *Introductory Network Theory.* Harper and Row, New York, 1965.

BRENNER, EGON, and MANSOUR JAVID. *Analysis of Electric Circuits.* McGraw-Hill Book Co., Inc., New York, 1959.

CASSELL, WALLACE L. *Linear Electric Circuits.* John Wiley and Sons, Inc., New York, 1964.

CLEMENT, PRESTON R., and WALTER C. JOHNSON. *Electrical Engineering Science.* McGraw-Hill Book Co., Inc., New York, 1960.

CLOSE, CHARLES M. *The Analysis of Linear Circuits.* Harcourt, Brace and World, Inc., New York, 1966.

CRAIG, EDWARD J. *Laplace and Fourier Transforms for Electrical Engineers.* Holt, Rinehart and Winston, Inc., New York, 1964.

DESOER, CHARLES A., and ERNEST S. KUH. *Basic Circuit Theory.* McGraw-Hill Book Co., Inc., New York, 1966.

FERRIS, C. D. *Linear Network Theory.* Charles E. Merrill Books, Inc., Columbus, Ohio, 1962.

FRIEDLAND, B., OMAR WING, and R. B. ASH. *Principles of Linear Networks.* McGraw-Hill Book Co., Inc., New York, 1961.

GUILLEMIN, E. A. *Introductory Circuit Theory.* John Wiley and Sons, Inc., New York, 1953.

HARMAN, W. W., and D. W. LYTLE. *Electrical and Mechanical Networks.* McGraw-Hill Book Co., Inc., New York, 1962.

HAYT, W. H., JR., and J. E. KEMMERLY. *Engineering Circuit Analysis.* McGraw-Hill Book Co., Inc., New York, 1962.

HENNYEY, Z. *Linear Electric Circuits.* Addison-Wesley Publishing Co., Inc., Reading, Massachusetts, 1962.

KUO, FRANKLIN F. *Network Analysis and Synthesis,* 2nd ed. John Wiley and Sons, Inc., New York, 1966.

MANNING, LAURENCE A. *Electrical Circuits.* McGraw-Hill Book Co., Inc., New York, 1965.

PASKUSZ, GERHARD F., and BERTRAM BUSSELL. *Linear Circuit Analysis.* Prentice-Hall, Inc., Englewood Cliffs, N. J., 1964.

PEARSON, S. I., and GEORGE J. MALER. *Introduction to Electric Circuit Analysis.* John Wiley and Sons, Inc., New York, 1964.

PESKIN, EDWARD. *Transient and Steady-State Analysis of Electric Networks.* D. Van Nostrand Co., Inc., Princeton, N. J., 1961.

POTTER, JAMES L., and SYLVAN J. FICH. *Theory of Networks and Lines.* Prentice-Hall, Inc., Englewood Cliffs, N. J., 1963.

REED, M. B. *Foundation for Electric Network Theory.* Prentice-Hall, Inc., Englewood Cliffs, N. J., 1961.

RUSTON, HENRY, and JOSEPH BORDOGNA. *Electric Networks: Functions, Filters, Analysis.* McGraw-Hill Book Co., Inc., New York, 1966.

SABBAGH, E. M. *Circuit Analysis.* The Ronald Press Co., New York, 1961.

SCOTT, R. E. *Elements of Linear Circuits.* Addison-Wesley Publishing Co., Inc., Reading, Massachusetts, 1965.

————. *Linear Circuits.* Addison-Wesley Publishing Co., Inc., Reading, Massachusetts, 1960.

SKILLING, H. H. *Electrical Engineering Circuits,* 2nd ed. John Wiley and Sons, Inc., New York, 1965.

SMITH, RALPH J. *Circuits, Devices and Systems.* John Wiley and Sons, Inc., New York, 1966.

VAN VALKENBURG, M. E. *Network Analysis,* 2nd ed. Prentice-Hall, Inc., Englewood Cliffs, N. J., 1964.

ZIMMERMANN, HENRY J., and S. J. MASON. *Electronic Circuit Theory: Devices, Models, and Circuits.* John Wiley and Sons, Inc., New York, 1959.

CIRCUIT ANALYSIS (ADVANCED)

BODE, H. W. *Network Analysis and Feedback Amplifier Design.* D. Van Nostrand Co., Inc., Princeton, N. J., 1945.

BROWN, WILLIAM M. *Analysis of Linear Time-Invariant Systems.* McGraw-Hill Book Co., Inc., New York, 1963.

CARLIN, HERBERT J., and ANTHONY B. GIORDANO. *Network Theory.* Prentice-Hall, Inc., Englewood Cliffs, N. J., 1964.

CHEN, WAYNE, H. *The Analysis of Linear Systems.* McGraw-Hill Book Co., Inc., New York, 1963.

GARDNER, MURRAY F., and J. L. BARNES. *Transients in Linear Systems.* John Wiley and Sons, Inc., New York, 1942.

GUILLEMIN, E. A. *The Mathematics of Circuit Analysis.* John Wiley and Sons, Inc., New York, 1949.

————. *Theory of Linear Physical Systems.* John Wiley and Sons, Inc., New York, 1963.

KARNI, SHLOMO. *Network Theory: Analysis and Synthesis.* Allyn and Bacon, Inc., Boston, 1966.

KU, T. H. *Transient Circuit Analysis.* D. Van Nostrand Co., Inc., Princeton, N. J., 1961.

LEY, B. J., S. G. LUTZ, and C. F. REHBERG. *Linear Circuit Analysis.* McGraw-Hill Book Co., Inc., New York, 1959.

REZA, F. M., and S. SEELY. *Modern Network Analysis.* McGraw-Hill Book Co., Inc., New York, 1959.

SESHU, SUNDARAM, and N. BALABANIAN. *Linear Network Analysis.* John Wiley and Sons, Inc., New York, 1959.

STERN, THOMAS E. *Theory of Nonlinear Networks and Systems, An Introduction.* Addison-Wesley Publishing Co., Inc., Reading, Massachusetts, 1965.

TUTTLE, DAVID F., JR. *Electric Networks: Analysis and Synthesis.* McGraw-Hill Book Co., Inc., New York, 1965.

WEINBERG, LOUIS. *Network Analysis and Synthesis.* McGraw-Hill Book Co., Inc., New York, 1962.

SYSTEMS ANALYSIS

ASELTINE, JOHN A. *Transform Method in Linear System Analysis.* McGraw-Hill Book Co., Inc., New York, 1958.

BOHN, ERIK V. *The Transform Analysis of Linear Systems.* Addison-Wesley Publishing Co., Inc., Reading, Massachusetts, 1963.

BROWN, R. G., and J. W. NILSSON. *Introduction to Linear Systems Analysis.* John Wiley and Sons, Inc., New York, 1962.

CHENG, DAVID K. *Analysis of Linear Systems.* Addison-Wesley Publishing Co., Inc., Reading, Massachusetts, 1959.

DeRUSSO, PAUL M., ROB J. ROY, and CHARLES M. CLOSE. *State Variables for Engineers.* John Wiley and Sons, Inc., New York, 1965.

GUILLEMIN, E. A. *Theory of Linear Physical Systems.* John Wiley and Sons, Inc., New York, 1963.

GUPTA, SOMESHWAR C. *Transform and State Variable Methods in Linear Systems.* John Wiley and Sons, Inc., New York, 1966.

HARRIS, L. DALE. *Introduction to Feedback Systems.* John Wiley and Sons, Inc., New York, 1961.

KAPLAN, WILFRED. *Operational Methods for Linear Systems.* Addison-Wesley Publishing Co., Inc., Reading, Massachusetts, 1962.

KOENIG, H. E., and WILLIAM A. BLACKWELL. *Electromechanical System Theory.* Mc-Graw-Hill Book Co., Inc., New York, 1960.

KOENIG, HERMAN E., YILMAX TOKAD, and HIREMAGLUR K. KESAVAN. *Analysis of Discrete Physical Systems.* McGraw-Hill Book Co., Inc., New York, 1966.

LYNCH, WILLIAM A., and JOHN G. TRUXAL. *Introductory System Analysis.* McGraw-Hill Book Co., Inc., New York, 1961.

―――. *Principles of Electronic Instrumentation.* McGraw-Hill Book Co., Inc., New York, 1962.

PFEIFFER, PAUL E. *Linear Systems Analysis.* McGraw-Hill Book Co., Inc., New York, 1961.

PORTER, WILLIAM A. *Modern Foundations of Systems Engineering.* The Macmillan Co., New York, 1966.

SCHWARZ, R., and B. FRIEDLAND. *Linear System Theory.* McGraw-Hill Book Co., Inc., New York, 1965.

SEELY, SAMUEL. *Dynamic Systems Analysis.* Reinhold Publishing Corp., New York, 1964.

ZADEH, L. A., and CHARLES A. DESOER. *Linear System Theory: The State Space Approach.* McGraw-Hill Book Co., Inc., New York, 1963.

CIRCUIT SYNTHESIS AND DESIGN

BALABANIAN, N. *Network Synthesis.* Prentice-Hall, Inc., Englewood Cliffs, N. J., 1958.

CALAHAN, D. A. *Modern Network Synthesis.* Hayden, New York, 1964.

CHEN, W. H. *Linear Network Design and Synthesis.* McGraw-Hill Book Co., Inc., New York, 1964.

CHRISTIAN, ERICH, and EGON EISENMANN. *Tables and Graphs for the Design of Filters.* John Wiley and Sons, Inc., New York, 1966.

GEFFE, P. R. *Simplified Modern Filter Design.* John F. Rider, New York, 1963.

GUILLEMIN, E. A. *Synthesis of Passive Networks.* John Wiley and Sons, Inc., New York, 1957.

HAZONY, D. *Elements of Network Synthesis.* Reinhold Publishing Corp., New York, 1963.

KARNI, SHLOMO. *Network Theory: Analysis and Synthesis.* Allyn and Bacon, Inc., Boston, 1966.

KUH, E. S., and D. O. PEDERSON. *Principles of Circuit Synthesis.* McGraw-Hill Book Co., Inc., New York, 1959.

KUO, FRANKLIN F. *Network Analysis and Synthesis,* 2nd ed. John Wiley and Sons, Inc., New York, 1966.

MATTHAEI, G. L., L. YOUNG, and E. M. T. JONES. *Microwave Filters, Impedance-Matching Networks and Coupling Structures.* McGraw-Hill Book Co., Inc., New York, 1964.

RUSTON, HENRY, and JOSEPH BORDOGNA. *Electric Networks: Functions, Filters, Analysis.* McGraw-Hill Book Co., Inc., New York, 1966.

SKWIRZYNSKI, J. K. *Design Theory and Data for Electrical Filters.* D. Van Nostrand Co., Inc., Princeton, N. J., 1965.

TUTTLE, DAVID F., JR. *Electrical Networks: Analysis and Synthesis.* McGraw-Hill Book Co., Inc., New York, 1965.

TUTTLE, D. F. *Network Synthesis*, Vol 1. John Wiley and Sons, Inc., New York, 1958.

VAN VALKENBURG, M. E. *Introduction to Modern Network Synthesis.* John Wiley and Sons, Inc., New York, 1960.

WEINBERG, L. *Network Analysis and Synthesis.* McGraw-Hill Book Co., Inc., New York, 1962.

YENGST, W. C. *Procedures of Modern Network Synthesis.* The Macmillan Company, New York, 1964.

ACTIVE CIRCUITS

ALLEY, CHARLES L., and KENNETH W. ATWOOD. *Electronic Engineering.* John Wiley and Sons, Inc., New York, 1962.

ANGELO, E. J. *Electronic Circuits*, 2nd ed. McGraw-Hill Book Co., Inc., New York, 1963.

DEPIAN, LOUIS. *Linear Active Network Theory.* Prentice-Hall, Inc., Englewood Cliffs, N. J., 1962.

HUELSMAN, LAWRENCE P. *Circuits, Matrices, and Linear Vector Spaces.* McGraw-Hill Book Co., Inc., New York, 1963.

MASON, S. J., and HENRY J. ZIMMERMANN. *Electronic Circuits, Signals, and Systems.* John Wiley and Sons, Inc., New York, 1960.

SU, KENDALL L. *Active Network Synthesis.* McGraw-Hill Book Co., Inc., New York, 1965.

ZIMMERMANN, HENRY J., and S. J. MASON. *Electronic Circuit Theory: Devices, Models, and Circuits.* John Wiley and Sons, Inc., New York, 1959.

DETERMINANTS AND MATRICES

AITKEN, A. C. *Determinants and Matrices*, 9th ed. Interscience Publishers, New York, 1956.

BODEWIG, E. *Matrix Calculus*, Second Revised and Enlarged Edition. North-Holland Publishing Co., Amsterdam, 1959.

GANTMACHER, F. R. *Applications of the Theory of Matrices.* Interscience Publishers, New York, 1959.

———. *The Theory of Matrices*, Vols. I and II. Chelsea Publishing Co., New York, 1959.

HOHN, F. E. *Elementary Matrix Algebra.* The Macmillan Company, New York, 1964.

HUELSMAN, L. P. *Circuits, Matrices, and Linear Vector Spaces.* McGraw-Hill Book Co., Inc., New York, 1963.

LECORBEILLER, P. *Matrix Analysis of Electric Networks.* John Wiley and Sons, Inc., New York, 1950.

MARCUS, M., and H. MING. *A Survey of Matrix Theory and Matrix Inequalities.* Allyn and Bacon, Boston, 1964.

NERING, E. D. *Linear Algebra and Matrix Theory.* John Wiley and Sons, Inc., New York, 1964.

PERLIS, S. *Theory of Matrices.* Addison-Wesley Publishing Co., Inc., Reading, Massachusetts, 1952.

STIGANT, S. AUSTEN. *Matrix and Tensor Analysis in Electrical Network Theory.* MacDonald, London, 1964.

TROPPER, A. M. *Matrix Theory for Electrical Engineering Students.* Harrop, London, 1962.

VON WEISS, A. *Matrix Analysis for Electrical Engineering.* D. Van Nostrand Co., Inc., Princeton, N. J., 1964.

Answers to Exercises

CHAPTER 1

1.1-1 At $t = \pi/2$, $v_1(t) = 5 \sin \left(2\frac{\pi}{2} + \frac{\pi}{6}\right) = -2.5$ volts. It is negative. Hence the plus reference terminal is negative with respect to the other terminal.

1.1-2 (a) At $t = \pi/2$, $i_{12}(t) = 5 \sin \left(2\frac{\pi}{2} + \frac{\pi}{6}\right) = -2.5$. The current is 2.5 amps. from 2 to 1. Electron flow is opposite, from 1 to 2.
(b) For $t = 0$, $i_{12}(0) = 2.5$ so the current is 2.5 amps. from 1 to 2; electron flow is from 2 to 1.

1.1-3 The algebraic sum is zero. The two readings are negatives of each other.

1.2-1 $f(x) = e^{-ax} \sin bx$; $f(\xi) = e^{-a\xi} \sin b\xi$; $f(\xi + 1) = e^{-a(\xi+1)} \sin b(\xi + 1)$.

1.2-2 $v(x + 2\pi)$ is shifted to the left by 2π compared to $v(x)$, and $v(x - \pi)$ is shifted to the right by π compared to $v(x)$.

1.2-3 $p(t) = \frac{1}{2}(\sin t)^2$; $w(t) = \frac{1}{4}t - \frac{1}{8}\sin 2t$.

1.2-4 (a) and (b) are shifted to the left by 5, and (c) and (d) are shifted to the right by 5.

1.2-5 Abscissas for (a) and (b) are compressed by 10 and abscissas for (c) and (d) are expanded by 10.

1.2-6 (a) Shift to right and compress scale; (b) shift to left and expand scale.

1.2-7 (a) $I_1 = 250$, (b) $I_2 = 250$, (c) $I_3 = 250$, (d) $I_4 = 250$.
Yes.

1.2-8 $I = 0$ for $t < 0$; $I = \frac{5}{2} t^2$ for $0 \le t \le 10$; $I = 250$ for $t > 10$.

1.2-9 The waveform in Figure 1.2(b) is rotated by 180° about the time axis to obtain the new waveform.

1.3-1 $v_{\text{out}}(t) = (1/T) \int_0^T |v_{\text{in}}(\tau)| d\tau.$

1.3-2 $v_1(t) = \dfrac{dv_3(t) - bv_4(t)}{ad - bc}.$

1.3-3 $LC \dfrac{d^2 v_2}{dt^2} + RC \dfrac{dv_2}{dt} + v_2 = v_1.$

CHAPTER 2

2.1-1 Yes.

2.1-2 $v_3 = -25e^{-t} + 55e^{-3t}.$

2.1-3 $|K| \le 1 \Big/ \left[\left| \left(\dfrac{\alpha}{\beta} \right)^{-\alpha/(\alpha-\beta)} - \left(\dfrac{\alpha}{\beta} \right)^{\beta/(\alpha-\beta)} \right| \right].$

2.1-4 (a) $y = \sigma x + \ln K$; (b) $\ln (d^n v/dt^n) = \ln (\sigma^n K) + \sigma t$. Since $\ln (\sigma^n K) = \ln K + n \ln \sigma$, the spacing is constant and equal to $\ln \sigma$.

2.1-5 $b = \dfrac{2\pi}{0.8} = (2.5)\pi$; $K = 4$; $\sigma = \dfrac{5}{3}.$

2.2-1 (a) Volt-seconds; (b) volts per second.

2.2-2 Delayed step function $v_2(t) = 3.4u(t - 2).$

2.2-3 $v_2(t) = 3\delta(t - t_0).$

2.2-4 Max. of $v_2(t)$ is at T_0, equal to $V_0 T_0$. Min. of $v_2(t)$ is $-V_0.$

2.2-5 $v_2(t) = 2i(t) + u'(t - 1) - 3u(t - 2).$

2.2-6 $v_2(t) = 2.34\delta(t - 1) + 2.06\delta(t - 2) - 4.4\delta(t - 3).$

2.2-7 $u_{-1}(t)$ — unit step; $u_{-2}(t)$ — unit ramp.

2.3-1 (a) $\omega = 380$ radians/sec.   (e) A: $7.6 \sin (380t).$
(b) $T = 16.64$ millisec. B: $170 \sin (380t - 45°).$
(c) $f = 60$ Hz. C: $12 \sin (380t - 112.5°).$
(d) B lags A by 45°.
     C lags A by 112.5°.

2.3-2 $v_1(t) = 2e^{1/4}e^{-2t} \sin 4\pi t.$

2.3-3 $v_3(t) = v_1 v_2 = 2 \sin 3t \sin 2t = \cos t - \cos 5t.$

2.3-4 $v_2(t) = \sqrt{5} \sin (2t + 116.5°).$

2.6-1 $v_2(t) = v_1(t - 4).$

2.6-2 $v_2(t) = K_1 e^{-\sigma_1(t-a)} \sin [\omega_1(t - a) + \phi_1] \, u(t - a).$

2.6-3 $v_2(t) = A_2 \sin [\omega_2(t - a) + \phi_2].$ Negative of phase shift due to delay is $\omega_2 a$, $[d(\omega_2 a)]/d\omega_2 = a.$

2.6-7 $v_2(t) = \sin 2t.$

2.6-9 $v(t) = \displaystyle\sum_{k=-\infty}^{\infty} v_1(t - kT).$

2.6-10 $v_2(t) = u(t) + u(t - a) + u(t - 2a) - 3u(t - 3a).$

CHAPTER 3

3.1-1 Period $= T_0.$

3.1-2 $\bar{v} = 1/\pi.$

3.1-3 No, does not satisfy condition for periodicity.

3.1-4 $\bar{v} = \dfrac{\sqrt{2} - 1}{2\pi}.$

3.1-5 $\bar{v} = \dfrac{K(T - a)}{T}.$

3.1-6 Average of v_{21} is $-V_0.$

3.2-1 (a) Peak value $= 25$, peak-to-peak $= 25 + 21 = 46$; (b) Peak value $= 2$, peak-to-peak $= 4$; (c) Peak value $= 3$, peak-to-peak $= 4.$

3.3-1 $V_{\text{rms}} = \dfrac{\sqrt{10}}{2}.$

3.3-2 (a) .648 volts.   (d) $.648/\sqrt{2}.$
       (b) .648 volts.   (e) $.648/\sqrt{2}.$
       (c) .648 volts.   (f) $.648/\sqrt{2}.$

3.3-3 (a) 1 watt, (b) 1 watt, (c) 1 watt, (d) 2 watts, (e) 4 watts.

3.3-4 $V_{\text{rms}} = \sqrt{\dfrac{11}{15}}.$

3.3-5 $V_{\text{rms}} = \dfrac{1}{\sqrt{2}}.$

3.3-6 $V_{\text{rms}} = \dfrac{V_m}{\sqrt{2}}.$

3.3-7 $V_{\text{rms}} = \sqrt{27}.$

3.3-8 $V_{\text{rms}} = \sqrt{21}.$

3.3-9 rms value of v_{21} is V.

3.3-10 $I_{rms} = \dfrac{1}{2} \sqrt{\dfrac{1}{2} - \dfrac{1}{\pi}}$.

3.4-1 Overshoot $= 5$; percent overshoot $= \frac{5}{100} (100) = 5\%$.

3.4-2 Overshoot $= e^{-\frac{1}{\omega}\left(\pi - \tan^{-1}\frac{1}{\omega}\right)} \left(\dfrac{\omega}{\sqrt{1 + \omega^2}}\right)$.

3.4-3 $t_2 - t_1 = \dfrac{1}{\sigma_1} \ln 9 = \dfrac{2.2}{\sigma_1}$.

3.4-4 Rise time $= 2.4 - .45 = 1.95$ millisec. Time delay $= 1.4$ millisec.

3.4-5 $t_1 = \dfrac{\ln 2}{\sigma_1} = \dfrac{.692}{\sigma_1}$.

3.4-6 $t_s = 2.99$.

CHAPTER 4

4.1-1 Reference directions for v and i provide the clue.

4.1-2 Capacitor is the model for the component; capacitance is the parameter describing the model.

4.1-3 $i = 1000v, \quad v > 0,$
$\quad\quad i = v, \quad\quad v \leq 0.$

4.1-4 $i = \psi^3$.

4.1-9 $\psi = (1 - e^{-t})i$.

4.1-10 $dq/dt = i = c(dv/dt) + v(dc/dt)$.

4.2-2 $v_2 = M(di_s/dt)$.

4.2-3 $v_2 = -M(di_s/dt)$.

4.2-4 $v_2 = M_{12}(di_s/dt)$.

4.2-5 $v_1 = -L_1(di_a/dt) + M(di_b/dt); v_2 = L_2(di_b/dt) - M(di_a/dt)$.

4.2-6 $v_a = -L_1(di_1/dt) - M(di_2/dt); v_2 = L_2(di_2/dt) + M(di_1/dt)$.

4.2-7 $v_1 = L_1(di_1/dt) - M(di_2/dt); v_2 = L_2(di_2/dt) - M(di_1/dt)$.

4.3-1 (a) $v_1 = (1/n^2)L(di_1/dt)$. (b) $i_1 = Cn^2(dv_1/dt)$.

4.3-2 (a) $v_1 = (K^2/R)i_1$. (b) $i_1 = (L/K^2)(dv_1/dt)$.
   (a) $v_2 = (K^2/R)i_2$. (b) $i_2 = (L/K^2)(dv_2/dt)$.

4.3-3 (a) $v_1 = -L(di_1/dt)$. $\therefore L_{eq} = -L$.
   (b) $i_1 = i_2 = C(dv_2/dt) = -C(dv_1/dt)$, $C_{eq} = -C$.

4.3-4 $v_1 = K_1(v_2/K_2)$. $\therefore v_2 = (K_2/K_1)v_1$,
   $i_2 = (1/K_2)v_4 = (1/K_2)(-K_1 i_1) = -(K_1/K_2)i_1$.
   Therefore, relations are like those of transformer with $n = (K_2/K_1)$.

4.4-1 $K = 1750$ newtons/meter.

4.4-2 $x(2) = \frac{1}{2} + 1 = \frac{3}{2}$ meters.

CHAPTER 5

5.1-1 (a) f, ad, be, bcd, ace.
(b) acd, ae, kf, amf, abf, khg, $amhg$, $abhg$.

5.1-2 (a) acd, ae, amf, abf, $amhg$, $abhg$, kf, khg, $kmcd$, kme.
(b) amk, abk, mb, $mcdf$, $bcdf$, cde, fgh, mef, bef, $acdfk$, $acdghk$, $mcdgh$, $bcdgh$, $megh$, $begh$, $aefk$, $aeghk$.

5.2-1 $i_a + i_b + i_f = 0$ (1).
$-i_a - i_c + i_d = 0$ (2).
$-i_d - i_e - i_f = 0$ (3).
$-i_b + i_c + i_e = 0$ (4).

5.2-2 $i_{12} + i_{14} + i_{13} = 0$ (1).
$i_{21} + i_{23} + i_{24} = 0$ (2).
$i_{32} + i_{34} + i_{31} = 0$ (3).
$i_{41} + i_{42} + i_{43} = 0$ (4).

5.2-3 Add (1) and (2) from Exercise 5.2-1: $i_f + i_b - i_c + i_d = 0$.

5.2-4 a, b, d, e; $i_a + i_b - i_e - i_d = 0$.

5.2-5 a, c, e, f; $i_a + i_f + i_c + i_e = 0$.

5.2-6 From Exercise 5.2-1, add (2), (3), (4): $-i_a - i_b - i_f = 0 \Rightarrow i_a + i_b + i_f = 0$(1).

5.2-7 Add (1), (3), (4): $i_a + i_c - i_d = 0$ or $-i_a - i_c + i_d = 0$ (2).

5.2-8 Add (1), (2), (4): $i_d + i_e + i_f = 0$ (4).

5.2-9 Add (1), (2), (3): $i_b - i_c - i_e = 0$ or $-i_b + i_c + i_e = 0$ (4).

5.3-1 (a) $v_a + v_d + v_e - v_b = 0$,
(b) $v_a - v_c - v_b = 0$,
(c) $v_d + v_e + v_c = 0$,
(d) $v_b - v_e - v_f = 0$.

5.3-2 (a) $v_{12} + v_{23} + v_{34} + v_{41} = 0$,
(b) $v_{12} + v_{24} + v_{41} = 0$,
(c) $v_{23} + v_{34} + v_{42} = 0$,
(d) $v_{14} + v_{43} + v_{31} = 0$.

5.3-3 (a) $v_{13} + v_{32} + v_{21} = 0$,
(b) $v_{34} + v_{45} + v_{53} = 0$,
(c) $v_{34} + v_{45} + v_{52} + v_{23} = 0$,
(d) $v_{56} + v_{62} + v_{25} = 0$.

5.3-4 $-v_a + v_b + v_c - v_d = 0$,
$5 + 3 + v_c + 6 = 0$,
$v_c = -14$.

5.3-5 $v_{32} = -4$; $v_{14} = -3$; $v_{43} = 9$.

5.4-1 $v_R = Ri = i$ if $R = 1$; then i is as shown in Figure Exercise 5.4-1A.
$v_L = L(di/dt) = di/dt$, as shown in Figure Exercise 5.4-1B.

5.4-2 $v_C = \int_0^t (\tau - 1) d\tau = \frac{1}{2} t^2 - t$ for $0 < t < 2$, as plotted in Figure Exercise 5.4-2A.
$v_C = (-t^2/2) + 3t - 4$ for $2 \le t \le 4$, as shown in Figure Exercise 5.4-2B.
$v_C(t)$ in $4 \le t \le 8$ is the same as that in $0 \le t \le 4$ in Figure Exercise 5.4-2C.

5.4-3 $v = v_L + v_C + v_R$ as in Figure Exercise 5.4-3.

5.4-4 $v_R = 5 \sin 5t$,
$v_L = 25 \cos 5t$,
$v = \begin{cases} 1 + 24 \cos 5t + 5 \sin 5t & \text{for} \quad 0 \le t \le 2\pi/5, \\ 0 \text{ elsewhere.} \end{cases}$

5.4-5 $i = \begin{cases} \sin 10t + 4 \cos 10t + 1 & \text{for} \quad t \ge 0, \\ 0 \quad \text{for} \quad t < 0. \end{cases}$

5.4-6 $i = \begin{cases} i_R + i_C + i_L = 10 & \text{for} \quad t > 2, \\ t + \frac{1}{2} + 5t^2 & \text{for} \quad 0 \le t \le 1, \\ -5t^2 + 19t - \frac{17}{2} & \text{for} \quad 1 \le t \le 2. \end{cases}$

5.5-1 $M \dfrac{d^2x}{dt^2} + D \dfrac{dx}{dt} = F$,
$x(0) = 0$.

CHAPTER 6

6.1-1 $p = +vi$.

6.1-2 $p = -vi$.

6.1-3 $p = +vi$.

6.1-4 $p = -vi$.

6.2-1 $P_{\text{av}} = \dfrac{L\omega_0 I_0^2}{2T} \displaystyle\int_0^T (\sin 2\omega_0 t) \, dt = 0.$

6.2-2 $P_{\text{av}} = \dfrac{1}{T} \displaystyle\int_0^T 3V_0^4 \omega_0 \sin^3 \omega_0 t \cos \omega_0 t \, dt = \dfrac{3}{T} V_0^4 \dfrac{1}{4} (\sin \omega_0 t)^4 \Big|_0^T = 0.$

6.2-3 $P_{\text{av}} = (1/T) \int_0^T \omega_0 I_0^2 \cos \omega_0 t [1 - \sin^2 \omega_0 t] dt = 0.$ Storing.

6.2-4 $P_{\text{av}} = (1/T) \int_0^T I_0 \cos \omega_0 t$
$\times [-2\omega_0 I_0 \sin \omega_0 t + \omega_0 I_0 \sin^2 \omega_0 t - I_0 \omega \cos^2 \omega_0 t] dt = 0.$ Storing.

6.2-5 No. It depends on the periodicity of R compared to that of v.

6.2-6 No.

6.2-7 $P_{\text{av}} = \dfrac{10}{T} \displaystyle\int_0^T [i^2] dt = \dfrac{10}{2} [(I_1 \cos \alpha_1 + I_2 \cos \alpha_2)^2 + (I_1 \sin \alpha_1 + I_2 \sin \alpha_2)^2].$

6.3-4 $P_{\text{av}} = \dfrac{1}{T} \displaystyle\int_0^T 0 \, dt = 0.$ Lossless.

6.3-5 Passive.

6.3-6 Yes.

6.4-1 W_{13} from source $= \int_0^t \dfrac{10}{12} \cdot 10 \, d\tau,$

$$W_{R_1} = \int_0^t 10 \left(\frac{10}{12}\right)^2 d\tau,$$

$$W_{R_2} = \int_0^t 2 \left(\frac{10}{12}\right)^2 d\tau.$$

6.4-2 $W_{13} = \int_0^t 10 \left[\dfrac{-5 \pm \sqrt{45}}{2}\right] d\tau,$

$$W_{R_1} = \int_0^t 10 \left[\frac{-5 \pm \sqrt{45}}{2}\right]^2 d\tau,$$

$$W_{R_2} = \int_0^t 2 \left[\frac{-5 \pm \sqrt{45}}{2}\right]^3 d\tau,$$

$$W_{R_1} + W_{R_2} = W_{13}.$$

6.4-3 $W_{13} = \int_0^t 10 \left(\dfrac{10}{8}\right) d\tau,$

$$W_{R_1} = \int_0^t 10 \left(\frac{10}{8}\right)^2 d\tau,$$

$$W_{R_2} = \int_0^t -2 \left(\frac{10}{8}\right)^2 d\tau,$$

$$W_{13} = W_{R_1} + W_{R_2}.$$

6.4-4 $W_R = 10\left(t + \dfrac{2L}{R} e^{-R/L\,t} - \dfrac{L}{2R} e^{-2R/L\,t} - 2\dfrac{L}{R} + \dfrac{L}{2R}\right),$

$$W_L = \frac{1}{2} L \left(1 - 2e^{-R/L\,t} + e^{-2R/L\,t}\right),$$

$$W_{13} = 10\left[t + \frac{L}{R} e^{-R/L\,t} - \frac{L}{R}\right],$$

$$W_{13} = W_L + W_R.$$

6.4-5 $P_R = 5,\ P_L = 0.$

6.4-6 $P_a = \left(\dfrac{3}{2}\right)^2 2,$

$$P_b = \left(\frac{5}{2}\right)^2 2,$$

$$P_c = \left(\frac{8}{2}\right)^2 2,$$

$$P_{12}(\text{out}) = 33/2,$$

$$P_{32}(\text{out}) = 65/2.$$

6.5-1 (a) $v_5 = v_1 + v_2$, $i_5 = i_1 = i_2$, $v_1 i_1 + v_2 i_2 - v_s i_s = 0$. (b) If v and i satisfy branch equations, then $v_1 i_1$ is instantaneous power into box 1, $v_2 i_2$ is instantaneous power into box 2, and $v_s i_s$ is instantaneous power out of source; $v_s i_s = v_1 i_1 + v_2 i_2$.

6.5-2 $v_1 = 3,$ 　　 $i_1 = e^{-t};$
$v_2 = 8,$ 　　 $i_2 = e^{-t};$
$v_s = 11,$ 　　 $i_s = e^{-t}.$

6.5-3 By Tellegen's theorem,

$$v_{11'}i_1 + v_{22'}i_2 + \cdots + v_{nn'}i_n - (v_1 i_1 + v_2 i_2 + \cdots + v_n i_n) = 0.$$

$$\therefore \underbrace{\sum_{k=1}^{n} v_{kk'}i_k}_{\substack{\text{power into} \\ n\text{-port}}} = \underbrace{\sum_{k=1}^{n} v_k i_k}_{\substack{\text{power out of} \\ \text{sources.}}}$$

6.6-1 (a) $W_C = \dfrac{1}{2C} q^2 = \dfrac{1}{2} (2t)^2$ for $0 \le t \le 1$.

$W_C = \dfrac{1}{2} (2)$ for $t > 1$.

(b) $W_C = \dfrac{1}{2} t^2$ for $0 \le t \le 1$.

$W_C = \dfrac{1}{2} (-t^2 + 4t - 3)^2$ for $1 < t < 2$.

For $t > 2$, W_C for (a) and W_C for (b) are equal. Reversing terminals has no effect on W_C.

6.6-2 (a) $W_R = \begin{cases} 8t & \text{for} \quad 0 \le t \le 1, \\ 8 & \text{for} \quad t > 1; \end{cases}$

(b) $W_R = \begin{cases} \frac{8}{3}t^3 & \text{for} \quad 0 < t < 1, \\ \frac{8}{3}t^3 - 16t^2 + 32t - 16 & \text{for} \quad 1 \le t \le 2, \\ \frac{16}{3} & \text{for} \quad t > 2. \end{cases}$

Reversing switch has no effect.

6.6-3 $v = \begin{cases} 2i, & i \ge 0, \\ 10i, & i < 0. \end{cases}$ $\qquad W_R = \begin{cases} 8t, & 0 \le t \le 1, \\ 8, & t > 1. \end{cases}$

If terminals are reversed,

$$W_R = \begin{cases} 40t, & 0 \le t \le 1, \\ 40, & t > 1. \end{cases}$$

6.6-4 $W_R = \begin{cases} \frac{8}{3}t^3 & \text{for} \quad 0 \le t \le 1, \\ \frac{8}{3} - 16t^2 + 32t - 16 & \text{for} \quad 1 \le t \le 2, \\ \frac{16}{3} & \text{for} \quad t > 2. \end{cases}$

If terminals are reversed,

$$W_R = \begin{cases} \frac{40}{3}t^3, & 0 \le t \le 1, \\ 5(\frac{8}{3}t^3 - 16t^2 + 32t - 16), & 1 \le t \le 2, \\ \frac{80}{3}, & t > 2. \end{cases}$$

6.6-5 $W_L = \frac{2}{3}, t > 1.$

6.6-6 $W_L = \dfrac{1}{2L} \psi^2 = \begin{cases} \frac{1}{6}t^2, & 0 \le t \le 1, \\ \frac{1}{6}(-t^2 + 4t - 2), & 1 \le t \le 2, \\ \frac{1}{6}(2), & t > 2. \end{cases}$

Reversing terminals has no effect on W_L.

6.6-7 $W_L = \frac{1}{3}\psi^3 - \frac{1}{2}\psi^2 = -\frac{1}{6}.$

6.6-8 $W_L = -\frac{1}{6}$. If terminals are reversed, $\psi(1) = -1$, $W_L = -\frac{1}{3} - \frac{1}{2} = -\frac{5}{6}$.

6.6-9 $W_L = \frac{23}{6}$.

CHAPTER 7

7.1-1 $v = R(t)i$.

If $\left.\begin{array}{c} v_1 = R(t)i_1, \\ v_2 = R(t)i_2, \end{array}\right\}$ then $K_1 v_1 + K_2 v_2 = R(t)[K_1 i_1 + K_2 i_2]$.

7.1-2 $\psi = Li = \int v \, d\tau$, $i = (1/L)\int_0^t v(\tau)\, d\tau + i(0)$. For $v \equiv 0$, $i = i(0)$ zero-input linear.

For $i(0) \equiv 0$, $i_1 = (1/L)\int_0^t v_1(\tau)\, d\tau \Rightarrow i_2 = K i_1 = (1/L)\int_0^t K v_1 \, d\tau$,

and if $v_3 = v_1 + v_2$, $i_3 = i_1 + i_2$. Therefore, 1-port is zero-state linear, and since the element satisfies the decomposition property, it is linear.

7.1-3 $Ri + L(di/dt) = v$. If $Ri_1 + L(di_1/dt) = v_1$, then $R(Ki_1) + L(d/dt)\,(Ki_1) = Kv_1$ (homogeneous); and if $Ri_2 + L(di_2/dt) = v_2$, then $R(i_1 + i_2) + L(d/dt)\,(i_1 + i_2) = v_1 + v_2$ (additive). Therefore, the system is zero-state linear.

7.1-4 $Ri + L(di/dt) = 0$. Let $i_1(0)$ be an initial state. And, since $i = Ke^{-(R/L)t}$, then $i(t) = i(0)e^{-(R/L)t}$. If $i_2(0) = K_1 i_1(0)$, then $i_2(t) = K_1 i_1(0)e^{-(R/L)t}$ (homogeneous). If $i_3(0) = i_2(0) + i_1(0)$, then $i_3(t) = [i_2(0) + i_1(0)]e^{-(R/L)t}$ (additive). Therefore, the system is zero-input linear.

7.1-5 Using the method of I.F., we have

$$\frac{d}{dt}e^{(R/L)t}\, i = v(t)e^{(R/L)t}$$

$$e^{(R/L)t}\, i(t) - i(0) = \int_0^t e^{(R/L)\tau}\, v(\tau)\, d\tau$$

$$i(t) = \underbrace{e^{-(R/L)t}\, i(0)}_{\substack{\text{zero-input} \\ \text{response}}} + \underbrace{\int_0^t e^{-(R/L)(t-\tau)}\, v(\tau)\, d\tau}_{\text{zero-state response}}.$$

Therefore, the system satisfies the decomposition property.

7.1-6 $v \neq f(q)$. Assuming that i is input, $v = f(\int i\, d\tau)$.

If f is a nonlinear function, then $f(Kq) \neq Kf(q)$. Nonlinear.

7.1-7 The system is nonlinear and zero-state homogeneous.

7.1-8 $x_1 \to y_1$, $x_2 \to y_2$, $x_1 + x_2 \to y_1 + y_2$. Therefore, if $x_2 = x_1$, $2x_1 \to 2y_1$. Repeat for $x_2 = x_1$, $2x_1 + x_2 \to 2y_1 + y_2$ or $3x_1 \to 3y_1$, etc. Therefore, $Cx_1 \to Cy_1$ for $C = $ integer.

7.1-9 $x_1 \to y_1$, $-x_1 \to -y_1$, $\therefore x_1 - x_1 = 0 \to y_1 - y_1 = 0$.

7.1-10 $v(t) = e^{-t}(\frac{41}{44}\cos 2t + \frac{6}{22}\sin 2t)\, u(t)$.

7.1-11 $v = e^{-t}(\frac{-5}{22}\cos 2t + \frac{20}{22}\sin 2t)\, u(t)$.

7.1-12 $v = e^{-t}(\frac{125}{44}\cos 2t + \frac{380}{44}\sin 2t)\,u(t)$.

7.1-13 $v(t) = -\frac{1}{2}[10e^{-t}\cos 2t]u(t) + 3[1 - e^{-t}\cos 2t]u(t)$.

7.2-1 $R_{eq} = R_2$
$v_{eq} = v$.

7.2-2 $R_{eq} = R_2$
$i_{eq} = v/R_2$.

7.2-3 $v_{eq} = 0$
$R_{eq} = 2R$.

7.2-4 (a) $v_{open} = (1/C)\displaystyle\int_0^t u(t) = (1/C)r(t)$ (ramp). (b) $v_{oc} = u(t)$.

7.2-5 $i_{sc} = C(dv/dt)$.

7.2-6 $v = L(di/dt)$.

7.2-7 $i = (1/L)\displaystyle\int_0^t v\,d\tau$.

7.3-1 No.

7.3-2 $i = (dq/dt) = (df/dv)(dv/dt)$. Let $i_1(t)$ be the output due to $v_1(t)$. Let $v_2(t) = v_1(t - \Delta)$. Then

$$i_2(t) = \frac{df}{dv}\bigg|_{v_2(t)}\frac{dv_2}{dt} = \frac{df}{dv}\bigg|_{v_1(t-\Delta)}\frac{d}{dt}v_1(t - \Delta) = i_1(t - \Delta).$$

7.3-3 $v = (d\psi/dt) = (dg/di)(di/dt)$. So if $v_1(t)$ is the output due to $i_1(t)$,

$$v_1(t) = \frac{dg}{dt}\bigg|_{i_1(t)}\frac{di_1}{dt}(t).$$

Now for $i_2(t) = i_1(t - \Delta)$, we have

$$v_2(t) = \frac{dg}{di}\bigg|_{i_1(t-\Delta)}\frac{di_1(t-\Delta)}{dt} = v_1(t - \Delta).$$

7.4-1 $\dfrac{R_1}{R_L}(R_2 + R_L)\,C\dfrac{dv_L}{dt} + \left(\dfrac{R_1 + R_2 + R_L}{R_L}\right)v_L = v$.

7.4-2 $v = -KC(dv_{ab}/dt)$.

7.4-3 $y = c_1 e^{jt} + c_2 e^{-jt}$.

7.4-4 $y = C_1 e^{-t} + C_2 e^{jt} + C_3 e^{-jt}$.

7.4-5 $y = C_1 e^{-3t} + C_2 e^{-2t} + C_3 t e^{-2t} + C_4 t^2 e^{-2t} + C_5 t^3 e^{-2t}$.

7.4-6 $y = \left(\dfrac{1-j}{2}\right)e^{jt} + \left(\dfrac{1+j}{2}\right)e^{-jt} = \cos t + \sin t$.

CHAPTER 8

8.1-2 $i = 2u(t - 1) - 2r(t - 1) + 2r(t - 2)$.
$y = 2v(t - 1)u(t - 1) - 2\int_0^t v(\tau - 1)u(\tau - 1)\,d\tau + 2\int_0^t v(\tau - 2)u(\tau - 2)\,d\tau$.

8.1-3 $y = 2 \int_0^t v(\tau - 1)u(\tau - 1) \, d\tau - 2 \int_0^t \int_0^\xi v(\lambda - 1)u(\lambda - 1) \, d\lambda \, d\xi +$
$\quad 2 \int_0^t \int_0^\xi v(\lambda - 2)u(\lambda - 2) \, d\lambda \, d\xi.$

8.1-4 $y = 2u(t - 1) - 2\delta(t - 2) - 2u(t - 2).$

8.1-5 $y = 2\delta(t - 1) - 2u(t - 1) + 2u(t - 2).$

8.2-1 $y = (1 - e^{-t})u(t).$

8.2-2 $y = (1 - e^{-t})u(t) - (1 - e^{-(t-1)})u(t - 1).$

8.2-3 Answer $= 2(t - 1)u(t - 1) - 2(1 - e^{-(t-1)})u(t - 1) - 2(t - 2)u(t - 2).$

8.2-4 It can be shown that if $x_1(t)$ produces $y_1(t)$, $Kx_1(t)$ produces $Ky_1(t)$; and if $x_1(t)$ produces $y_1(t)$, and $x_2(t)$ produces $y_2(t)$, then $x_1(t) + x_2(t)$ produces $y_1(t) + y_2(t)$.

8.2-5 $y = \frac{1}{2} e^{-t} + \frac{1}{2} \sin t - \frac{1}{2} \cos t$, for $t \geq 0$.

8.3-1 $y(1) = 1 - 1/e.$

8.3-2 $y = \begin{cases} 0 & \text{for} \quad t < 1, \\ -t^2 + 4t - 3 & \text{for} \quad 1 \leq t < 2, \\ t^2 - 6t + 9 & \text{for} \quad 2 \leq t < 3, \\ 0 & \text{for} \quad t > 3. \end{cases}$

8.3-3 $y = \begin{cases} 0 & \text{for} \quad t < 0, \\ t & \text{for} \quad 0 \leq t < 1, \\ -t + 2 & \text{for} \quad 1 \leq t < 2, \\ 0 & \text{for} \quad t \geq 2. \end{cases}$

8.3-4 From $h(t)$, form $h(\tau)$; then form $h(t + \tau)$ which is shifted to the left by t, compared to $h(\tau)$. Finally fold $h(t + \tau)$ versus τ, with respect to the vertical axis. This means replacing τ by $-\tau$, so that we have $h(t - \tau)$.

8.3-5 $y = \begin{cases} 0 & \text{for} \quad t < 2, \\ \frac{2}{3} t^3 - 2t + 4/3 & \text{for} \quad 2 \leq t < 3, \\ -\frac{2}{3} t^3 + 4t^2 - 4t - 16/3 & \text{for} \quad 3 \leq t < 4, \\ 0 & \text{for} \quad t \geq 4. \end{cases}$

8.3-6 $y(t) = \begin{cases} t & \text{for} \quad 0 \leq t < 1, \\ 1 & \text{for} \quad t \geq 1, \\ 0 & \text{for} \quad t < 0. \end{cases}$

8.4-1 $v_{23}(t) = (1/RC)e^{-t/RC} \, u(t).$

8.4-2 $v_{12}(t) = (1/RC)\delta(t) - (1/R^2C^2)e^{-t/RC} \, u(t).$

8.4-3 $h(t) = (e^{-t} + 2te^{-t})u(t).$

8.4-4 $h(t) = (-\frac{1}{8} e^{-4t} + \frac{1}{8} + \frac{1}{2} t)u(t).$

8.4-5 Substitute y of Equation 8.42 in left-hand side of Equation 8.34 and this comes out to be equal to 1. Hence Equation 8.34 is satisfied.

8.4-6 Hint: Use Euler's identity for trigonometric functions.

8.5-1 $v_2(t) = \frac{2}{3} e^{-2t} + \frac{2}{3} e^{-(1/2)t} \cos\left(\frac{\sqrt{3}}{2} t + 60°\right)$.

8.5-2 $\dfrac{d^2 v_3}{dt^2} + \dfrac{R}{L} \dfrac{dv_3}{dt} + \dfrac{1}{LC} v_3 = \dfrac{1}{LC} v_1$.

$v_3 = \dfrac{(1/LC) e^{st}}{s^2 + (R/L)s + 1/LC}$.

8.5-3 $v_C(0+) + v_2(0+) = v_1(0+)$. Since v_C is continuous, $v_C(0+) = v_C(0-) = 0$. Therefore, $v_2(0+) = v_1(0+)$ and $v_C'(t) + v_2'(t) = v_1'(t)$. But $i(t)$ (through the inductor) is continuous, so that $i(0+) = i(0-) = 0$. But $Cv_C'(0+) = i(0+) = 0$. Therefore, $v_2'(0+) = v_1'(0+)$.

Since $v_C(0+) + v_2(0+) = v_1(0+)$ if $v_2(0+) = 1$, and since $v_1(0+) = 1$, then $v_C(0+) = 0$. Also $v_C'(0+) + v_2'(0+) = v_1'(0+)$ and $v_2'(0+) = -2$, $v_1'(0+) = -2$. Therefore $v_C'(0+) = 0$. But $i(0+) = Cv_C'(0+) = 0$. Hence the initial conditions on C and L for $t = 0+$ are zero.

8.5-4 $y(t) = \displaystyle\sum_{k=-\infty}^{\infty} C_k \dfrac{b_m (jk\omega_0)^m + \cdots + b_0}{a_n (jk\omega_0)^n + \cdots + a_0} e^{jk\omega_0 t}$.

CHAPTER 9

9.1-1 (a) $i_1 = 5 \sin\left(t + \tan^{-1} \frac{4}{3}\right)$.
(b) $v_2 = \sqrt{(15)^2 + (7)^2} \sin\left(3t + \tan^{-1} \frac{7}{15}\right)$.
(c) $i_3 = \sqrt{(3 - 2\sqrt{2})^2 + 8} \sin\left(t + \tan^{-1} \dfrac{2\sqrt{2}}{3 - 2\sqrt{2}}\right)$.
(d) $q_1 = 18 \sin(t - \pi/4)$.
(e) $v_1 = 3 \sin(t + \pi/2)$.

9.1-2 (a) $i_1 = 5 \cos\left(t + \tan^{-1} \frac{4}{3} - \pi/2\right)$.
(b) $v_2 = \sqrt{274} \cos\left(3t + \tan^{-1} \frac{7}{15} - \pi/2\right)$.
(c) $i_3 = \sqrt{(3 - 2\sqrt{2})^2 + 8} \cos\left(t + \tan^{-1} \dfrac{2\sqrt{2}}{3 - 2\sqrt{2}} - \pi/2\right)$.
(d) $q_1 = 18 \cos(t - 3\pi/4)$.
(e) $v_1 = 3 \cos t$.

9.2-1 (a) $5 \underline{/-53.2°}$ (d) $6.8 \underline{/17.1°}$ (g) $5 \underline{/180°}$
(b) $5 \underline{/233.2°}$ (e) $13.09 \underline{/83.4°}$ (h) $8 \underline{/90°}$
(c) $5 \underline{/126.8°}$ (f) $13 \underline{/157.3°}$ (i) $8 \underline{/-90°}$
           (j) $25 \underline{/-1.7°}$.

9.2-2 (a) $0 + j5$ (f) $3\sqrt{3} + j3$
(b) $\sqrt{2} + j\sqrt{2}$ (g) $3\sqrt{3} - j3$
(c) $0 - j10$ (h) $-12 \cos 75° + j12 \sin 75°$
(d) $-4\sqrt{3} + j4$ (i) $-\sqrt{2} + j\sqrt{2}$
(e) $-3 + j0$ (j) $4.5 + j0$.

9.2-3 (a) $14.5 + j15$,

    (b) $(-12 \cos 75° + 3\sqrt{3}) + j(12 \sin 75° + 3)$,

    (c) $-4\sqrt{3} + j4 + 3\sqrt{3} - j3 = -\sqrt{3} + j1$.

9.2-4 (a) $25e^{j\pi}$,

    (b) $170.2e^{j240.7°}$,

    (c) $45e^{j178.1°}$.

9.2-5 $(e^{j\theta})* = (\cos \theta + j \sin \theta)* = \cos \theta - j \sin \theta = e^{-j\theta}$.

9.2-6 $(c_1 c_2)* = [(a_1 + jb_1)(a_2 + jb_2)]* = [(a_1 a_2 - b_1 b_2) + j(b_1 a_2 + b_2 a_1)]* = a_1 a_2 - b_1 b_2 - j(b_1 a_2 + b_2 a_1)$; $c_1* c_2* = (a_1 - jb_1)(a_2 - jb_2) = a_1 a_2 - b_1 b_2 - j(b_1 a_2 + a_1 b_2)$; $\therefore (c_1 c_2)* = c_1* c_2*$.

9.3-1 $6.65 \; \underline{/114.9°}$.

9.3-2 (a) jA leads A by 90°.

    (b) $-2jA$ lags A by 90° and it is twice as long as A.

    (c) $(1 - 2j)A$ lags A by 63.5° and it is 2.24 times as long.

    (d) $A*$ is the mirror image of A with respect to the real axis.

9.3-3 $5.33 \sin (377t + 16°)$.

9.3-4 $5.33 \sin (377t + 26°)$; $5.33 \sin (377t - 14°)$; yes.

9.3-5 $V_0 = I_0 \sqrt{R^2 + (\omega L)^2}$,

$$\theta_V = \theta_0 + \tan^{-1} \frac{\omega L}{R}.$$

9.4-1 $\dfrac{d^2 v_{12}}{dt^2} + \dfrac{R}{L} \dfrac{dv_{12}}{dt} + \dfrac{1}{LC} v_{12} = \dfrac{1}{C} \dfrac{di}{dt} + \dfrac{R}{LC} i$,

$v_{12} = 2 \sin (10^4 t + 119.4°)$.

9.4-2 $i(t) = \frac{1}{2} \times 10^{-3} \sin (10^4 t - 89.4°)$.

9.4-3 $\dfrac{d^2 v_{13}}{dt^2} + \dfrac{3dv_{13}}{dt} + v_{13} = \dfrac{dv}{dt} + v$,

$v_{13}(t) = 1.05 \cos (t - 71.5°)$.

9.4-4 $\dfrac{d^2 v_{23}}{dt^2} + \dfrac{3dv_{23}}{dt} + v_{23} = v$,

$v_{23} = 0.745 \cos (t - 116.5°)$.

CHAPTER 10

10.1-1 $i = 5\sqrt{2} \sin (3t + 15°)$.

10.1-2 $G = \dfrac{R}{R^2 + X^2}$, $B = \dfrac{-X}{R^2 + X^2}$.

10.1-3 $G = \dfrac{1}{|Z|} \cos \theta$, $B = \dfrac{-1}{|Z|} \sin \theta$.

10.2-1 Capacitor. $C = 1/40\pi$.

10.2-2 Inductor. $L = 1/2\pi$.

10.2-3 Resistor. $R = 10/3$.

10.3-1 $v_R(t) + v_L(t) + v_C(t) = v(t)$. Since we are considering only the sinusoidal steady state, the voltages are of the form

$$v_R(t) = |V_R| \sin(\omega t + \theta_R) = Im[|V_R|e^{j(\omega t + \theta_R)}]$$
$$v_L(t) = |V_L| \sin(\omega t + \theta_L) = Im[|V_L|e^{j(\omega t + \theta_L)}]$$
$$v_C(t) = |V_C| \sin(\omega t + \theta_C) = Im[|V_C|e^{j(\omega t + \theta_C)}]$$
$$v(t) = |V| \sin(\omega t + \theta) = Im[|V|e^{j(\omega t + \theta)}]$$
$$v_R(t) + v_L(t) + v_C(t) = Im[(V_R + V_L + V_C)e^{j\omega t}] = v = Im[Ve^{j\omega t}],$$

where $V_R = |V_R|e^{j\theta_R}$; $V_L = |V_L|e^{j\theta_L}$; $V_C = |V_C|e^{j\theta_C}$; and $V = |V|e^{j\theta}$.

Since the time-domain equation holds for all t, it holds for time equal to $t + \pi/2$. But if $\sin(\omega t + \theta + \pi/2) = \cos(\omega t + \theta)$, then $v_R(t + \pi/2) + v_L(t + \pi/2) + v_C(t + \pi/2) = |V_R| \cos(\omega t + \theta_R) + |V_L| \cos(\omega t + \theta_L) + |V_C| \cos(\omega t + \theta_C) = v(t + \pi/2) = |V| \cos(\omega t + \theta) = Re[(V_R + V_L + V_C)e^{j\omega t}] = Re[Ve^{j\omega t}]$.

Since the real parts and imaginary parts of the above rotating phasors are equal for all time, the rotating phasors are equal:

$$(V_R + V_L + V_C)e^{j\omega t} = Ve^{j\omega t}.$$

Hence

$$V_R + V_L + V_C = V,$$

which verifies Equation 10.24.

10.3-2 Using a procedure similar to that for Exercise 10.3-1, show that the imaginary parts of the corresponding rotating phasors are equal. Similarly, show that the real parts of the rotating phasors match. Hence the corresponding rotating phasors are equal thus verifying Equation 10.41.

10.3-3 $V_{a_i} = 6.3$ volts; $V_{c_g} = 1$ volt.

10.3-4 $|V_2| = 76.9$ volts.

10.3-5 $|V_L| = 2$ volts; $|V_R| = .707$ volt; $V_C = 1.293$ volts.

10.3-6 $|V_R| = 12$; $|V_L| = 16$; $V_C = 7$ or 25.

10.3-7 For $\omega = 1$, $Z = 1 - j\,1/4$; For $\omega = 2$, $Z = 1 - j\,1/2$.

10.3-8 $Z = \frac{7}{5} - j\frac{13}{10}$.

10.3-9 $|V_1| = 130$ volts.

10.4-1 $v = 2 \sin(t - 75°)$.

10.4-2 $v_1(t) = 7.2 \sin(2t + 168.8°)$.

10.4-3 $V_{Irms} = 3$ volts.

10.4-4 (a) $v_1(t) = 2\sqrt{2} \sin(\frac{1}{2}t + 15°)$
       (b) $v_1(t) = 11.65 \sin(2t + 120.9°)$
       (c) $v_1(t) = \sqrt{2} \sin(0.1t + 45°)$

(d) $v_1(t) = 2\sqrt{5} \sin (0.5t - 33.4°)$

(e) $v_1(t) = 2.91 \sin (0.5t + 14.1°)$

(f) $v_1(t) = 3.09 \sin (t + 30.9°)$

(g) $v_1(t) = 20\sqrt{2} \sin (0.5t - 45°)$

(h) $v_1(t) = 2 \sin (2t)$

(i) $v_1(t) = 4 \sin (4t - 7.5°)$

(j) $v_1(t) = 150\sqrt{2} \sin (t - 0.6°)$

(k) $v_1(t) = \frac{5}{3} \sin (\frac{1}{16}t - 33.1°)$

(l) $v_1(t) = 4 \sin (0.5t + 120°)$

(m) $v_1(t) = \frac{11}{12} \sin (t + 240°)$

(n) $v_1(t) = (7/\sqrt{2}) \sin (27t + 713°)$

(o) $v_1(t) = 5.54 \sin (0.25t + 51.2°)$

(p) $v_1(t) = \sqrt{2} \sin (t - 180°)$

(q) $v_1(t) = 6.18 \sin (t - 45.9°)$

(r) $v_1(t) = (3/\sqrt{2}) \sin (t + 135°)$

(s) $v_1(t) = 7.28 \sin (2t - 75.9°)$

(t) $v_1(t) = (3\sqrt{10}/2) \sin (0.5t - 1.6°)$

(u) $v_1(t) = 8 \sin (t - 45°)$

(v) $v_1(t) = 1.95 \sin (0.5t + 68.6°)$

(w) $v_1(t) = 152.5 \sin (t - 101.3°)$

(x) $v_1(t) = 1.21 \sin (0.5t + 39.1°)$

(y) $v_1(t) = (15/\sqrt{2}) \sin (t - 90°)$.

10.5-1 $G_{21} = \dfrac{2000s + \frac{8}{3} \times 10^6}{s^2 + 4 \times 10^3 s + \frac{8}{3} \times 10^6}$.

$$v_2(t) = \frac{10[(\frac{8}{3} \times 10^6)^2 + (2000\omega)^2]^{1/2}}{[(\frac{8}{3} \times 10^6 - \omega^2)^2 + (4000\omega)^2]^{1/2}}$$
$$\times \sin \left(\omega t + 45° + \tan^{-1}\frac{3\omega}{4000} - \tan^{-1}\frac{4000\omega}{\frac{8}{3} \times 10^6 - \omega^2}\right).$$

10.5-2 $G_{21}(j\omega) = \dfrac{1}{(1 - \omega^2 + \omega^4)^{1/2}} \left/ -\tan^{-1}\dfrac{\omega}{1 - \omega^2}\right.$.

10.5-3 (a) $Z_{21} = (V_2/I_1) = \frac{2}{5} + j\frac{1}{5}$; (b) $Y_{21} = (I_2/V_1) = j\frac{1}{3}$; (c) $Z_{21} \neq (1/Y_{21})$.

10.5-4 $\alpha_{21} = I_2/I_1 = \frac{2}{5} + j\frac{1}{5}$.

10.5-5 $G_{21} = s^2/(s^2 + 3s + 1)$.

10.5-6 $\alpha_{21} = s/(2s + 1)$.

10.6-1 $I = I_R + I_L + I_C = (V/R) + (V/Ls) + CsV$. Hence, $I/V = Y = (1/R) + (1/Ls) + Cs$.

10.6-2 (a) $Z_{21}(s) = \dfrac{s}{2s + 1}$,   (c) $G_{21}(s) = \dfrac{s^2}{s^2 + 3s + 1}$,

(b) $Y_{21}(s) = \dfrac{s^2}{s^2 + 3s + 1}$,   (d) $\alpha_{21}(s) = \dfrac{s}{2s + 1}$.

For $s = -1$, $Z_{21} = 1$, $Y_{21} = -1$, $G_{21} = -1$, $\alpha_{21} = 1$.

10.6-3 $G_{21}(s) = \dfrac{2s^2}{2s^2 + s + 1}$.

10.6-4 $G_{21}(s) = 1/(s^2 + s + 1)$; $v_2(t) = \frac{10}{13} e^{3t}$.

CHAPTER 11

11.1-1 Time constant $= RC$; bandwidth $= \omega_c = 1/$(time constant).

11.1-2 $v_0(t) = 100 + 0.531 \sin (377t - 178.5°)$.

11.1-3 $v_0(t) = 20 \cos (377t - 178.5°)$.

11.1-4 $\phi = -\tan^{-1} (\omega RC)$; $\phi_c = -45°$.

11.1-5 $\phi = 90° - \tan^{-1} (\omega RC)$; $\phi_c = 45°$.

11.2-1 (a) Replace L by $1/\omega_r^2 C$ in Equation 11.35 and obtain $Q = 1/\omega_r RC$; (b) Replace ω_r by $1/\sqrt{LC}$ in Equation 11.35 and obtain $Q = (1/R)\sqrt{L/C}$.

11.2-2 From Equation 11.35, $V_{Cm} = V_m/(\omega_r RC)$. But from Equation 11.40, $V_{Lm} = \omega_r L V_m/R$. Since $1/(\omega_r RC) = Q = \omega_r L/R$, then $V_{Lm} = V_{Cm}$.

11.2-3 Let $\omega \to \infty$ in Equation 11.40 and obtain $V_{Lm} \to V_m$.

11.2-4 $|Y| = 1/\sqrt{R^2 + (\omega L - 1/\omega C)^2}$.

11.2-5 Selectivity $= \omega_r/\Delta\omega = \omega_r/(R/L) = \omega_r L/R$. But for the series RLC, $\omega_r L/R = Q$. Hence the Q expressions in Exercise 11.2-1 are also equal to S for the series RLC circuit.

11.3-1 $\omega_r \approx 10^6$ radians/sec; $S \approx 10$; $\Delta\omega = 10^5$ radians/sec; $Q = 10$.

11.3-2 $|Z|$ at resonance $\approx L/RC = 10^5$ ohms.
At $\omega = 0$, $|Z| = R = 1000$.
At $\omega = \infty$, $|Z| = 0$.
At $\omega = \omega_r - \frac{1}{4}\Delta\omega = 10^6(.975)$, $|Z| = .865 \times 10^5$ ohms.
At $\omega = \omega_r + \frac{1}{4}\Delta\omega = 10^6(1.025)$, $|Z| = .913 \times 10^5$ ohms.
At $\omega = \frac{1}{2}\omega_r = .5 \times 10^6$, $|Z| = .675 \times 10^4$.
At $\omega = 2\omega_r = 2 \times 10^6$, $|Z| = .667 \times 10^4$.

11.3-3 $v(t) = 10^4 \cos \omega_r t + 0.667 \times 10^3 \sin 2\omega_r t$. There is a filtering effect.

11.3-4 $\omega_r = 1/\sqrt{LC}$.

11.3-5 $\Delta\omega = 1/RC$; $S = R\sqrt{C/L}$; $Q = R/\omega_r L$.

11.3-6 $\omega_r = 1/\sqrt{LC}$.

11.4-1 From the locus diagram, form a right triangle with the hypotenuse equal to the maximum value of I, and one side corresponding to an angle of 45°. It is clear that the sides are $1/\sqrt{2}$ times the length of the hypotenuse.

11.4-2 Plot the values of I in the complex plane corresponding to the three values of C. Draw a circle passing through the three points. Then compute the value of I corresponding to the fourth value of C. Verify that the point lies on the circle that was drawn.

11.4-3 The diameter of the circular locus is 1. For $C \to \infty$, $I = 1/(1 + jl)$ so that the locus consists of $\frac{3}{4}$ of the circle starting at I lagging V by 45° ($C \to \infty$) up to I leading V by 90° ($C = 0$).

11.4-4 (a) $I_L = V_m/(R_L + j\omega L)$; (b) the locus of I_C with C as parameter is similar to that in Figure 11.16; (c) the locus of I with C as parameter is similar to that in Figure 11.19.

11.4-5 The locus is similar to that in Figure 11.21.

11.5-1 $|I|_{min} = 4.78$; $|Z|_{max} = 20.9$ ohms.

11.5-2 $C_1 = .0887 \times 10^{-3}$ F; $C_2 = .480 \times 10^{-3}$ F.

11.5-3 For resonance $L = .01125$H or $.00209$H; for I minimum, the angle of lead is 28.8°.

11.5-4 (a) Maximum $|Z| = 33.8$ ohms; (b) $C = 142 \ \mu$F.

11.5-5 The Z locus is a circle.

11.5-6 This applies only to a series RLC situation.

11.6-1 Poles are at $-500 \pm j\,500\sqrt{3}$; zero at the origin.

11.6-2 Compare your result with that in Exercise 11.3-2.

11.6-3 (a) Pole is at $s = -1/RC$; no finite zero; (b) pole at $s = -1/RC$; zero at $s = 0$.

11.6-4 $Y = \dfrac{1}{R} + Cs + \dfrac{1}{Ls}$

$$Z = 1 \Big/ \Big(Cs + \frac{1}{R} + \frac{1}{Ls}\Big) = Ls \Big/ \Big(LCs^2 + \frac{Ls}{R} + 1\Big)$$

$$Z = \frac{1}{C}s \Big/ \Big(s^2 + \frac{1}{RC}s + \frac{1}{LC}\Big)$$

Zero is at $s = 0$. If $(1/RC)^2 - (4/LC) > 0$, there are two real poles at

$$s = \Big(-\frac{1}{RC} \pm \sqrt{\Big(\frac{1}{RC}\Big)^2 - \frac{4}{LC}}\Big)\Big/ 2.$$

If $(1/RC)^2 - (4/LC) = 0$, there is a double pole at $s = -1/2RC$. If $(1/RC)^2 - (4/LC) < 0$, there are two complex poles at

$$s = \Big(-\frac{1}{RC} \pm j \sqrt{\frac{4}{LC} - \Big(\frac{1}{RC}\Big)^2}\Big)\Big/ 2.$$

CHAPTER 12

12.1-1 Sets (b) and (d) are redundant.

12.1-2 At (a): $i_{af} + i_1 + i_5 = 0$.   At (c): $-i_3 + i_4 - i_5 = 0$.
At (b): $-i_1 + i_2 + i_3 = 0$.   At (e): $-i_{af} - i_2 - i_4 = 0$.
The four equations are not linearly independent.

12.1-3 1. $v_1 + v_2 - v_s = 0$.   2. $-v_2 + v_3 + v_4 = 0$.   3. $-v_1 + v_5 - v_3 = 0$.   4. $v_1 + v_3 + v_4 - v_s = 0$.   5. $-v_s + v_5 + v_4 = 0$.   6. $-v_s + v_5 - v_3 + v_2 = 0$.
These six equations are not linearly independent.

12.1-4 $v_1 = v_a - v_b$; $v_2 = v_b$; $v_3 = v_b - v_c$; $v_4 = v_c$; $v_5 = v_a - v_c$; $v_s = v_a$.

12.1-5 $i_2 = i_1 - i_3$; $i_4 = i_3 + i_5$; $i_{af} = -i_1 - i_5$.

12.2-1 (a) *cad*, (b) *efd*, (c) *eda*, (d) *dcb*, (e) *cef*.   There are many more.

12.2-2 (a) *bfe*, (b) *abc*, (c) *bfc*, (d) *aef*, (e) *abd*.

12.2-3 *c*, *ab*, *de*, *afe*, *dfb*.

12.2-4 1673, 5678, 5724, 1683, 1237, 1238, 1235, 2347, 2456, 1268.

12.2-5 2458, 1234, 1368, 2457, 4568, 4567, 4678, 1568, 1378, 3457, respectively.

12.3-1 (a) 3, (b) 3.   12.3-2 (a) 3, (b) 3.   12.3-3 (a) 4, (b) 4.   12.3-4 (a) 4, (b) 4.

12.3-5 1. $i_{ed} + i_{eg} = 0$.   5. $i_{ab} + i_{cf} + i_{kb} + i_{eg} = 0$.
      2. $+i_{kd} + i_{kb} = 0$.   6. $i_{bh} + i_{cf} + i_{eg} = 0$.
      3. $i_{dc} + i_{kb} + i_{eg} = 0$.   7. $i_{hg} + i_{eg} = 0$.
      4. $i_{ca} + i_{cf} + i_{kb} + i_{eg} = 0$.   8. $i_{fh} + i_{cf} = 0$.

12.3-6 1. $v_{ac} + v_{cf} - v_{hf} - v_{bh} - v_{ab} = 0$.
      2. $v_{kd} + v_{dc} - v_{ac} + v_{ab} - v_{kb} = 0$.
      3. $v_{ed} + v_{dc} - v_{ac} + v_{ab} + v_{bh} + v_{hg} - v_{eg} = 0$.

12.4-1 *acb*, *cde*, *afd*.

12.4-2 *adf*, *bfe*, *cde*.

12.4-3 $i_{12} + i_{13} + i_{14} = 0$; $-i_{12} + i_{24} + i_{23} = 0$; $-i_{23} - i_{13} + i_{34} = 0$.

12.4-4 $v_{12} + v_{24} - v_{14} = 0$; $v_{23} + v_{34} - v_{24} = 0$; $v_{13} - v_{23} - v_{12} = 0$.

12.4-5 $i_{12} + i_{13} + i_{14} + i_{15} = 0$; $-i_{12} + i_{23} + i_{24} + i_{25} = 0$; $-i_{13} - i_{23} + i_{34} + i_{35} = 0$; $-i_{14} - i_{24} - i_{34} + i_{45} = 0$.

12.4-6 (a) No, because it is nonplanar; (b) Yes, since it is planar, but first it has to be redrawn in planar form.

12.5-1 $i_{14} = -i_{13} + i_{21}$; $i_{34} = i_{13} + i_{23}$; $i_{24} = -i_{21} - i_{23}$.

12.5-2 i_{12}, i_{23}, i_{34}, i_{45}, i_{56}, $i_{6,12}$, $i_{12,18}$, $i_{18,24}$, $i_{24,23}$, $i_{23,22}$, $i_{22,21}$, $i_{21,20}$, $i_{20,19}$, $i_{19,13}$, $i_{13,7}$, i_{71}.

12.5-3 Choose a tree such as (15, 54, 43, 32); then the chords are appropriate variables: 12, 24, 14, 25, 35, and 13.

12.5-4 No. It is nonplanar.

12.5-5 v_{15}, v_{25}, v_{35}, v_{45}.

12.5-6 v_{15}, v_{54}, v_{43}, v_{32}.

CHAPTER 13

13.1-1 Let v_1, v_2, v_4 and v_5 be the node voltages of nodes 1, 2, 4, and 5 with respect to node 3. Then

$$C_1 \frac{dv_1}{dt} + \frac{1}{R_1} v_1 - \frac{1}{R_1} v_2 = i,$$

$$-\frac{1}{R_1}v_1 + C_3\frac{dv_2}{dt} + \left(\frac{1}{R_1} + \frac{1}{R_2}\right)v_2 - \frac{1}{R_2}v_4 - C_3\frac{dv_5}{dt} = 0,$$

$$-\frac{1}{R_2}v_2 + C_2\frac{dv_4}{dt} + \left(\frac{1}{R_2} + \frac{1}{R_4}\right)v_4 - \frac{1}{R_4}v_5 = 0,$$

$$-C_3\frac{dv_2}{dt} - \frac{1}{R_4}v_4 + C_3\frac{dv_5}{dt} + \left(\frac{1}{R_3} + \frac{1}{R_4}\right)v_5 = -i.$$

13.1-2 Let v_1, v_2, v_3, v_5 be the node voltages of nodes 1, 2, 3, and 5 with respect to node 4. Then

$$C_1\frac{dv_1}{dt} + \frac{1}{R_1}v_1 - \frac{1}{R_1}v_2 - C_1\frac{dv_3}{dt} = i,$$

$$-\frac{1}{R_1}v_1 + C_3\frac{dv_2}{dt} + \left(\frac{1}{R_1} + \frac{1}{R_2}\right)v_2 - C_3\frac{dv_5}{dt} = 0,$$

$$-C_1\frac{dv_1}{dt} + (C_1 + C_2)\frac{dv_3}{dt} + \frac{1}{R_3}v_3 - \frac{1}{R_3}v_5 = 0,$$

$$-C_3\frac{dv_2}{dt} - \frac{1}{R_3}v_3 + C_3\frac{dv_5}{dt} + \left(\frac{1}{R_3} + \frac{1}{R_4}\right)v_5 = -i.$$

13.1-3 Let V_1, V_2, V_4, V_5, V_6 and V_7 be the node voltages with respect to node 3. Then

$$\left(\frac{1}{R_5} + j\omega C_1\right)V_1 - j\omega C_1 V_2 - \frac{1}{R_5}V_7 = I_1,$$

$$-j\omega C_1 V_1 + \left(j\omega C_1 + \frac{1}{R_2} + \frac{1}{j\omega L_1}\right)V_2 - \frac{1}{R_2}V_4 = 0,\ _{\text{\tiny `}}$$

$$-\frac{1}{R_2}V_2 + \left(\frac{1}{R_2} + \frac{1}{R_6} + j\omega C_2\right)V_4 - j\omega C_2 V_5 - \frac{1}{R_6}V_6 = 0,$$

$$-j\omega C_2 V_4 + \left(j\omega C_2 + \frac{1}{R_3}\right)V_5 - \frac{1}{R_3}V_7 = 0,$$

$$-\frac{1}{R_6}V_4 + \left(\frac{1}{R_6} + \frac{1}{R_4}\right)V_6 - \frac{1}{R_4}V_7 = 0.$$

$$-\frac{1}{R_5}V_1 - \frac{1}{R_3}V_5 - \frac{1}{R_4}V_6 + \left(\frac{1}{R_5} + \frac{1}{R_1} + \frac{1}{R_3} + \frac{1}{R_4}\right)V_7 = -I_1.$$

13.1-4
$$\left(\frac{1}{R_5} + j\omega C_1\right)V_1 - j\omega C_2 V_2 - \frac{1}{R_5}V_7 = I_1,$$

$$-j\omega C_1 V_1 + \left(j\omega C_1 + \frac{1}{R_2} + \frac{1}{j\omega L_1}\right)V_2 - \frac{1}{j\omega L_1}V_3 - \frac{1}{R_2}V_4 = 0,$$

$$-\frac{1}{j\omega L_1}V_2 + \left(\frac{1}{R_1} + \frac{1}{j\omega L_1}\right)V_3 - \frac{1}{R_1}V_7 = 0,$$

$$-\frac{1}{R_2}V_2 + \left(\frac{1}{R_2} + \frac{1}{R_6} + j\omega C_2\right)V_4 - \frac{1}{R_6}V_6 = 0,$$

$$-\frac{1}{R_6}V_4 + \left(\frac{1}{R_6} + \frac{1}{R_4}\right)V_6 - \frac{1}{R_4}V_7 = 0,$$

$$-\frac{1}{R_5}V_1 - \frac{1}{R_4}V_6 + \left(\frac{1}{R_5} + \frac{1}{R_1} + \frac{1}{R_3} + \frac{1}{R_4}\right)V_7 = -I_1.$$

13.1-5
$$\left(\frac{1}{R_5} + j\omega C_1\right)V_1 - \frac{1}{R_5}V_7 = I_1,$$

$$\left(\frac{1}{R_1} + \frac{1}{j\omega L_1}\right)V_3 - \frac{1}{R_1}V_7 = 0,$$

$$\left(j\omega C_2 + \frac{1}{R_2} + \frac{1}{R_6}\right)V_4 - j\omega C_2 V_5 - \frac{1}{R_6}V_6 = 0,$$

$$-j\omega C_2 V_4 + \left(j\omega C_2 + \frac{1}{R_3}\right)V_5 - \frac{1}{R_3}V_7 = 0,$$

$$-\frac{1}{R_6}V_4 + \left(\frac{1}{R_6} + \frac{1}{R_4}\right)V_6 - \frac{1}{R_4}V_7 = 0,$$

$$-\frac{1}{R_5}V_1 - \frac{1}{R_1}V_3 - \frac{1}{R_3}V_5 - \frac{1}{R_4}V_6 + \left(\frac{1}{R_5} + \frac{1}{R_1} + \frac{1}{R_3} + \frac{1}{R_4}\right)V_7 = -I_1.$$

13.1-6
$$\left(C_1 s + \frac{1}{R_5}\right)V_1 - C_1 s V_2 = I_1,$$

$$-C_1 s V_1 + \left(C_1 s + \frac{1}{R_2} + \frac{1}{L_1 s}\right)V_2 - \frac{1}{L_1 s}V_3 = 0,$$

$$-\frac{1}{L_1 s}V_2 + \left(\frac{1}{L_1 s} + \frac{1}{R_1}\right)V_3 - \frac{1}{R_1}V_7 = 0,$$

$$\left(C_2 s + \frac{1}{R_3}\right)V_5 - \frac{1}{R_3}V_7 = 0,$$

$$\left(\frac{1}{R_6} + \frac{1}{R_4}\right)V_6 - \frac{1}{R_4}V_7 = 0,$$

$$-\frac{1}{R_5}V_1 - \frac{1}{R_1}V_3 - \frac{1}{R_3}V_5 - \frac{1}{R_4}V_6 + \left(\frac{1}{R_5} + \frac{1}{R_1} + \frac{1}{R_3} + \frac{1}{R_4}\right)V_7 = 0.$$

13.1-7
$$\left(C_1 s + \frac{1}{R_5}\right)V_1 - C_1 s V_2 - \frac{1}{R_5}V_7 = I_1,$$

$$-C_1 s V_1 + \left(C_1 s + \frac{1}{R_2} + \frac{1}{L_1 s}\right)V_2 - \frac{1}{L_1 s}V_3 - \frac{1}{R_2}V_4 = 0,$$

$$-\frac{1}{L_1 s}V_2 + \left(\frac{1}{L_1 s} + \frac{1}{R_1}\right)V_3 - \frac{1}{R_1}V_7 = 0,$$

$$-\frac{1}{R_2}V_2 + \left(\frac{1}{R_2} + \frac{1}{R_6} + C_2 s\right)V_4 - C_2 s V_5 = 0,$$

$$-C_2 s V_4 + \left(C_2 s + \frac{1}{R_3}\right)V_5 - \frac{1}{R_3}V_7 = 0,$$

$$-\frac{1}{R_5}V_1 - \frac{1}{R_1}V_3 - \frac{1}{R_3}V_5 + \left(\frac{1}{R_5} + \frac{1}{R_1} + \frac{1}{R_3} + \frac{1}{R_4}\right)V_7 = -I_1.$$

13.1-8
$$\left(C_1 s + \frac{1}{L_1 s} + \frac{1}{R_2}\right)V_2 - \frac{1}{L_1 s}V_3 - \frac{1}{R_2}V_4 = 0,$$

$$-\frac{1}{L_1 s}V_2 + \left(\frac{1}{L_1 s} + \frac{1}{R_1}\right)V_3 - \frac{1}{R_1}V_7 = 0,$$

$$-\frac{1}{R_2}V_2 + \left(C_2 s + \frac{1}{R_2} + \frac{1}{R_6}\right)V_4 - C_2 s V_5 - \frac{1}{R_6}V_6 = 0,$$

$$-C_2 s V_4 + \left(C_2 s + \frac{1}{R_3}\right)V_5 - \frac{1}{R_3}V_7 = 0,$$

$$-\frac{1}{R_6}V_4 + \left(\frac{1}{R_6} + \frac{1}{R_4}\right)V_6 - \frac{1}{R_4}V_7 = 0,$$

$$-\frac{1}{R_1}V_3 - \frac{1}{R_3}V_5 - \frac{1}{R_4}V_6 + \left(\frac{1}{R_5} + \frac{1}{R_1} + \frac{1}{R_3} + \frac{1}{R_4}\right)V_7 = -I_1.$$

13.1-9   Let v_1, v_3, and v_4 be the voltages of nodes 1, 3, and 4 with respect to node 2. Then

$$C_1 \frac{dv_1}{dt} + \frac{1}{R_1}v_1 - \frac{1}{R_1}v_4 = i_1,$$

$$\frac{1}{R_3} v_3 + \frac{1}{L_1} \int_{-\infty}^{t} v_3(\tau) \, d\tau - \frac{1}{R_3} v_4 = i_2 \,,$$

$$-\frac{1}{R_1} v_1 - \frac{1}{R_3} v_3 + \left(\frac{1}{R_1} + \frac{1}{R_2} + \frac{1}{R_3}\right) v_4 = -i_1 - i_2 \,.$$

The inductor current $i_{32}(t)$ may be written as

$$i_{32}(t) = \frac{1}{L_1} \int_{t_1}^{t} v_3(\tau) \, d\tau + i_{32}(t_1),$$

where $i_{32}(t_1)$ is the initial current at the instant t_1.

13.1-10
$$C_1 \frac{dv_1}{dt} + \frac{1}{R_1} v_1 - C_1 \frac{dv_2}{dt} - \frac{1}{R_1} v_4 = i_1 \,,$$

$$-C_1 \frac{dv_1}{dt} + C_1 \frac{dv_2}{dt} + \frac{1}{R_2} v_2 + \frac{1}{L_1} \int_{t_1}^{t} v_3(\tau) \, d\tau + i_{23}(t_1) - \frac{1}{R_2} v_4 = 0,$$

$$-\frac{1}{R_1} v_1 - \frac{1}{R_2} v_2 + \left(\frac{1}{R_1} + \frac{1}{R_2} + \frac{1}{R_3}\right) v_4 = -i_1 - i_2 \,.$$

13.1-11
$$\begin{bmatrix} \dfrac{1}{R_1} + \dfrac{1}{R_2} & -\dfrac{1}{R_2} & 0 & 0 \\[2mm] -\dfrac{1}{R_1} & \dfrac{1}{R_2} + \dfrac{1}{R_3} + \dfrac{1}{R_4} & -\dfrac{1}{R_4} & 0 \\[2mm] 0 & -\dfrac{1}{R_4} & \dfrac{1}{R_4} + \dfrac{1}{R_5} + \dfrac{1}{R_6} & -\dfrac{1}{R_6} \\[2mm] 0 & 0 & -\dfrac{1}{R_6} - G & \dfrac{1}{R_6} + \dfrac{1}{R_7} \end{bmatrix} = y$$

No, y is not symmetric.

13.1-12
$$\left(C_1 s + \frac{1}{R_5}\right) V_1 - C_1 s V_2 = I_1 \,,$$

$$-C_1 s V_1 + \left(C_1 s + \frac{1}{L_1 s} + \frac{1}{R_2}\right) V_2 - \frac{1}{L_1 s} V_3 - \frac{1}{R_2} V_4 = 0,$$

$$-\frac{1}{L_1 s} V_2 + \left(\frac{1}{L_1 s} + \frac{1}{R_1}\right) V_3 = 0,$$

$$-\frac{1}{R_2} V_2 + \left(\frac{1}{R_2} + \frac{1}{R_6} + C_2 s\right) V_4 - C_2 s V_5 - \frac{1}{R_6} V_6 = 0,$$

$$-\frac{K}{L_1 s} V_2 + \frac{K}{L_1 s} V_3 - C_2 s V_4 + \left(C_2 s + \frac{1}{R_3}\right) V_5 = 0,$$

$$-\frac{1}{R_6} V_4 + \left(\frac{1}{R_6} + \frac{1}{R_4}\right) V_6 = 0.$$

13.2-1
$$\left(R_1 + j\omega L_1 + \frac{1}{j\omega C}\right) I_a + \frac{1}{j\omega C} I_b - (R_1 + j\omega L_1) I_c = V_1 \,,$$

$$\frac{1}{j\omega C} I_a + \left(R_2 + R_3 + j\omega L_2 + \frac{1}{j\omega C}\right) I_b + R_2 I_c = 0,$$

$$-(R_1 + j\omega L_1) I_a + R_2 I_b + (R_1 + R_2 + R_4 + j\omega L_1) I_c = 0,$$

$$Z = \begin{bmatrix} R_1 + j\omega L_1 + \dfrac{1}{j\omega C} & \dfrac{1}{j\omega C} & -(R_1 + j\omega L_1) \\[2mm] \dfrac{1}{j\omega C} & R_2 + R_3 + j\omega L_2 + \dfrac{1}{j\omega C} & R_2 \\[2mm] -(R_1 + j\omega L_1) & R_2 & R_1 + R_2 + R_4 + j\omega L_1 \end{bmatrix}.$$

13.2-2
$$\begin{bmatrix} R_1 + j\omega L_1 + \dfrac{1}{j\omega C} & -\dfrac{1}{j\omega C} & R_1 + j\omega L_1 \\[2mm] -\dfrac{1}{j\omega C} & R_2 + R_3 + j\omega L_2 + \dfrac{1}{j\omega C} & R_2 \\[2mm] R_1 + j\omega L_1 & R_2 & R_1 + R_2 + R_4 + j\omega L_1 \end{bmatrix} \begin{bmatrix} I_a \\[2mm] I_b \\[2mm] I_c \end{bmatrix} = \begin{bmatrix} V_1 \\[2mm] 0 \\[2mm] 0 \end{bmatrix}.$$

13.2-3
$$(R_4 + R_7)i_a + (R_4 + R_7)i_b + R_4 i_c - R_5 i_d - R_7 i_e = v_1,$$
$$(R_4 + R_7)i_a + (R_4 + R_6 + R_7)i_b + R_4 i_c - (R_1 + R_4)i_d - R_7 i_e = 0,$$
$$R_4 i_a + R_4 i_b + (R_1 + R_2 + R_4)i_c - (R_4 + R_1)i_d = 0,$$
$$-R_4 i_a - (R_4 + R_1)i_b - (R_4 + R_1)i_c + (R_1 + R_3 + R_4 + R_5)i_d - R_3 i_e = 0,$$
$$-R_7 i_a - R_7 i_b + 0 - R_3 i_d + (R_3 + R_7 + R_8)i_d = 0.$$

13.2-4
$$(R_1 + R_6)i_a - R_6 i_b - R_6 i_e = v_1,$$
$$-R_6 i_a + (R_2 + R_6 + R_7)i_b - R_7 i_c + R_7 i_d + R_6 i_e = 0,$$
$$-R_7 i_b + (R_3 + R_7 + R_8)i_c - R_7 i_d + R_8 i_e = 0,$$
$$R_7 i_b - R_7 i_c + (R_4 + R_7)i_d = v_1,$$
$$-R_6 i_a + R_6 i_b + R_8 i_c + (R_5 + R_6 + R_8)i_e = 0.$$

13.2-5 (1)
$$R_7 i_0 + \frac{1}{C_2}\int_{t_1}^{t} i_0(\tau)\, d\tau - R_7 i_1 - \frac{1}{C_2}\int_{t_1}^{t} i_1(\tau)\, d\tau + v_{cf}(t_1) + \frac{1}{C_2}\int_{t_1}^{t} i_2(\tau)\, d\tau$$
$$- \frac{1}{C_2}\int_{t_1}^{t} i_3(\tau)\, d\tau - \frac{1}{C_2}\int_{t_1}^{t} i_5(\tau)\, d\tau = v_1.$$

(2)
$$-R_7 i_0 - \frac{1}{C_2}\int_{t_1}^{t} i_0(\tau)\, d\tau + (R_1 + R_7)i_1 + \left(\frac{1}{C_1} + \frac{1}{C_2}\right)\int_{t_1}^{t} i_1(\tau)\, d\tau + v_{bf}(t_1)$$
$$- v_{cf}(t_1) + \frac{1}{C_2}\int_{t_1}^{t} i_3(\tau)\, d\tau - \left(\frac{1}{C_1} + \frac{1}{C_2}\right)\int_{t_1}^{t} i_2(\tau)\, d\tau$$
$$+ \frac{1}{C_2}\int_{t_1}^{t} i_5(\tau)\, d\tau - \frac{1}{C_1}\int_{t_1}^{t} i_6(\tau)\, d\tau = 0.$$

(3)
$$-\frac{1}{C_2}\int_{t_1}^{t} i_0(\tau)\, d\tau + \frac{1}{C_2}\int_{t_1}^{t} i_1(\tau)\, d\tau - \frac{1}{C_2}\int_{t_1}^{t} i_2(\tau)\, d\tau + R_3 i_3$$
$$+ \left(\frac{1}{C_2} + \frac{1}{C_3}\right)\int_{t_1}^{t} i_3(\tau)\, d\tau + v_{df}(t_1) - v_{cf}(t_1) - \frac{1}{C_3}\int_{t_1}^{t} i_4(\tau)\, d\tau$$
$$+ \frac{1}{C_2}\int_{t_1}^{t} i_5(\tau)\, d\tau + \frac{1}{C_3}\int_{t_1}^{t} i_6(\tau)\, d\tau = 0.$$

(4)
$$R_2 i_2 + \frac{1}{C_2}\int_{t_1}^{t} \left[i_2(\tau) + i_0(\tau) - i_1(\tau) - i_3(\tau) - i_5(\tau)\right] d\tau$$
$$+ v_{cf}(t_1) + \frac{1}{C_1}\int_{t_1}^{t} \left[-i_1(\tau) + i_2(\tau) + i_6(\tau)\right] d\tau - v_{bf}(t_1) = 0.$$

(5)
$$R_4 i_4 + v_2 + \frac{1}{C_3}\int_{t_1}^{t} \left[-i_3(\tau) + i_4(\tau) - i_6(\tau)\right] d\tau - v_{df}(t_1) = 0.$$

(6)
$$R_5 i_5 + v_2 + \frac{1}{C_2}\int_{t_1}^{t} \left[-i_0(\tau) + i_1(\tau) - i_2(\tau) + i_3(\tau) + i_5(\tau)\right] d\tau - v_{cf}(t_1) = 0.$$

(7)
$$R_6 i_6 + \frac{1}{C_3}\int_{t_1}^{t} \left[i_3(\tau) - i_4(\tau) + i_6(\tau)\right] d\tau + v_{df}(t_1)$$
$$+ \frac{1}{C_1}\int_{t_1}^{t} \left[-i_1(\tau) + i_2(\tau) + i_6(\tau)\right] d\tau - v_{bf}(t_1) = 0.$$

13.2-6
$$\begin{bmatrix} R_1 + R_2 & -R_2 & 0 \\[2mm] -R_2 & R_2 + R_3 + \dfrac{1}{Cs} & -\dfrac{1}{Cs} \\[2mm] 0 & -\dfrac{1}{Cs} - R & Ls + R_4 + \dfrac{1}{Cs} \end{bmatrix} \begin{bmatrix} I_a \\[2mm] I_b \\[2mm] I_c \end{bmatrix} = \begin{bmatrix} V_1 \\[2mm] 0 \\[2mm] 0 \end{bmatrix}.$$

No, Z is not symmetric.

13.2-7 $(10 - j100)I_1 + j100I_2 = 10,$
$j100I_1 + (40 - j90)I_2 - 30I_3 = 0,$
$-30I_2 + 50I_3 = -5e^{-j30°}.$

Note that the phasor $V_1 = 10$ corresponds to $v_1 = 10 \sin 1000t$.

13.2-8 (1) $(R_1 + L_1s)(I_a - I_c) - MsI_b + \dfrac{1}{Cs}(I_a - I_b) = V_1.$

(2) $\dfrac{1}{Cs}(I_b - I_a) + R_2(I_b - I_c) + (R_3 + L_2s)I_b + MsI_c = 0.$

(3) $(R_1 + L_1s)(I_c - I_a) + MsI_b + R_4I_c - R(I_a - I_b) + R_2(I_c - I_b) = 0.$

13.3-1 $I_c = (V_b - V_c - V_2)j\omega C.$ This is not the same as the current through C in the transformed network.

13.3-2 Yes. If a source transformation is performed with respect to a branch (voltage source in series is converted to current source in parallel), then the current through the transformed branch is not the same as that in the original branch.

13.3-3 Two node equations. Use node d as reference. Denote the unknown node voltages by V_b and V_c. Then

$$\frac{V_b - V_1}{R_1} + j\omega C V_b + \frac{V_b - V_c}{j\omega L} = 0,$$
$$\frac{V_c - V_b}{j\omega L} + \frac{V_c}{R_2} = I_1.$$

13.3-4 Two-node equations:

$$\left(j\omega C + \frac{1}{R_1} + \frac{1}{j\omega L}\right)V_b - \frac{1}{j\omega L}V_c = \frac{V_1}{R_1}$$

and

$$-\frac{1}{j\omega L}V_b + \left(\frac{1}{j\omega L} + \frac{1}{R_2}\right)V_c = I_1 + I_2.$$

13.3-5 Three loop equations. Assign mesh currents directed clockwise, I_a, I_b, and I_c, for the first three meshes from left to right. The fourth mesh current is I_2.

$$R_1 I_a - R_1 I_b = V_1$$
$$-R_1 I_a + (R_1 + R_2 + R_3 + j\omega L)I_b - (R_3 + j\omega L)I_c = 0$$
$$-(R_3 + j\omega L)I_b + \left(R_3 + R_4 + j\omega L + \frac{1}{j\omega C}\right)I_c = -R_4 I_2.$$

13.4-1 $a_{21} = \dfrac{R_2}{L_1(R_1 + R_2)}, \qquad a_{22} = \dfrac{1}{L_1}\left(R_3 + \dfrac{R_1 R_2}{R_1 + R_2}\right).$

13.4-2 Three-state variables.

13.4-3 Three-state variables.

13.4-4 Two-state variables.

13.4-5 $a_{11} = -\dfrac{R_3R_4 + R_2R_4 + R_2R_3}{C_1[R_1R_3R_4 + R_1R_2R_4 + R_1R_2R_3 + R_2R_3R_4]}$,

$a_{21} = -\dfrac{R_2R_3 + R_3R_4}{C_2[R_1R_3R_4 + R_1R_2R_4 + R_1R_2R_3 + R_2R_3R_4]}$,

$a_{31} = \dfrac{R_2R_3 + R_2R_4}{C_3[R_1R_3R_4 + R_1R_2R_4 + R_1R_2R_3 + R_2R_3R_4]}$.

13.4-6 $a_{12} = \dfrac{-(R_2R_3 + R_3R_4)}{C_1[R_1R_3R_4 + R_1R_2R_4 + R_1R_2R_3 + R_2R_3R_4]}$,

$a_{22} = -\dfrac{R_1R_2 + R_1R_4 + R_2R_3 + R_3R_4}{C_2[R_1R_3R_4 + R_1R_2R_4 + R_1R_2R_3 + R_2R_3R_4]}$,

$a_{32} = \dfrac{R_2R_3 - R_1R_4}{C_3[R_1R_3R_4 + R_1R_2R_4 + R_1R_2R_3 + R_2R_3R_4]}$.

13.4-7 $a_{13} = \dfrac{R_2R_3 + R_2R_4}{C_1[R_1R_3R_4 + R_1R_2R_4 + R_1R_3R_4 + R_2R_3R_4]}$,

$a_{23} = \dfrac{R_2R_3 - R_1R_4}{C_2[R_1R_3R_4 + R_1R_2R_4 + R_1R_3R_4 + R_2R_3R_4]}$,

$a_{33} = -\dfrac{R_1R_3 + R_1R_4 + R_2R_3 + R_2R_4}{C_3[R_1R_3R_4 + R_1R_2R_4 + R_1R_3R_4 + R_2R_3R_4]}$.

13.5-1 Assign mesh variables i_a and i_b in the inside meshes, with clockwise directions, and assign i_1 and i_2 as mesh variables in the outer meshes. Two loop equations are needed:

$$R_1(t)i_a - R_1 i_1 + \frac{C_1(t_1)}{C_1(t)} v_{12}(t_1) + \frac{1}{C_1(t)} \int_{t_1}^t i_a(\tau)\, d\tau + R_2(t)[i_a - i_b] = 0,$$

$$R_2(t)[i_b - i_a] + \frac{d}{dt}[L_1(t)i_b(t)] + R_3(t)[i_b + i_2] = 0.$$

13.5-2 $R_1(t)[i_a - i_c] + \dfrac{d}{dt}[L_1(t)\{i_a - i_c\}] + \dfrac{C(t_1)}{C(t)} v_{36}(t_1)$

$$+ \frac{1}{C(t)} \int_{t_1}^t [i_a(\tau) - i_b(\tau)]\, d\tau = 0,$$

$-\dfrac{C(t_1)}{C(t)} v_{36}(t_1) + \dfrac{1}{C(t)} \displaystyle\int_{t_1}^t [i_b(\tau) - i_a(\tau)]\, d\tau$

$$+ R_2(t)[i_b - i_c] + R_3(t)i_c + \frac{d}{dt}[L_2(t)i_b] = 0,$$

$$\frac{d}{dt}[L_1(t)\{i_c - i_a\}] + R_1(t)[i_c - i_a] + R_4(t)i_c + R_2(t)[i_c - i_b] = 0.$$

13.5-3 Use node 6 as reference. Since v_1 is known, only 4-node voltages are unknown:

$$\frac{v_2 - v_1}{R_1(t)} + \frac{L_1(t_1)}{L_1(t)} i_{23}(t_1) + \frac{1}{L_1(t)} \int_{t_1}^t [v_2(\tau) - v_3(\tau)]\, d\tau = 0,$$

$$-\frac{L_1(t_1)}{L_1(t)} i_{23}(t_1) + \frac{1}{L_1(t)} \int_{t_1}^t [v_3(\tau) - v_2(\tau)]\, d\tau + \frac{d}{dt}[C(t)v_3] + \frac{v_3 - v_4}{R_2(t)} = 0,$$

$$\frac{v_4 - v_1}{R_4(t)} + \frac{v_4 - v_3}{R_2(t)} + \frac{v_4 - v_5}{R_3(t)} = 0,$$

$$\frac{v_5 - v_4}{R_3(t)} + \frac{L_2(t_1)}{L_2(t)} i_{56}(t_1) + \frac{1}{L_2(t)} \int_{t_1}^t v_5(\tau)\, d\tau = 0.$$

13.5-4 $(i_a - i_c)^2 + \dfrac{d}{dt}\left[(i_a - i_c)^2\right] + \left[\displaystyle\int_{t_1}^{t}\{i_a(\tau) - i_b(\tau)\}\,d\tau + q_{36}(t_1)\right]^2 - v_1 = 0,$

$-\left[\displaystyle\int_{t_1}^{t}\{i_a(\tau) - i_b(\tau)\}\,d\tau + q_{36}(t_1)\right]^2 + (i_b - i_c)^2 + (i_b)^2 + \dfrac{d}{dt}\left[(i_b)^2\right] = 0,$

$-\dfrac{d}{dt}\left[(i_a - i_c)^2\right] - [i_a - i_b]^2 + (i_c)^2 - (i_b - i_c)^2 = 0.$

13.5-5 $\dfrac{dq}{dt} = -\dfrac{1}{R_1}q^2 - \psi^2 + \dfrac{V_1}{R_1}.$

CHAPTER 14

14.1-1 (a) An LC 2-port terminated in R_1 and R_2; (b) A resistive 4-port terminated in L_1, L_2, C_1 and C_2.

14.1-2 (a) An LC 4-port terminated in R_1, R_2, R_3, and R_4; (b) A resistive 5-port terminated in C_1, C_2, C_3, L_1 and L_2.

14.1-3 $R_1 = \dfrac{R_a R_b}{R_a + R_b + R_c},\qquad R_2 = \dfrac{R_a R_c}{R_a + R_b + R_c},\qquad R_3 = \dfrac{R_b R_c}{R_a + R_b + R_c}.$

14.2-1 (a) $y_{11} = 1/Z_1$, $y_{22} = 1/Z_1$, $y_{12} = y_{21} = -1/Z_1$.
   Z-parameters do not exist.
   $h_{11} = Z_1$, $h_{12} = 1$, $h_{21} = -1$, $h_{22} = 0$.
   $g_{11} = 0$, $g_{12} = -1$, $g_{21} = 1$, $g_{22} = Z_1$.
   (b) y-parameters do not exist.
   $z_{11} = z_{12} = z_{21} = z_{22} = Z_2$.
   $h_{11} = 0$, $h_{12} = 1$, $h_{21} = -1$, $h_{22} = 1/Z_2$.
   $g_{11} = 1/Z_2$, $g_{12} = -1$, $g_{21} = 1$, $g_{22} = 0$.
   (c) $y_{11} = 1/Z_1$, $y_{12} = -1/Z_1$, $y_{21} = -1/Z_1$, $y_{22} = (1/Z_1) + (1/Z_2)$.
   $z_{11} = Z_1 + Z_2$, $z_{12} = z_{21} = Z_2$, $z_{22} = Z_2$.
   $h_{11} = Z_1$, $h_{12} = 1$, $h_{21} = -1$, $h_{22} = 1/Z_2$.
   $g_{11} = 1/(Z_1 + Z_2)$, $g_{12} = -Z_2/(Z_1 + Z_2)$, $g_{21} = 1$, $g_{22} = Z_1 Z_2/(Z_1 + Z_2)$.

14.2-2 (a) $y_{11} = \frac{3}{2}$, $y_{12} = y_{21} = -\frac{1}{2}$, $y_{22} = \frac{3}{4}$.
   $z_{11} = \frac{6}{7}$, $z_{12} = z_{21} = \frac{4}{7}$, $z_{22} = \frac{12}{7}$.
   $h_{11} = \frac{2}{3}$, $h_{12} = \frac{1}{3}$, $h_{21} = -\frac{1}{3}$, $h_{22} = \frac{7}{12}$.
   $g_{11} = \frac{7}{6}$, $g_{12} = -\frac{2}{3}$, $g_{21} = \frac{2}{3}$, $g_{22} = \frac{4}{3}$.
   (b) $y_{11} = \frac{5}{14}$, $y_{12} = y_{21} = -\frac{2}{7}$, $y_{22} = \frac{3}{7}$.
   $z_{11} = 6$, $z_{12} = z_{21} = 4$, $z_{22} = 5$.
   $h_{11} = \frac{14}{5}$, $h_{12} = \frac{4}{5}$, $h_{21} = -\frac{4}{5}$, $h_{22} = \frac{1}{5}$.
   $g_{11} = \frac{1}{6}$, $g_{12} = -\frac{2}{3}$, $g_{21} = \frac{2}{3}$, $g_{22} = \frac{7}{3}$.

14.2-3 $k_{21} = 3$.

14.2-4 Assume that the 2-port measurements are made with the two bottom nodes of the two ports connected to ground. Then $V_1 = \frac{7}{23}$, $V_2 = -\frac{3}{23}$.

14.2-5 (a) No. h_{11} is a short circuit driving-point impedance, but h_{22} is an open circuit driving-point admittance. (b) Not necessarily. If $h_{12} = -h_{21}$, the network is reciprocal. (See Table 14.1.)

14.3-1
$$\frac{I_{2b}}{I_{1b}}\bigg|V_{2b}=0 = -\frac{V_{1a}}{V_{2a}}\bigg|I_{1a}=0.$$

This is the same result as in Equation 14.60, except that the roles of ports 1 and 2 are interchanged.

14.3-2
$$\frac{V_2}{V_1}\bigg|I_2=0 = \frac{z_{21}}{z_{11}}, \qquad \frac{I_1}{I_2}\bigg|V_1=0 = -\frac{z_{12}}{z_{11}}.$$

Hence, if $z_{12} = z_{21}$, Equation 14.60 is verified.

14.3-3 $h_{12} = -h_{21}$.

14.3-4 $z_{21} = 2(1 - \alpha)$; $z_{12} = 2$. For the network to be reciprocal, $\alpha = 0$.

14.3-5 As long as the 2-port can be represented as an interconnection of 1-ports, it is reciprocal.

14.3-6 Replace the 2-ohm resistor in Figure Exercise 14.2-2(a) by a 1-port, using port 1 of the network in Figure Exercise 14.3-4, and leaving port 2 of the network of Figure Exercise 14.3-4 unused.

CHAPTER 15

15.1-1 (a) The solution is the same as before; (b) the solutions are equal.

15.1-2 $v_1 = 1$, $v_2 = 3/4$, $v_3 = 5/4$. The answer is twice the answer in Example 15.1-1.

15.1-3 (a) $v_1 = 191$, $v_2 = 139.6$, $v_3 = 288.5$.
(b) $v_1 = 191 \sin 1000t$, $v_2 = 139.6 \sin 1000t$, $v_3 = 288.5 \sin 1000t$.
(c) $v_1 = 143.5 \sin 3000t + 47.6 \sin 500t$, $v_2 = 105 \sin 3000t + 34.7 \sin 500t$, $v_3 = 217 \sin 3000t + 71.9 \sin 500t$.

15.1-4 The answer is the same. There are four others, but the answers are all the same.

15.1-5 $V_1 = .467 + j.0625$; $V_2 = .341 + j.1875$; $V_3 = .558 + j.25$.

15.2-1 (a) $\det A = -a_{12}(a_{21}a_{33} - a_{23}a_{31}) + a_{22}(a_{11}a_{33} - a_{13}a_{31}) - a_{32}(a_{11}a_{23} - a_{13}a_{21})$.
(b) $\det A = a_{13}(a_{21}a_{32} - a_{22}a_{31}) - a_{23}(a_{11}a_{32} - a_{12}a_{31}) + a_{33}(a_{11}a_{22} - a_{12}a_{21})$.

15.2-2 (a) $\det A = a_{11}(a_{22}a_{33} - a_{23}a_{32}) - a_{12}(a_{21}a_{33} - a_{23}a_{31}) + a_{13}(a_{21}a_{32} - a_{22}a_{31})$.
(b) $\det A = -a_{21}(a_{12}a_{33} - a_{13}a_{32}) + a_{22}(a_{11}a_{33} - a_{13}a_{31}) - a_{23}(a_{11}a_{32} - a_{12}a_{31})$.
(c) $\det A = a_{31}(a_{12}a_{23} - a_{13}a_{22}) - a_{32}(a_{11}a_{23} - a_{13}a_{21}) + a_{33}(a_{11}a_{22} - a_{12}a_{21})$.

15.2-3 (a) $x_2 = [-b_1(a_{21}a_{33} - a_{23}a_{31}) + b_2(a_{11}a_{33} - a_{13}a_{31}) - b_3(a_{11}a_{23} - a_{13}a_{21})]/\det A$.
(b) $x_3 = [b_1(a_{21}a_{32} - a_{22}a_{31}) - b_2(a_{11}a_{32} - a_{12}a_{31}) + b_3(a_{11}a_{22} - a_{12}a_{21})]/\det A$.

15.2-4
$$\begin{vmatrix} a_{11} & a_{12} \\ a_{21} & a_{22} \end{vmatrix} = \begin{vmatrix} a_{11} & a_{12} \\ 0 & a_{22} - \dfrac{a_{21}a_{12}}{a_{11}} \end{vmatrix} = \begin{vmatrix} a_{11} & 0 \\ 0 & a_{22} - \dfrac{a_{21}a_{12}}{a_{11}} \end{vmatrix}$$
$$= a_{11}\left(a_{22} - \frac{a_{21}a_{12}}{a_{11}}\right)\begin{vmatrix} 1 & 0 \\ 0 & 1 \end{vmatrix} = a_{11}a_{22} - a_{12}a_{21}.$$

15.2-5 (a) From Cramer's rule: 6 multiplications, 2 divisions, 3 subtractions; (b) from Gauss's elimination: 3 multiplications, 3 divisions, 3 subtractions.

15.3-1 $3\dfrac{d^3x_1}{dt^3} + 18\dfrac{d^2x_1}{dt^2} + 29\dfrac{dx_1}{dt} + 7x_1 = 4\dfrac{d^2u_1}{dt^2} + 18\dfrac{du_1}{dt} + 18u_1 + \dfrac{d^2u_2}{dt^2} + 4\dfrac{du_2}{dt} + 2u_2$

$+ 4\dfrac{d^2u_3}{dt^2} + 28\dfrac{du_3}{dt} + 40u_3$. Three initial conditions are needed.

15.3-2 $3\dfrac{d^3x_2}{dt^3} + 18\dfrac{d^2x_2}{dt^2} + 29\dfrac{dx_2}{dt} + 7x_2 = 2\dfrac{d^2u_1}{dt^2} + 8\dfrac{du_1}{dt} + 4u_1 + 2\dfrac{d^2u_2}{dt^2} + 7\dfrac{du_2}{dt} + 2u_2$

$+ 8\dfrac{d^2u_3}{dt^2} + 28\dfrac{du_3}{dt} + 12u_3$. Three initial conditions are required.

15.3-3 $3\dfrac{d^3x_3}{dt^3} + 18\dfrac{d^2x_3}{dt^2} + 29\dfrac{dx_3}{dt} + 7x_3 = 2\dfrac{d^2u_1}{dt^2} + 14\dfrac{du_1}{dt} + 20u_1 + 2\dfrac{d^2u_2}{dt^2} + 7\dfrac{du_2}{dt} + 3u_2$

$+ 20\dfrac{d^2u_3}{dt^2} + 76\dfrac{du_3}{dt} + 60u_3$. Three initial conditions are needed.

15.3-4 $-2x_1 - (p+1)x_2 + (p+2)x_3 = 4u_3$,
$(7p+17)x_2 - (p+2)x_3 = 4u_1 + 4u_2 + 12u_3$,
$(3p^3 + 18p^2 + 29p + 7)x_3 = (p^2 + 7p + 10)2u_1 + (2p^2 + 7p + 3)u_2 + (20p^2 + 76p + 60)u_3$.

15.3-5 (a) $C\dfrac{d}{dt}(v_2 - v_1) + \dfrac{v_2}{R_2} + \dfrac{v_2 - v_3}{R_3} = 0$;

$\dfrac{v_3 - v_2}{R_3} + \dfrac{1}{L}\displaystyle\int_0^t v_3(\tau)\,d\tau + i_L(0) = 0$;

(b) $\left[p^2 + \left(\dfrac{R_3}{L} + \dfrac{1}{R_2C}\right)p + \dfrac{1}{LC}\left(1 + \dfrac{R_3}{R_2}\right)\right]v_2 = \left(p^2 + \dfrac{R_3}{L}p\right)v_1$;

(c) $v_2(t) = -1.049e^{-.869\times10^6 t} - .049e^{-.23\times10^6 t}$.

Index